1950
9c
-M-

FOUNDATIONS

OF

ELECTROMAGNETIC
THEORY

This book is in the

ADDISON-WESLEY SERIES IN PHYSICS

FOUNDATIONS OF ELECTROMAGNETIC THEORY

by

JOHN R. REITZ

Department of Physics
Case Institute of Technology

and

FREDERICK J. MILFORD

Mathematical Physics Division
Battelle Memorial Institute

ADDISON-WESLEY PUBLISHING COMPANY, INC.

READING, MASSACHUSETTS · PALO ALTO · LONDON

JAPAN PUBLICATIONS TRADING COMPANY, LTD.

TOKYO, JAPAN

PREFACE

Although Maxwell's equations were formulated more than seventy years ago, the subject of Electricity and Magnetism has not remained static. The progress of the 1930's on the microscopic constitution of matter, and the growth of solid-state physics after World War II, have led to a better understanding of electric and magnetic fields inside matter. The advanced undergraduate student in Science (this is the student to whom we are directing our attention) approaches the subject of electricity with a qualitative understanding of atomic phenomena. At the same time, he has acquired a good background in mathematics, and for the first time in his career he is in the position of being able to solve some of the important mathematical problems of classical physics. It appeared to us that there was no well-designed text in Electricity and Magnetism to meet the special needs of this group of students.

The present volume has evolved from the teaching of a course in Electricity and Magnetism to physics majors at Case Institute of Technology. These students have been introduced to vector analysis both in mathematics and mechanics courses, they have encountered some of the important partial differential equations in physics, and they have been introduced to boundary-value problems. A course in Electricity and Magnetism is ideally suited to a further development of these mathematical concepts, and we have attempted to exploit this idea in the present book. Although a previous introduction to these concepts is desirable, the sections on vector analysis and boundary-value problems have been written in such a way that little previous knowledge of the subject is required.

We feel that the approach of building up Electricity and Magnetism from the basic experimental laws is still the correct one at the intermediate level, and we have followed this approach. Although a rigorous exposition of the fundamentals is to be preferred to teaching by example, we have been careful to include a substantial number of well-chosen example problems to bridge the gap between the formal development of the subject and the problems. Experience has shown that a deficiency of examples can detract from an otherwise good textbook.

It is our belief that a full understanding of the electric and magnetic fields inside matter can be obtained only after the atomic nature of matter is appreciated. Hence we have used elementary atomic concepts freely in the development of macroscopic theory. We have tried to use the physical approach in our treatment of polarization and magnetization, as well as in our discussion of the auxiliary vectors **D** and **H**. We believe our book has something extra to offer in this area.

Separate short chapters have been written on the microscopic theory of dielectric and magnetic material. This is a subject usually neglected in a book on formal theory, but it seems to us that many of the concepts involved are simple, and best presented early.

The special features of our book are: (1) a full vector treatment of the subject, including the use of vector identities to simplify proofs of theorems, (2) a utilitarian approach to boundary-value problems and their solution, (3) a rigorous development of Electricity and Magnetism from experimental laws, with no essential proofs relegated to more advanced texts, (4) use of atomic concepts to simplify the understanding of macroscopic theory of fields inside matter, (5) the relation of the microscopic and macroscopic pictures of electric and magnetic fields inside matter, (6) an introduction to plasma physics, and (7) a substantial list of nontrivial problems which have been carefully related to the textual material.

As an aid to the instructor, the more difficult problems have been labeled with an asterisk. Sections of the text which are starred are not essential to its further development, and may be omitted if the course must be shortened for some reason or other.

June 1959

J. R. R.
F. J. M.

CONTENTS

Starred sections and chapters may be omitted without loss of continuity

CHAPTER 1

VECTOR ANALYSIS

In the study of electricity and magnetism a great saving in complexity of notation may be accomplished by using the notation of vector analysis. In providing this valuable shorthand, vector analysis also brings to the forefront the physical ideas involved in equations. It is the purpose of this chapter to give a brief but self-contained exposition of basic vector analysis and to provide the rather utilitarian knowledge of the field which is required for a treatment of electricity and magnetism. Those already familiar with vector analysis will find it a useful review and an introduction to the notation of the text.

1–1 Definitions. In the study of elementary physics several kinds of quantities have been encountered; in particular, the division into vectors and scalars has been made. For our purposes it will be sufficient to define a scalar as follows:

A scalar is a quantity which is completely characterized by its magnitude.

Examples of scalars are numerous: mass, time, volume, etc. A simple extension of the idea of a scalar is a *scalar field*, i.e., a function of position which is completely specified by its magnitude at all points in space.

A vector may be defined as follows:

A vector is a quantity which is completely characterized by its magnitude and direction.

As examples of vectors we cite position from a fixed origin, velocity, acceleration, force, etc. The generalization to a vector field gives a function of position which is completely specified by its magnitude and direction at all points in space.

These definitions may be refined and extended; in fact, in more advanced treatments they are usually replaced by more subtle definitions in terms of transformation properties. In addition, more complicated kinds of quantities, such as tensors, are sometimes encountered. Scalars and vectors will, however, suffice for our purposes.

1–2 Vector algebra. Since the algebra of scalars is familiar to the reader, this algebra will be used to develop vector algebra. In order to proceed with this development it is convenient to have a representation of vectors, for which purpose we introduce a three-dimensional cartesian coordinate system. This three-dimensional system will be denoted by the three variables x, y, z or, when it is more convenient, x_1, x_2, x_3. With respect to this coordinate system a vector is specified by its x-, y-, and z-components. Thus a vector* $\mathbf{V}$ is specified by its components V_x, V_y, V_z, where $V_x = |\mathbf{V}| \cos \alpha_1$, $V_y = |\mathbf{V}| \cos \alpha_2$, $V_z = |\mathbf{V}| \cos \alpha_3$, the α's being the angles between $\mathbf{V}$ and appropriate coordinate axes. In the case of vector fields, each of the components is to be regarded as a function of x, y, and z. It should be emphasized at this point that we introduce a representation of the vectors with respect to a cartesian coordinate system only for simplicity and ease of understanding; all of the definitions and operations are, in fact, independent of any special choice of coordinates.

The sum of two vectors is defined as the vector whose components are the sums of the corresponding components of the original vectors. Thus if $\mathbf{C}$ is the sum of $\mathbf{A}$ and $\mathbf{B}$, we write

$$\mathbf{C} = \mathbf{A} + \mathbf{B} \tag{1-1}$$

and

$$C_x = A_x + B_x, \qquad C_y = A_y + B_y, \qquad C_z = A_z + B_z. \tag{1-2}$$

This definition of the vector sum is completely equivalent to the familiar parallelogram rule for vector addition.

Vector subtraction is defined in terms of the negative of a vector, which is the vector whose components are the negatives of the corresponding components of the original vector. Thus if $\mathbf{A}$ is a vector, $-\mathbf{A}$ is defined by

$$(-\mathbf{A})_x = -A_x, \qquad (-\mathbf{A})_y = -A_y, \qquad (-\mathbf{A})_z = -A_z. \tag{1-3}$$

The operation of subtraction is then defined as the addition of the negative. This is written

$$\mathbf{A} - \mathbf{B} = \mathbf{A} + (-\mathbf{B}). \tag{1-4}$$

Since the addition of real numbers is associative, it follows that vector addition (and subtraction) is also associative. In vector notation this appears as

$$\mathbf{A} + (\mathbf{B} + \mathbf{C}) = (\mathbf{A} + \mathbf{B}) + \mathbf{C} = (\mathbf{A} + \mathbf{C}) + \mathbf{B} = \mathbf{A} + \mathbf{B} + \mathbf{C}. \tag{1-5}$$

In other words, the parentheses are not needed, as indicated by the last form.

Proceeding now to the process of multiplication, we note that the simplest product is a scalar times a vector. This operation results in a

---

* Vector quantities will be denoted by boldface symbols.

vector each component of which is the scalar times the corresponding component of the original vector. If c is a scalar and $\mathbf{A}$ a vector, the product $c\mathbf{A}$ is a vector, $\mathbf{B} = c\mathbf{A}$, defined by

$$B_x = cA_x, \qquad B_y = cA_y, \qquad B_z = cA_z. \tag{1–6}$$

It is clear that if $\mathbf{A}$ is a *vector field* and c a *scalar field* then $\mathbf{B}$ is a new vector field which is *not* necessarily a simple multiple of the original field.

If, now, two vectors are to be multiplied, there are two possibilities, known as the vector and scalar products. Considering first the scalar product, we note that this name derives from the scalar nature of the product, although the alternative names, inner product and dot product, are sometimes used. The definition of the scalar product, written $\mathbf{A} \cdot \mathbf{B}$, is

$$\mathbf{A} \cdot \mathbf{B} = A_x B_x + A_y B_y + A_z B_z. \tag{1–7}$$

This definition is equivalent to another, and perhaps more familiar, definition, i.e., as the product of the magnitudes of the original vectors times the cosine of the angle between these vectors.

The vector product of two vectors is a vector, which accounts for the name. Alternative names are outer and cross product. The vector product is written $\mathbf{A} \times \mathbf{B}$; if $\mathbf{C}$ is the vector product of $\mathbf{A}$ and $\mathbf{B}$, then $\mathbf{C} = \mathbf{A} \times \mathbf{B}$, or

$$C_x = A_y B_z - A_z B_y, \qquad C_y = A_z B_x - A_x B_z, \qquad C_z = A_x B_y - A_y B_x. \tag{1–8}$$

This definition is equivalent to the following: the vector product is the product of the magnitudes times the sine of the angle between the original vectors, with the direction given by a right-hand screw rule.*

It is important to note that the cross product depends on the order of the factors; interchanging the order introduces a minus sign. The vector product may be easily remembered in terms of a determinant. If $\mathbf{i}$, $\mathbf{j}$, and $\mathbf{k}$ are unit vectors, i.e., vectors of unit magnitude, in the x-, y-, and z-directions, respectively, then

$$\mathbf{A} \times \mathbf{B} = \begin{vmatrix} \mathbf{i} & \mathbf{j} & \mathbf{k} \\ A_x & A_y & A_z \\ B_x & B_y & B_z \end{vmatrix}. \tag{1–9}$$

---

* Let $\mathbf{A}$ be rotated into $\mathbf{B}$ through the smallest possible angle. A right-hand screw rotated in this manner will advance in a direction perpendicular to both $\mathbf{A}$ and $\mathbf{B}$; this direction is the direction of $\mathbf{A} \times \mathbf{B}$.

If this determinant is evaluated by the usual rules, the result is precisely our definition of the cross product.

At this point one might well inquire as to the possibility of vector division. Division of a vector by a scalar can, of course, be defined as multiplication by the reciprocal of the scalar. Division of a vector by another vector, however, is possible only if the two vectors are parallel. On the other hand, it is possible to write general solutions to vector equations and so accomplish something closely akin to division. Consider the equation

$$c = \mathbf{A} \cdot \mathbf{X}, \tag{1-10}$$

where c is a known scalar, $\mathbf{A}$ a known vector, and $\mathbf{X}$ an unknown vector. A general solution to this equation is

$$\mathbf{X} = \frac{c\mathbf{A}}{\mathbf{A} \cdot \mathbf{A}} + \mathbf{B}, \tag{1-11}$$

where $\mathbf{B}$ is a vector of arbitrary magnitude which is perpendicular to $\mathbf{A}$, that is, $\mathbf{A} \cdot \mathbf{B} = 0$. What we have done is very nearly to divide c by $\mathbf{A}$; more correctly, we have found the general form of the vector $\mathbf{X}$ which satisfies Eq. (1-10). There is no unique solution, and this fact accounts for the vector $\mathbf{B}$. In the same fashion we may consider the vector equation

$$\mathbf{C} = \mathbf{A} \times \mathbf{X}, \tag{1-12}$$

where $\mathbf{A}$ and $\mathbf{C}$ are known vectors and $\mathbf{X}$ is an unknown vector. The general solution of this equation is

$$\mathbf{X} = \frac{\mathbf{C} \times \mathbf{A}}{\mathbf{A} \cdot \mathbf{A}} + k\mathbf{A}, \tag{1-13}$$

where k is an arbitrary scalar. This again is very nearly the quotient of $\mathbf{C}$ by $\mathbf{A}$; the scalar k takes account of the nonuniqueness of the process. If $\mathbf{X}$ is required to satisfy both (1-10) and (1-12), then the result is unique and given by

$$\mathbf{X} = \frac{\mathbf{C} \times \mathbf{A}}{\mathbf{A} \cdot \mathbf{A}} + \frac{c\mathbf{A}}{\mathbf{A} \cdot \mathbf{A}}. \tag{1-14}$$

The algebraic operations discussed above may be combined in many ways. Most of the results so obtained are obvious; however, there are two triple products of sufficient importance to merit explicit mention. The triple scalar product $D = \mathbf{A} \cdot \mathbf{B} \times \mathbf{C}$ is easily found to be given by the determinant

$$D = \mathbf{A} \cdot \mathbf{B} \times \mathbf{C} = \begin{vmatrix} A_x & A_y & A_z \\ B_x & B_y & B_z \\ C_x & C_y & C_z \end{vmatrix} = -\mathbf{B} \cdot \mathbf{A} \times \mathbf{C}. \tag{1-15}$$

This product is unchanged by an exchange of dot and cross or by a cyclic permutation of the three vectors; parentheses are not needed, since the cross product of a scalar and a vector is undefined. The other interesting triple product is the triple vector product $\mathbf{D} = \mathbf{A} \times (\mathbf{B} \times \mathbf{C})$. By a repeated application of the definition of the cross product, Eq. (1–8), we find

$$\mathbf{D} = \mathbf{A} \times (\mathbf{B} \times \mathbf{C}) = \mathbf{B}(\mathbf{A} \cdot \mathbf{C}) - \mathbf{C}(\mathbf{A} \cdot \mathbf{B}), \tag{1–16}$$

which is frequently known as the "back cab rule." It should be noted that in the cross product the parentheses are vital; without them the product is not well defined.

1–3 Gradient. The extensions of the ideas introduced above to differentiation and integration, i.e., vector calculus, will now be considered. The simplest of these is the relation of a particular vector field to the derivatives of a scalar field. It is convenient to first introduce the idea of the *directional derivative* of a function of several variables. This is just the rate of change of the function in a specified direction. The directional derivative of a scalar function φ is usually denoted by $d\varphi/ds$; it must be understood that $d\mathbf{s}$ represents an infinitesimal displacement in the direction being considered, and that ds is the scalar magnitude of $d\mathbf{s}$. If $d\mathbf{s}$ has the components dx, dy, dz, then

$$\frac{d\varphi}{ds} = \lim_{\Delta s \to 0} \frac{\varphi(x + \Delta x, y + \Delta y, z + \Delta z) - \varphi(x, y, z)}{\Delta s}$$
$$= \frac{\partial \varphi}{\partial x}\frac{dx}{ds} + \frac{\partial \varphi}{\partial y}\frac{dy}{ds} + \frac{\partial \varphi}{\partial z}\frac{dz}{ds}.$$

In order to clarify the idea of a directional derivative, consider a scalar function of two variables. Thus, $\varphi(x, y)$ represents a two-dimensional scalar field. We may plot φ as a function of x and y as is done in Fig. 1–1 for the function $\varphi(x, y) = x^2 + y^2$. The directional derivative at the point x_0, y_0 depends on the direction. If we choose the direction corresponding to $dy/dx = -x_0/y_0$, then we find

$$\frac{d\varphi}{ds}\bigg|_{x_0, y_0} = \frac{\partial \varphi}{\partial x}\frac{dx}{ds} + \frac{\partial \varphi}{\partial y}\frac{dy}{ds} = \left[2x_0 - 2y_0\frac{x_0}{y_0}\right]\frac{dx}{ds} = 0. \tag{1–17a}$$

Alternatively, if we choose $dy/dx = y_0/x_0$, we find

$$\frac{d\varphi}{ds}\bigg|_{x_0, y_0} = \left(2x_0 + 2\frac{y_0^2}{x_0}\right)\sqrt{\frac{x_0^2}{x_0^2 + y_0^2}} = 2\sqrt{x_0^2 + y_0^2}. \tag{1–17b}$$

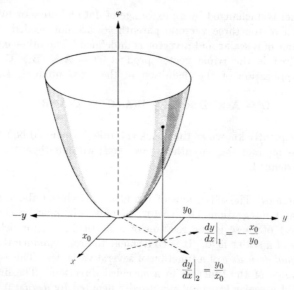

$$\frac{dy}{dx}\bigg|_1 = -\frac{x_0}{y_0}$$

$$\frac{dy}{dx}\bigg|_2 = \frac{y_0}{x_0}$$

Fig. 1–1. The function $\varphi(x, y) = x^2 + y^2$ plotted against x and y in a three-dimensional graph.

As a third possibility choose $dy/dx = \alpha$; then

$$\frac{d\varphi}{ds}\bigg|_{x_0, y_0} = (2x_0 + 2\alpha y_0)(1 + \alpha^2)^{-1/2}. \tag{1–17c}$$

If this result is differentiated with respect to α and the derivative set equal to zero, then the value of α for which the derivative is a maximum or minimum is found. When we perform these operations, we obtain $\alpha = y_0/x_0$, which simply means that the direction of maximum rate of change of the function $\varphi = x^2 + y^2$ is the radial direction. If the direction is radially outward then the maximum is the maximum rate of increase; if it is radially inward it is a maximum rate of decrease or minimum rate of increase. In the direction specified by $dy/dx = -x_0/y_0$ the rate of change of $x^2 + y^2$ is zero. This direction is tangent to the circle $x^2 + y^2 = x_0^2 + y_0^2$. Clearly, on this curve, $\varphi = x^2 + y^2$ does not change. The direction in which $d\varphi/ds$ vanishes gives the direction of the curve $\varphi = constant$ through the point being considered. These lines, which are circles for the function $x^2 + y^2$, are completely analogous to the familiar contour lines or lines of constant altitude which appear on topographic maps. Figure 1–2 shows the function $\varphi = x^2 + y^2$ replotted as a contour map.

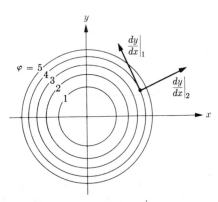

FIG. 1–2. The function $\varphi(x, y)$ of Fig. 1–1 expressed as a contour map in two dimensions.

The idea of contour lines may be generalized to a function of three variables, in which case the surfaces, $\varphi(x, y, z) = constant$, are called *level surfaces* or *equipotential surfaces*. The three-dimensional analog to Fig. 1–2 is the only practical way of graphing a scalar field for a three-dimensional space.

The gradient of a scalar function may now be defined as follows:

The gradient of a scalar function φ is a vector whose magnitude is the maximum directional derivative at the point being considered and whose direction is the direction of the maximum directional derivative at the point.

It is evident that the gradient has the direction normal to the level surface of φ through the point being considered. The most common symbols for the gradient are ∇ and **grad**; of these we will most often use the latter. In terms of the gradient the directional derivative is given by

$$\frac{d\varphi}{ds} = |\mathbf{grad}\ \varphi|\ \cos\theta, \tag{1–18}$$

where θ is the angle between the direction of $d\mathbf{s}$ and the direction of the gradient. This is immediately evident from the geometry of Fig. 1–3. If we write $d\mathbf{s}$ for the vector displacement of magnitude ds, then (1–18) can be written

$$\frac{d\varphi}{ds} = \mathbf{grad}\ \varphi \cdot \frac{d\mathbf{s}}{ds}. \tag{1–19}$$

This equation enables us to find the explicit form of the gradient in any coordinate system in which we know the form of $d\mathbf{s}$. In rectangular coordinates we know that $d\mathbf{s} = \mathbf{i}\,dx + \mathbf{j}\,dy + \mathbf{k}\,dz$. We also know that

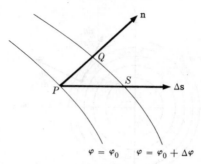

FIG. 1–3. Parts of two level surfaces of the function $\varphi(x, y, z)$. $|\mathbf{grad}\,\varphi|$ at P equals the limit as $\overline{PQ} \to 0$ of $\Delta\varphi/\overline{PQ}$, and $d\varphi/ds$ is the corresponding limit of $\Delta\varphi/\overline{PS}$.

$$d\varphi = \frac{\partial\varphi}{\partial x}\,dx + \frac{\partial\varphi}{\partial y}\,dy + \frac{\partial\varphi}{\partial z}\,dz.$$

From this and Eq. (1–19) it follows that

$$\frac{\partial\varphi}{\partial x}\,dx + \frac{\partial\varphi}{\partial y}\,dy + \frac{\partial\varphi}{\partial z}\,dz = (\mathbf{grad}\,\varphi)_x\,dx + (\mathbf{grad}\,\varphi)_y\,dy + (\mathbf{grad}\,\varphi)_z\,dz.$$

Equating coefficients of differentials of independent variables on both sides of the equation gives

$$\mathbf{grad}\,\varphi = \mathbf{i}\,\frac{\partial\varphi}{\partial x} + \mathbf{j}\,\frac{\partial\varphi}{\partial y} + \mathbf{k}\,\frac{\partial\varphi}{\partial z} \qquad (1\text{–}20)$$

in rectangular coordinates. In a more complicated case the procedure is the same. In spherical polar coordinates, with r, θ, ϕ as defined in Fig. 1–4, we have

$$d\varphi = \frac{\partial\varphi}{\partial r}\,dr + \frac{\partial\varphi}{\partial\theta}\,d\theta + \frac{\partial\varphi}{\partial\phi}\,d\phi, \qquad (1\text{–}21)$$

and

$$d\mathbf{s} = \mathbf{a}_r\,dr + \mathbf{a}_\theta r\,d\theta + \mathbf{a}_\phi r \sin\theta\,d\phi, \qquad (1\text{–}22)$$

where $\mathbf{a}_r$, $\mathbf{a}_\theta$, and $\mathbf{a}_\phi$ are unit vectors in the r, θ, and ϕ directions respectively. Applying (1–19) and equating coefficients of independent variables yields

$$\mathbf{grad}\,\varphi = \mathbf{a}_r\,\frac{\partial\varphi}{\partial r} + \mathbf{a}_\theta\,\frac{1}{r}\,\frac{\partial\varphi}{\partial\theta} + \mathbf{a}_\phi\,\frac{1}{r \sin\theta}\,\frac{\partial\varphi}{\partial\phi} \qquad (1\text{–}23)$$

in spherical coordinates.

1–4 Vector integration. There are, of course, other aspects to differentiation involving vectors; however, it is convenient to discuss vector

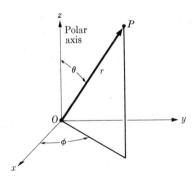

FIG. 1-4. Definition of the polar coordinates r, θ, ϕ.

integration first. For our purposes we may consider three kinds of integrals: line, surface, and volume, according to the nature of the differential appearing in the integral. The integrand may be either a vector or a scalar; however, certain combinations of integrands and differentials give rise to uninteresting integrals. Those of interest here are the line integral of a vector, the surface integral of a vector, and the volume integrals of both vectors and scalars.

If **F** is a vector, the line integral of **F** is written

$$\int_{aC}^{b} \mathbf{F} \cdot d\mathbf{l}, \tag{1-24}$$

where C is the curve along which the integration is performed, a and b the initial and final points on the curve, and $d\mathbf{l}$ an infinitesimal vector displacement along the curve C. Since $\mathbf{F} \cdot d\mathbf{l}$ is a scalar it is clear that the line integral is a scalar. The definition of the line integral follows closely the Riemann definition of the definite integral. The segment of C between a and b is divided into a large number of small increments $\Delta\mathbf{l}_i$; for each increment an interior point is chosen and the value of **F** at that point found. The scalar product of each increment with the corresponding value of **F** is found and the sum of these computed. The line integral is then defined as the limit of this sum as the number of increments becomes infinite in such a way that each increment goes to zero. This definition may be compactly written as

$$\int_{aC}^{b} \mathbf{F} \cdot d\mathbf{l} = \lim_{N \to \infty} \sum_{i=1}^{N} \mathbf{F}_i \cdot \Delta\mathbf{l}_i.$$

It is important to note that the line integral usually depends not only on the endpoints a and b but also on the curve C along which the integration is to be done. The line integral around a closed curve is of sufficient importance that a special notation is used for it, namely,

$$\oint_C \mathbf{F} \cdot d\mathbf{l}. \qquad (1\text{--}25)$$

The integral around a closed curve may or may not be zero; the class of vectors for which the line integral around any closed curve is zero is of considerable importance. For this reason one often encounters line integrals around undesignated closed paths, e.g.,

$$\oint \mathbf{F} \cdot d\mathbf{l}. \qquad (1\text{--}26)$$

This notation is useful only in those cases where the integral is independent of the contour C within rather wide limits. If any ambiguity is possible, it is wise to specify the contour. The basic approach to the evaluation of line integrals is to obtain a one-parameter description of the curve and then use this description to express the line integral as the sum of three ordinary one-dimensional integrals. In all but the simplest cases this is a long and tedious procedure; fortunately, however, it is seldom necessary to evaluate the integrals in this fashion. As will be seen later, it is often possible to convert the line integral into a more tractable surface integral or to show that it does not depend on the path between the endpoints. In the latter case a simple path may be chosen to simplify the integration.

If $\mathbf{F}$ is again a vector, the surface integral of $\mathbf{F}$ is written

$$\int_S \mathbf{F} \cdot \mathbf{n} \, da, \qquad (1\text{--}27)$$

where S is the surface over which the integration is to be performed, da is an infinitesimal area on S and $\mathbf{n}$ is a unit normal to da. There is a twofold ambiguity in the choice of $\mathbf{n}$, which is resolved by taking $\mathbf{n}$ to be the outward drawn normal if S is a closed surface. If S is not closed and is finite then it has a boundary, and the sense of the normal is important only with respect to the arbitrary positive sense of traversing the boundary. The positive sense of the normal is the direction in which a right-hand screw would advance if rotated in the direction of the positive sense on the bounding curve. This is illustrated in Fig. 1–5. The surface integral of $\mathbf{F}$ over a closed surface S is sometimes denoted by

$$\oint_S \mathbf{F} \cdot \mathbf{n} \, da.$$

Comments exactly parallel to those made for the line integral can be made for the surface integral. The surface integral is clearly a scalar; it usually depends on the surface S, and cases where it does not are particularly important. The definition of the surface integral is made in a way exactly comparable to that of the line integral. The detailed formulation is left as an exercise.

If **F** is a vector and φ a scalar then the two volume integrals in which we are interested are

$$J = \int_V \varphi\, dv, \qquad \mathbf{K} = \int_V \mathbf{F}\, dv. \tag{1–28}$$

Clearly J is a scalar and **K** a vector. The definitions of these integrals reduce quickly to just the Riemann integral in three dimensions except that in **K** one must note that there is one integral for each component of **F**. These integrals are sufficiently familiar to require no further comment.

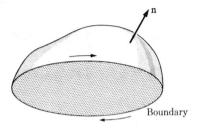

Fig. 1–5. Relation of normal **n** to a surface, and the direction of traversal of the boundary.

1–5 Divergence. Another important operator, which is essentially a derivative, is the divergence operator. The divergence of vector **F**, written div **F**, is defined as follows:

The divergence of a vector is the limit of its surface integral per unit volume as the volume enclosed by the surface goes to zero. That is,

$$\operatorname{div} \mathbf{F} = \lim_{V \to 0} \frac{1}{V} \oint_S \mathbf{F} \cdot \mathbf{n}\, da.$$

The divergence is clearly a scalar point function (scalar field), and it is defined at the limit point of the surface of integration. The above definition has several virtues: it is independent of any special choice of coordinate system, and it may be used to find the explicit form of the divergence operator in any particular coordinate system.

In rectangular coordinates the volume element $\Delta x\, \Delta y\, \Delta z$ provides a convenient basis for finding the explicit form of the divergence. If one corner of the rectangular parallelepiped is at the point $x_0,\ y_0,\ z_0$, then

$$F_x(x_0 + \Delta x, y, z) = F_x(x_0, y, z) + \Delta x \left.\frac{\partial F_x}{\partial x}\right|_{x_0, y, z},$$

$$F_y(x, y_0 + \Delta y, z) = F_y(x, y_0, z) + \Delta y \left.\frac{\partial F_y}{\partial y}\right|_{x, y_0, z}, \qquad (1\text{--}29)$$

$$F_z(x, y, z_0 + \Delta z) = F_z(x, y, z_0) + \Delta z \left.\frac{\partial F_z}{\partial z}\right|_{x, y, z_0},$$

where higher-order terms in Δx, Δy, and Δz have been omitted. Since the area element $\Delta y\, \Delta z$ is perpendicular to the x-axis, $\Delta z\, \Delta x$ perpendicular to the y-axis, and $\Delta x\, \Delta y$ perpendicular to the z-axis, the definition of the divergence becomes

$$\operatorname{div} \mathbf{F} = \lim_{V \to 0} \frac{1}{\Delta x\, \Delta y\, \Delta z} \left\{ \int\!\!\int F_x(x_0, y, z)\, dy\, dz \right.$$

$$+ \Delta x\, \Delta y\, \Delta z \frac{\partial F_x}{\partial x} + \int F_y(x, y_0, z)\, dx\, dz$$

$$+ \Delta x\, \Delta y\, \Delta z \frac{\partial F_y}{\partial y} + \int F_z(x, y, z_0)\, dx\, dy$$

$$+ \Delta x\, \Delta y\, \Delta z \frac{\partial F_z}{\partial z} - \int F_x(x_0, y, z)\, dy\, dz$$

$$\left. - \int F_y(x, y_0, z)\, dx\, dz - \int F_z(x, y, z_0)\, dx\, dy \right\}. \qquad (1\text{--}30)$$

The minus signs associated with the last three terms account for the fact that the outward drawn normal is in the direction of the negative axes in these cases. The limit is easily taken, and the divergence in rectangular coordinates is found to be

$$\operatorname{div} \mathbf{F} = \frac{\partial F_x}{\partial x} + \frac{\partial F_y}{\partial y} + \frac{\partial F_z}{\partial z}. \qquad (1\text{--}31)$$

In spherical coordinates the procedure is similar. The volume enclosed by the coordinate intervals Δr, $\Delta \theta$, $\Delta \phi$ is chosen as the volume of integration. This volume is $r^2 \sin \theta\, \Delta r\, \Delta \theta\, \Delta \phi$. Because the area enclosed by the coordinate intervals depends on the values of the coordinates (note that this is not the case with rectangular coordinates), it is best to write $\mathbf{F} \cdot \mathbf{n}\, \Delta a$ in its explicit form:

$$\mathbf{F} \cdot \mathbf{n}\, \Delta a = F_r r^2 \sin \theta\, \Delta \theta\, \Delta \phi + F_\theta r \sin \theta\, \Delta \phi\, \Delta r + F_\phi r\, \Delta r\, \Delta \theta. \qquad (1\text{--}32)$$

It is clear from this expression that $r^2 F_r \sin \theta$, rather than just F_r, must be expanded in Taylor series. Similarly, it is the coefficient of the products of coordinate intervals which must be expanded in the other terms. Making these expansions and using them to evaluate the surface integral in the definition of the divergence gives

$$\text{div } \mathbf{F} = \lim_{V \to 0} \frac{1}{r^2 \sin \theta \, \Delta r \, \Delta \theta \, \Delta \phi} \left\{ \frac{\partial}{\partial r} (F_r r^2 \sin \theta) \, \Delta r \, \Delta \theta \, \Delta \phi \right.$$

$$\left. + \frac{\partial}{\partial \theta} (F_\theta r \sin \theta) \, \Delta \theta \, \Delta r \, \Delta \phi + \frac{\partial}{\partial \phi} (F_\phi r) \, \Delta \phi \, \Delta r \, \Delta \theta \right\}. \quad (1\text{-}33)$$

Taking the limit, the explicit form of the divergence in spherical coordinates is found to be

$$\text{div } \mathbf{F} = \frac{1}{r^2} \frac{\partial}{\partial r} (r^2 F_r) + \frac{1}{r \sin \theta} \frac{\partial}{\partial \theta} (\sin \theta F_\theta) + \frac{1}{r \sin \theta} \frac{\partial F_\phi}{\partial \phi}. \quad (1\text{-}34)$$

This method of finding the explicit form of the divergence is applicable to any coordinate system provided the forms of the volume and surface elements or, alternatively, the elements of length are known.

The physical significance of the divergence is readily seen in terms of an example taken from fluid mechanics. If $\mathbf{V}$ is the velocity of a fluid, given as a function of position, and ρ is its density, then $\oint_S \rho \mathbf{V} \cdot \mathbf{n} \, da$ is clearly the net amount of fluid per unit time that leaves the volume enclosed by S. If the fluid is incompressible, the surface integral measures the total source of fluid enclosed by the surface. The above definition of the divergence then indicates that it may be interpreted as the limit of the source strength per unit volume, or the source density of an incompressible fluid.

An extremely important theorem involving the divergence may now be stated and proved.

DIVERGENCE THEOREM. *The integral of the divergence of a vector over a volume V is equal to the surface integral of the normal component of the vector over the surface bounding V. That is,*

$$\int_V \text{div } \mathbf{F} \, dv = \oint_S \mathbf{F} \cdot \mathbf{n} \, da.$$

Consider the volume to be subdivided into a large number of small cells. Let the ith cell have volume ΔV_i and be bounded by the surface S_i. It is clear that

$$\sum_i \oint_{S_i} \mathbf{F} \cdot \mathbf{n} \, da = \oint_S \mathbf{F} \cdot \mathbf{n} \, da, \quad (1\text{-}35)$$

where in each integral on the left the normal is directed outward from the volume being considered. Since outward to one cell is inward to the appropriate adjacent cell, all contributions to the left side of (1–35) cancel except those which arise from the surface of S, and Eq. (1–35) is essentially proved. The divergence theorem is now obtained by letting the number of cells go to infinity in such a way that the volume of each cell goes to zero.

$$\oint_S \mathbf{F} \cdot \mathbf{n} \, da = \lim_{\Delta V_i \to 0} \sum_i \left\{ \frac{1}{\Delta V_i} \oint_{S_i} \mathbf{F} \cdot \mathbf{n} \, da \right\} \Delta V_i. \qquad (1\text{–}36)$$

In the limit, the sum on i becomes an integral over V and the ratio of the integral over S_i to ΔV_i becomes the divergence of $\mathbf{F}$. Thus,

$$\oint_S \mathbf{F} \cdot \mathbf{n} \, da = \int_V \operatorname{div} \mathbf{F} \, dv, \qquad (1\text{–}37)$$

which is the divergence theorem. We shall have frequent occasion to exploit this theorem, both in the development of the theoretical aspects of electricity and magnetism and for the very practical purpose of evaluating integrals.

1–6 Curl. The third interesting vector differential operator is the curl. The curl of a vector, written **curl F**, is defined as follows:

The curl of a vector is the limit of the ratio of the integral of its cross product with the outward drawn normal, over a closed surface, to the volume enclosed by the surface as the volume goes to zero. That is,

$$\mathbf{curl\ F} = \lim_{V \to 0} \frac{1}{V} \oint_S \mathbf{n} \times \mathbf{F} \, da. \qquad (1\text{–}38)$$

The parallelism between this definition and the definition of the divergence is quite apparent; instead of the scalar product of the vector with the outward drawn normal, one has the vector product. Otherwise the definitions are the same. This definition is convenient for finding the explicit form of the curl in various coordinate systems; however, for other purposes a different but equivalent definition is more useful. This alternative definition is:

The component of **curl F** *in the direction of the unit vector* **a** *is the limit of a line integral per unit area, as the enclosed area goes to zero, this area being perpendicular to* **a**. *That is,*

$$\mathbf{a} \cdot \mathbf{curl\ F} = \lim_{S \to 0} \frac{1}{S} \oint_C \mathbf{F} \cdot d\mathbf{l}, \qquad (1\text{–}39)$$

where the curve C, which bounds the surface S, is in a plane normal to **a**. It is easy to see the equivalence of the two definitions by considering a plane curve C and the volume swept out by this curve when it is displaced a distance ξ in the direction of the normal to its plane, as shown in

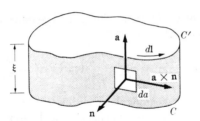

Fig. 1-6. Volume swept out by displacing the plane curve C in the direction of its normal, **a**.

Fig. 1-6. If **a** is normal to this plane, then taking the dot product of **a** with the first definition of the curl, (1-38), gives

$$\mathbf{a} \cdot \mathbf{curl\, F} = \lim_{V \to 0} \frac{1}{V} \oint_S \mathbf{a} \cdot \mathbf{n} \times \mathbf{F}\, da. \tag{1-40}$$

Since **a** is parallel to the normal for all of the bounding surface except the narrow strip bounded by C and C', only the integral over this surface need be considered. For this surface we note that $\mathbf{a} \times \mathbf{n}\, da$ is just $\xi\, d\mathbf{l}$, where $d\mathbf{l}$ is an infinitesimal displacement along C. Since, in addition, $V = \xi S$, the limit of the volume integral is just

$$\mathbf{a} \cdot \mathbf{curl\, F} = \lim_{V \to 0} \frac{1}{\xi S} \oint \xi \mathbf{F} \cdot d\mathbf{l},$$

which reduces to the second form of our definition upon cancelling the ξ's. This equivalence can be shown without the use of the special volume used here; however, so doing sacrifices much of the simplicity of the proof given above.

The form of the curl in various coordinate systems can be calculated in much the same way as was done with the divergence. In rectangular coordinates the volume $\Delta x\, \Delta y\, \Delta z$ is convenient. For the x-component of the curl only the faces perpendicular to the y- and z-axes contribute. Recalling that $\mathbf{j} \times \mathbf{k} = -\mathbf{k} \times \mathbf{j} = \mathbf{i}$, the nonvanishing contributions from the faces of the parallelepiped to the x-component of the curl give

$$(\mathbf{curl\, F})_x = \lim_{V \to 0} \frac{1}{V}\, \{[-F_y(x, y, z + \Delta z) + F_y(x, y, z)]\, \Delta x\, \Delta y$$

$$+ [F_z(x, y + \Delta y, z) - F_z(x, y, z)]\, \Delta x\, \Delta z\}. \tag{1-41}$$

Making a Taylor series expansion and taking the limit gives

$$(\mathbf{curl\, F})_x = \frac{\partial F_z}{\partial y} - \frac{\partial F_y}{\partial z} \tag{1-42}$$

for the x-component of the curl. The y- and z-components may be found in exactly the same way. They are

$$(\text{curl } \mathbf{F})_y = \frac{\partial F_x}{\partial z} - \frac{\partial F_z}{\partial x}, \qquad (\text{curl } \mathbf{F})_z = \frac{\partial F_y}{\partial x} - \frac{\partial F_x}{\partial y}. \qquad (1\text{--}43)$$

The form of the curl in rectangular coordinates can be easily remembered if it is noted that it is just the expansion of a three-by-three determinant, namely,

$$\text{curl } \mathbf{F} = \begin{vmatrix} \mathbf{i} & \mathbf{j} & \mathbf{k} \\ \dfrac{\partial}{\partial x} & \dfrac{\partial}{\partial y} & \dfrac{\partial}{\partial z} \\ F_x & F_y & F_z \end{vmatrix}. \qquad (1\text{--}44)$$

The problem of finding the form of the curl in other coordinate systems is only slightly more complicated and is left to the exercises.

As with the divergence, we encounter an important and useful theorem involving the curl, known as Stokes' theorem.

STOKES' THEOREM. *The line integral of a vector around a closed curve is equal to the integral of the normal component of its curl over any surface bounded by the curve.* That is,

$$\oint_C \mathbf{F} \cdot d\mathbf{l} = \int_S \text{curl } \mathbf{F} \cdot \mathbf{n} \, da, \qquad (1\text{--}45)$$

where C is a closed curve which bounds the surface S. The proof of this theorem is quite analogous to the proof of the divergence theorem. The surface S is divided into a large number of cells. The surface of the ith cell is called ΔS_i and the curve bounding it is C_i. Since each of these cells must be traversed in the same sense, it is clear that the sum of the line integrals around the C_i's is just the line integral around the bounding curve; all of the other contributions cancel. Thus

$$\oint_C \mathbf{F} \cdot d\mathbf{l} = \sum_i \oint_{C_i} \mathbf{F} \cdot d\mathbf{l}. \qquad (1\text{--}46)$$

It remains only to take the limit as the number of cells becomes infinite in such a way that the area of each goes to zero. The result of this limiting process is

$$\oint_C \mathbf{F} \cdot d\mathbf{l} = \lim_{\Delta S_i \to 0} \sum_i \frac{1}{\Delta S_i} \oint_{C_i} \mathbf{F} \cdot d\mathbf{l} \, \Delta S_i$$

$$= \int_S \text{curl } \mathbf{F} \cdot \mathbf{n} \, da, \qquad (1\text{--}47)$$

which is Stokes' theorem. This theorem, like the divergence theorem, is useful both in the development of electromagnetic theory and in the evaluation of integrals. It is perhaps worth noting that both the divergence theorem and Stokes' theorem are essentially partial integrations.

1-7 Further developments. The operations of taking the gradient, divergence, or curl of appropriate kinds of fields may be repeated. For example, it makes sense to take the divergence of the gradient of a scalar field. Some of these repeated operations give zero for any well-behaved field. One is of sufficient importance to have a special name; the others can be expressed in terms of simpler operations. An important double operation is the divergence of the gradient of a scalar field. This combined operator is known as the *Laplacian operator* and is usually written ∇^2. In rectangular coordinates,

$$\nabla^2 \varphi = \frac{\partial^2 \varphi}{\partial x^2} + \frac{\partial^2 \varphi}{\partial y^2} + \frac{\partial^2 \varphi}{\partial z^2}. \tag{1-48}$$

This operator is of great importance in electrostatics and will be considered at length in Chapter 3.

The curl of the gradient of any scalar field is zero. This statement is most easily verified by writing it out in rectangular coordinates. If the scalar field is φ, then

$$\text{curl grad } \varphi = \begin{vmatrix} \mathbf{i} & \mathbf{j} & \mathbf{k} \\ \dfrac{\partial}{\partial x} & \dfrac{\partial}{\partial y} & \dfrac{\partial}{\partial z} \\ \dfrac{\partial \varphi}{\partial x} & \dfrac{\partial \varphi}{\partial y} & \dfrac{\partial \varphi}{\partial z} \end{vmatrix} = \mathbf{i}\left(\frac{\partial^2 \varphi}{\partial y\, \partial z} - \frac{\partial^2 \varphi}{\partial z\, \partial y} \right) + \cdots = 0, \tag{1-49}$$

which verifies the original statement. The divergence of any curl is also zero. This is verified directly in rectangular coordinates by writing

$$\text{div curl } \mathbf{F} = \frac{\partial}{\partial x}\left(\frac{\partial F_z}{\partial y} - \frac{\partial F_y}{\partial z} \right) + \frac{\partial}{\partial y}\left(\frac{\partial F_x}{\partial z} - \frac{\partial F_z}{\partial x} \right) + \cdots = 0. \tag{1-50}$$

The other possible second-order operation is taking the curl of the curl of a vector field. It is left as an exercise to show that in rectangular coordinates

$$\text{curl curl } \mathbf{F} = \text{grad div } \mathbf{F} - \nabla^2 \mathbf{F}, \tag{1-51}$$

where the Laplacian of a vector is the vector whose rectangular components are the Laplacians of the rectangular components of the original vector. In any coordinate system other than rectangular the Laplacian of a vector is *defined* by Eq. (1-51).

Another way in which the application of the vector differential operators may be extended is to apply them to various products of vectors and scalars. There are many possible combinations of differential operators and products; those of most interest are tabulated in Table 1–1. These identities may be readily verified in rectangular coordinates, which is sufficient to assure their validity in any coordinate system.

TABLE 1–1

FORMULAS FROM VECTOR ANALYSIS INVOLVING
DIFFERENTIAL OPERATORS

(I–1)	$\nabla(\varphi + \psi) = \nabla\varphi + \nabla\psi$
(I–2)	$\nabla\varphi\psi = \varphi\nabla\psi + \psi\nabla\varphi$
(I–3)	$\text{div }(\mathbf{F} + \mathbf{G}) = \text{div }\mathbf{F} + \text{div }\mathbf{G}$
(I–4)	$\text{curl }(\mathbf{F} + \mathbf{G}) = \text{curl }\mathbf{F} + \text{curl }\mathbf{G}$
(I–5)	$\nabla(\mathbf{F} \cdot \mathbf{G}) = (\mathbf{F} \cdot \nabla)\mathbf{G} + (\mathbf{G} \cdot \nabla)\mathbf{F} + \mathbf{F} \times \text{curl }\mathbf{G} + \mathbf{G} \times \text{curl }\mathbf{F}$
(I–6)	$\text{div }\varphi\mathbf{F} = \varphi \text{ div }\mathbf{F} + \mathbf{F} \cdot \nabla\varphi$
(I–7)	$\text{div }(\mathbf{F} \times \mathbf{G}) = \mathbf{G} \cdot \text{curl }\mathbf{F} - \mathbf{F} \cdot \text{curl }\mathbf{G}$
(I–8)	$\text{div curl }\mathbf{F} = 0$
(I–9)	$\text{curl }\varphi\mathbf{F} = \varphi \text{ curl }\mathbf{F} + \nabla\varphi \times \mathbf{F}$
(I–10)	$\text{curl }(\mathbf{F} \times \mathbf{G}) = \mathbf{F} \text{ div }\mathbf{G} - \mathbf{G} \text{ div }\mathbf{F} + (\mathbf{G} \cdot \nabla)\mathbf{F} - (\mathbf{F} \cdot \nabla)\mathbf{G}$
(I–11)	$\text{curl curl }\mathbf{F} = \text{grad div }\mathbf{F} - \nabla^2\mathbf{F}$
(I–12)	$\text{curl }\nabla\varphi = 0$
(I–13)	$\oint_S \mathbf{F} \cdot \mathbf{n} \, da = \int_V \text{div }\mathbf{F} \, dv$
(I–14)	$\oint_C \mathbf{F} \cdot d\mathbf{l} = \int_S \text{curl }\mathbf{F} \cdot \mathbf{n} \, da$
(I–15)	$\oint_S \varphi\mathbf{n} \, da = \int_V \nabla\varphi \, dv$
(I–16)	$\oint_S \mathbf{F}(\mathbf{G} \cdot \mathbf{n}) \, da = \int_V \mathbf{F} \text{ div }\mathbf{G} \, dv + \int_V (\mathbf{G} \cdot \nabla)\mathbf{F} \, dv$
(I–17)	$\oint_S \mathbf{n} \times \mathbf{F} \, da = \int_V \text{curl }\mathbf{F} \, dv$
(I–18)	$\oint_C \varphi \, d\mathbf{l} = \int_S \mathbf{n} \times \nabla\varphi \, da$

There are several possibilities for the extension of the divergence theorem and of Stokes' theorem. The most interesting of these is Green's theorem, which is

$$\int_V (\psi\nabla^2\varphi - \varphi\nabla^2\psi) \, dv = \oint_S (\psi \text{ grad } \varphi - \varphi \text{ grad } \psi) \cdot \mathbf{n} \, da. \quad (1\text{-}52)$$

This theorem follows from the application of the divergence theorem to the vector

$$\mathbf{F} = \psi \text{ grad } \varphi - \varphi \text{ grad } \psi. \quad (1\text{-}53)$$

Using this $\mathbf{F}$ in the divergence theorem, we obtain

$$\int_V \text{div} \, [\psi \, \textbf{grad} \, \varphi - \varphi \, \textbf{grad} \, \psi] \, dv = \oint_S (\psi \, \textbf{grad} \, \varphi - \varphi \, \textbf{grad} \, \psi) \cdot \textbf{n} \, da.$$

$$(1\text{--}54)$$

Using the identity (Table 1–1) for the divergence of a scalar times a vector gives

$$\text{div} \, (\psi \, \textbf{grad} \, \varphi) - \text{div} \, (\varphi \, \textbf{grad} \, \psi) = \psi \nabla^2 \varphi - \varphi \nabla^2 \psi. \qquad (1\text{--}55)$$

Combining (1–54) and (1–55) yields Green's theorem.

This concludes our brief discussion of vector analysis. In the interests of brevity, many well-known results have been relegated to the exercises. No attempt has been made to achieve a high degree of rigor; the approach has been utilitarian. What we will need we have developed; everything else has been omitted.

PROBLEMS

1–1. The vectors from the origin to the points A, B, C, D are

$$\textbf{A} = \textbf{i} + \textbf{j} + \textbf{k},$$
$$\textbf{B} = 2\textbf{i} + 3\textbf{j},$$
$$\textbf{C} = 3\textbf{i} + 5\textbf{j} - 2\textbf{k},$$
$$\textbf{D} = \textbf{k} - \textbf{j}.$$

Show that the lines $\overline{AB}$ and $\overline{CD}$ are parallel and find the ratio of their lengths.

1–2. Show that the following vectors are perpendicular:

$$\textbf{A} = \textbf{i} + 4\textbf{j} + 3\textbf{k},$$
$$\textbf{B} = 4\textbf{i} + 2\textbf{j} - 4\textbf{k}.$$

1–3. Show that the vectors

$$\textbf{A} = 2\textbf{i} - \textbf{j} + \textbf{k},$$
$$\textbf{B} = \textbf{i} - 3\textbf{j} - 5\textbf{k},$$
$$\textbf{C} = 3\textbf{i} - 4\textbf{j} - 4\textbf{k}$$

form the sides of a right triangle.

1–4. By squaring both sides of the equation

$$\textbf{A} = \textbf{B} - \textbf{C}$$

and interpreting the result geometrically, prove the "law of cosines."

1–5. Show that

$$\textbf{A} = \textbf{i} \cos \alpha + \textbf{j} \sin \alpha,$$
$$\textbf{B} = \textbf{i} \cos \beta + \textbf{j} \sin \beta$$

are unit vectors in the xy-plane making angles α, β with the x-axis. By means of a scalar product, obtain the formula for $\cos (\alpha - \beta)$.

1-6. If **A** is a constant vector and **r** is the vector from the origin to the point (x, y, z), show that

$$(\mathbf{r} - \mathbf{A}) \cdot \mathbf{A} = 0$$

is the equation of a plane.

1-7. With **A** and **r** defined as in Problem 1-6, show that

$$(\mathbf{r} - \mathbf{A}) \cdot \mathbf{r} = 0$$

is the equation of a sphere.

1-8. If **A**, **B**, **C**, are vectors from the origin to the points A, B, C, show that

$$(\mathbf{A} \times \mathbf{B}) + (\mathbf{B} \times \mathbf{C}) + (\mathbf{C} \times \mathbf{A})$$

is perpendicular to the plane ABC.

1-9. Verify that Eq. (1-13) is a solution to (1-12) by direct substitution. [Note that Eq. (1-12) implies that **C** is perpendicular to **A**.]

1-10. Find the gradient of φ in cylindrical coordinates, given that $ds = dr\mathbf{a}_r + r\,d\theta\mathbf{a}_\theta + dz\mathbf{k}$. It should be noted that r and θ have different meanings here than in Eqs. (1-21) and (1-22). In spherical coordinates r is the magnitude of the radius vector from the origin and θ is the polar angle. In cylindrical coordinates, r is the perpendicular distance from the cylinder axis and θ is the azimuthal angle about this axis.

1-11. From the definition of the divergence, obtain an expression for div **F** in cylindrical coordinates.

1-12. Find the divergence of the vector

$$\mathbf{i}(x^2 + yz) + \mathbf{j}(y^2 + zx) + \mathbf{k}(z^2 + xy).$$

Also find the curl.

1-13. If **r** is the vector from the origin to the point (x, y, z), prove the formulas

$$\text{div } \mathbf{r} = 3; \quad \text{curl } \mathbf{r} = 0; \quad (\mathbf{u} \cdot \text{grad}) \mathbf{r} = \mathbf{u}.$$

[*Note:* **u** is any vector.]

1-14. If **A** is a constant vector, show that

$$\text{grad } (\mathbf{A} \cdot \mathbf{r}) = \mathbf{A}.$$

1-15. Prove identities (I-6) and (I-9) in Table 1-1.

1-16. If r is the magnitude of the vector from the origin to the point (x, y, z), and $f(r)$ is an arbitrary function of r, prove that

$$\text{grad } f(r) = \frac{\mathbf{r}}{r} \frac{df}{dr}.$$

1-17. Verify Eq. (1-51) in rectangular coordinates, where $\nabla^2\mathbf{F}$ in these coordinates is as defined in the text.

1-18. Prove identities (I-15) and (I-16) in Table 1-1. [*Hint:* Use the divergence theorem and one or more identities from the first half of Table 1-1.]

CHAPTER 2

ELECTROSTATICS

2–1 Electric charge. The first observation of the electrification of objects by rubbing is lost in antiquity; however, it is common experience that rubbing a hard rubber comb on a piece of wool endows the rubber with the ability to pick up small pieces of paper. As a result of rubbing the two objects together (strictly speaking, as a result of bringing them into close contact), both the rubber and the wool acquire a new property; they are *charged*. This experiment serves to introduce the concept of *charge*. But charge, itself, is not created during this process; the total charge, or the sum of the charges on the two bodies, is still the same as before electrification. In the light of modern physics we know that microscopic charged particles, specifically electrons, are transferred from the wool to the rubber, leaving the wool positively charged and the rubber comb negatively charged.

Charge is a fundamental and characteristic property of the elementary particles which make up matter. In fact, all matter is composed ultimately of protons, neutrons, and electrons, and two of these particles bear charges. But even though on a microscopic scale matter is composed of a large number of charged particles, the powerful electrical forces associated with these particles are fairly well hidden in a macroscopic observation. The reason is that there are two kinds of charge, positive and negative, and an ordinary piece of matter contains approximately equal amounts of each kind. From the macroscopic viewpoint, then, charge refers to net charge, or excess charge. When we say that an object is charged, we mean that it has an excess charge, either an excess of electrons (negative) or an excess of protons (positive). In this and the following chapters, charge will usually be denoted by the symbol q.

It is an experimental observation that charge can be neither created nor destroyed. The total charge of a closed system cannot change. From the macroscopic point of view charges may be regrouped and combined in different ways; nevertheless, we may state that *net charge is conserved in a closed system.*

2–2 Coulomb's law. Towards the end of the eighteenth century techniques in experimental science achieved sufficient sophistication to make possible refined observations of the forces between electric charges. The results of these observations, which were extremely controversial at the time, can be summarized in three statements. (a) There are two and only two kinds of electric charge, now known as positive and negative. (b) Two point charges exert on each other forces which act along the line joining them and which are inversely proportional to the square of the distance between them. (c) These forces are also proportional to the product of the charges, are repulsive for like charges, and attractive for unlike charges. The last two statements, with the first as preamble, are known as *Coulomb's law* in honor of Charles Augustin de Coulomb (1736–1806), who was one of the leading eighteenth century students of electricity. Coulomb's law for point charges may be concisely formulated in the vector notation of Chapter 1 as

$$\mathbf{F}_1 = C \frac{q_1 q_2}{r_{21}^2} \frac{\mathbf{r}_{21}}{r_{21}}, \tag{2-1}$$

where $\mathbf{F}_1$ is the force on charge q_1, $\mathbf{r}_{21}$ is the vector from q_2 to q_1, r_{21} is the magnitude of $\mathbf{r}_{21}$, and C is a constant of proportionality about which more will be said later. In Eq. (2-1) a unit vector in the direction of $\mathbf{r}_{21}$ has been formed by dividing $\mathbf{r}_{21}$ by its magnitude, a device of which frequent use will be made. If the force on q_2 is to be found, it is only necessary to change every subscript 1 to 2 and every 2 to 1. Understanding this notation is important, since in future work it will provide a technique for keeping track of field and source variables.

Coulomb's law applies to point charges. In the macroscopic sense a "point charge" is one whose spatial dimensions are very small compared with any other length pertinent to the problem under consideration, and we shall use the term "point charge" in this sense. To the best of our knowledge, Coulomb's law also applies to the interactions of elementary particles such as protons and electrons. Equation (2-1) is found to hold for the electrostatic repulsion between nuclei at distances greater than about 10^{-14} meter; at smaller distances, the powerful, but short-ranged, nuclear forces dominate the picture.

Equation (2-1) is an experimental law; nevertheless, there is both theoretical and experimental evidence to indicate that the inverse square law is exact, i.e., that the exponent of r_{21} is exactly 2. By an indirect experiment[*] it has been shown that the exponent of r_{21} can differ from 2 by no more than one part in 10^9.

The constant C in Eq. (2-1) requires some comment, since it determines the system of units. The units of force and distance are presumably those belonging to one of the systems used in mechanics; the most direct procedure here would be to set $C = 1$, and choose the unit of charge such that Eq. (2-1) agrees with experiment. Other procedures are also

---

[*] Plimpton and Lawton, *Phys. Rev.* **50**, 1066 (1936). The same experiment was performed earlier by Kelvin and by Maxwell. Maxwell established the exponent of 2 to within one part in 20,000.

possible and may have certain advantages; e.g., the unit of charge may
be specified in advance. It was shown by Giorgi in 1901 that all of the
common electrical units, such as the ampere, volt, ohm, henry, etc.,
can be combined with one of the mechanical systems (namely, the mks
or meter-kilogram-second system) to form a system of units for all electric and magnetic problems. There is considerable advantage to having
the results of calculations come out in the same units as those which
are used in the laboratory; hence we shall use the rationalized *mks* or
Giorgi system of units in the present volume. Since in this system q is
measured in coulombs, r in meters and $\mathbf{F}$ in newtons, it is clear that C
must have the dimensions of newton·meters^2/coulomb^2. The size of
the unit of charge, the coulomb, is established from magnetic experiments; this requires that $C = 8.9874 \times 10^9$ n·m^2/coul^2. We make the
apparently complicated substitution, $C = 1/4\pi\epsilon_0$, in the interest of
future simplicity. The constant ϵ_0 will occur repeatedly; it represents
a property of free space known as the *permittivity of free space*, and is
numerically equal to 8.854×10^{-12} coul^2/n·m^2. In Appendix I the
definitions of the coulomb, the ampere, the permeability, and permittivity
of free space are related to one another and to the velocity of light in a
logical way; since a logical formulation of these definitions requires a
knowledge of magnetic phenomena and of electromagnetic wave propagation, it is not appropriate to pursue them now. In Appendix II other
systems of electrical units, in particular the gaussian system, are discussed.

If more than two point charges·are present, the mutual forces are
determined by the repeated application of Eq. (2–1). In particular, if a
system of N charges is considered, the force on the ith charge is given by

$$\mathbf{F}_i = q_i \sum_{j \neq i}^{N} \frac{q_j}{4\pi\epsilon_0} \frac{\mathbf{r}_{ji}}{r_{ji}^3}, \tag{2–2}$$

where the summation on the right is extended over all of the charges
except the ith. (This is, of course, just the superposition principle for
forces, which says that the total force acting on a body is the vector sum
of the individual forces which act on it.)

A simple extension of the ideas of N interacting point charges is the
interaction of a point charge with a continuous charge distribution. We
deliberately choose this configuration to avoid certain difficulties which
may be encountered when the interaction of two continuous charge distributions is considered. Before proceeding further the meaning of a continuous distribution of charge should be examined. It is now well known
that electric charge is found in multiples of a basic charge, that of the
electron. In other words, if any charge were examined in great detail,
its magnitude would be found to be an integral multiple of the magnitude
of the electronic charge. For the purposes of macroscopic physics this

discreteness of charge causes no difficulties simply because the electronic charge has a magnitude of 1.6019×10^{-19} coul, which is extremely small. The smallness of the basic unit means that macroscopic charges are invariably composed of a very large number of electronic charges; this in turn means that in a macroscopic charge distribution any small element of volume contains a large number of electrons. One may then describe a charge distribution in terms of a charge density function defined as the limit of the charge per unit volume as the volume becomes infinitesimal. Care must be used, however, in applying this kind of description to atomic problems, since in these cases only a small number of electrons is involved, and the process of taking the limit is meaningless. Leaving aside these atomic cases, we may proceed as if a segment of charge might be subdivided indefinitely, and describe the charge distribution by means of point functions:

a *volume charge density* defined by

$$\rho = \lim_{\Delta V \to 0} \frac{\Delta q}{\Delta V}, \tag{2-3}$$

and a *surface charge density* defined by

$$\sigma = \lim_{\Delta S \to 0} \frac{\Delta q}{\Delta S}. \tag{2-4}$$

From what has been said about q, it is evident that ρ and σ are net charge, or excess charge, densities. It is worth while mentioning that in typical solid materials even a very large charge density ρ will involve a change in the local electron density of only about one part in 10^9.

If charge is distributed through a volume V with a density ρ, and on the surface S which bounds V with a density σ, then the force exerted by this charge distribution on a point charge q located at $\mathbf{r}$ is obtained from (2-2) by replacing q_j with $\rho_j \, dv_j'$ (or with $\sigma_j \, da_j'$) and proceeding to the limit:

$$\mathbf{F}_q = \frac{q}{4\pi\epsilon_0} \int_V \frac{\mathbf{r} - \mathbf{r}'}{|\mathbf{r} - \mathbf{r}'|^3} \rho(r') \, dv' + \frac{q}{4\pi\epsilon_0} \int_S \frac{\mathbf{r} - \mathbf{r}'}{|\mathbf{r} - \mathbf{r}'|^3} \sigma(r') \, da'. \tag{2-5}$$

The variable $\mathbf{r}'$ is used to locate a point within the charge distribution, that is, it plays the role of the source point $\mathbf{r}_j$ in Eq. (2-2). It may appear at first sight that if point $\mathbf{r}$ falls inside the charge distribution, the first integral of (2-5) should diverge. This is not the case; the region of integration in the vicinity of $\mathbf{r}$ contributes a negligible amount, and the integral is well behaved (see Problem 2-5).

It is clear that the force on q as given by Eq. (2-5) is proportional to q; the same is true in Eq. (2-2). This observation leads us to introduce a vector field which is independent of q, namely, the force per unit charge.

This vector field, known as the *electric field*, is considered in detail in the following section.

2–3 The electric field. The electric field at a point is defined as the limit of the following ratio: the force on a test charge placed at the point, to the charge of the test charge, the limit being taken as the magnitude of the test charge goes to zero. The customary symbol for the electric field is **E**. In vector notation the definition of **E** becomes

$$\mathbf{E} = \lim_{q \to 0} \frac{\mathbf{F}_q}{q}. \tag{2–6}$$

The limiting process is included in the definition of **E** to ensure that the test charge does not affect the charge distribution which produces **E**. If, for example, positive charge is distributed on the surface of a conductor (a conductor is a material in which charge is free to move), then bringing a test charge into the vicinity of the conductor will cause the charge on the conductor to redistribute itself. If the electric field were calculated using the ratio of force to charge for a finite test charge, the field obtained would be that due to the redistributed charge rather than that due to the original charge distribution. In the special case where one of the charges of the charge distribution can be used as a test charge the limiting process is unnecessary. In this case the electric field at the location of the test charge will be that produced by all of the rest of the charge distribution; there will, of course, be no redistribution of charge, since the proper charge distribution obtains under the influence of the entire charge distribution, including the charge being used as test charge. In certain other cases, notably those in which the charge distribution is *specified*, the force will be proportional to the size of the test charge. In these cases, too, the limit is unnecessary; however, if any doubt exists, it is always safe to use the limiting process.

Equations (2–2) and (2–5) provide a ready means for obtaining an expression for the electric field due to a given distribution of charge. Let the charge distribution consist of N point charges $q_1, q_2, \ldots, q_N$ located at the points $\mathbf{r}_1, \mathbf{r}_2, \ldots, \mathbf{r}_N$ respectively, and a volume distribution of charge specified by the charge density $\rho(\mathbf{r}')$ in the volume V and a surface distribution characterized by the surface charge density $\sigma(\mathbf{r}')$ on the surface S. If a test charge q is located at the point $\mathbf{r}$, it experiences a force $\mathbf{F}$ given by

$$\mathbf{F} = \frac{q}{4\pi\epsilon_0} \sum_{i=1}^{N} q_i \frac{\mathbf{r} - \mathbf{r}_i}{|\mathbf{r} - \mathbf{r}_i|^3} + \frac{q}{4\pi\epsilon_0} \int_V \frac{\mathbf{r} - \mathbf{r}'}{|\mathbf{r} - \mathbf{r}'|^3} \rho(\mathbf{r}') \, dv'$$

$$+ \frac{q}{4\pi\epsilon_0} \int_S \frac{\mathbf{r} - \mathbf{r}'}{|\mathbf{r} - \mathbf{r}'|^3} \sigma(\mathbf{r}') \, da', \tag{2–7}$$

due to the given charge distribution. The electric field at **r** is the limit of the ratio of this force to the test charge q. Since the ratio is independent of q, the electric field at **r** is just

$$\mathbf{E}(\mathbf{r}) = \frac{1}{4\pi\epsilon_0} \sum_{i=1}^{N} q_i \frac{\mathbf{r} - \mathbf{r}_i}{|\mathbf{r} - \mathbf{r}_i|^3} + \frac{1}{4\pi\epsilon_0} \int_V \frac{\mathbf{r} - \mathbf{r}'}{|\mathbf{r} - \mathbf{r}'|^3} \rho(\mathbf{r}') \, dv'$$

$$+ \frac{1}{4\pi\epsilon_0} \int_S \frac{\mathbf{r} - \mathbf{r}'}{|\mathbf{r} - \mathbf{r}'|^3} \sigma(\mathbf{r}') \, da'. \quad (2\text{--}8)$$

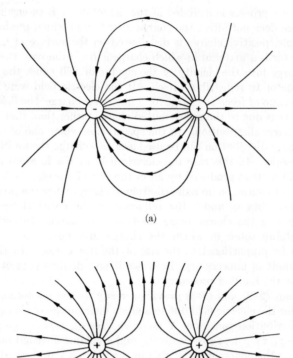

(a)

(b)

Fig. 2-1. The mapping of an electric field with the aid of lines of force.

Equation (2–8) is very general; in most cases one or more of the terms will not be needed.

The quantity we have just defined, the electric field, may be calculated at each point in space in the vicinity of a system of charges or of a charge distribution. Thus $\mathbf{E} = \mathbf{E}(\mathbf{r})$ is a vector point function, or a vector field. This field has a number of interesting mathematical properties which we shall proceed to develop in the following sections and in the next chapter. As an aid to visualizing the electric field structure associated with a particular distribution of charge, Michael Faraday (1791–1867) introduced the concept of *lines of force.* A line of force is an imaginary line (or curve) drawn in such a way that its direction at any point is the direction of the electric field at that point.

Consider, for example, the electric field structure associated with a single positive point charge q_1. The lines of force are radial lines radiating outward from q_1. Similarly, the lines of force associated with an isolated negative point charge are also radial lines, but this time the direction is inward (i.e., toward the negative charge). These two examples are extremely simple, but they nevertheless illustrate an important property of the field lines: the lines of force terminate on the sources of the electric field, i.e., upon the charges which produce the electric field.

Figure 2–1 shows several simple electric fields which have been mapped with the aid of lines of force.

2–4 The electrostatic potential. It has been noted in Chapter 1 that if the curl of a vector vanishes, then the vector may be expressed as the gradient of a scalar. The electric field given by Eq. (2–8) satisfies this criterion. To verify this, we note that taking the curl of Eq. (2–8) involves differentiating with respect to r. This variable appears in the equation only in functions of the form $(\mathbf{r} - \mathbf{r}')/|\mathbf{r} - \mathbf{r}'|^3$, and hence it will suffice to show that functions of this form have zero curl. Using the formula from Table 1–1 for the curl of the product (vector times scalar) gives

$$\operatorname{curl} \frac{\mathbf{r} - \mathbf{r}'}{|\mathbf{r} - \mathbf{r}'|^3} = \frac{1}{|\mathbf{r} - \mathbf{r}'|^3} \operatorname{curl} (\mathbf{r} - \mathbf{r}') + \left[\operatorname{grad} \frac{1}{|\mathbf{r} - \mathbf{r}'|^3} \right] \times [\mathbf{r} - \mathbf{r}'].$$

$$(2\text{--}9)$$

A direct calculation (see Problem 1–13) shows that

$$\operatorname{curl} (\mathbf{r} - \mathbf{r}') = 0, \qquad\qquad (2\text{--}10)$$

and (see Problem 1–16) that

$$\operatorname{grad} \frac{1}{|\mathbf{r} - \mathbf{r}'|^3} = -3 \frac{\mathbf{r} - \mathbf{r}'}{|\mathbf{r} - \mathbf{r}'|^5}. \qquad\qquad (2\text{--}11)$$

These results, together with the observation that the vector product of a vector with a parallel vector is zero, suffice to prove that

$$\text{curl} \frac{\mathbf{r} - \mathbf{r}'}{|\mathbf{r} - \mathbf{r}'|^3} = 0. \tag{2-12}$$

Since each contribution of Eq. (2–8) to the electric field is of this form, we have demonstrated that the curl of the electric field is zero. Equation (2–12) indicates that a scalar function exists whose gradient is the electric field; it remains to find this function. That is, we now know that a function exists which satisfies

$$\mathbf{E}(\mathbf{r}) = -\text{grad} \, U(\mathbf{r}), \tag{2-13}$$

but we have yet to find the form of the function U. It should be noted that it is conventional to include the minus sign in Eq. (2–13) and to call U the electrostatic potential.

It is easy to find the electrostatic potential due to a point charge q_1; it is just

$$U(\mathbf{r}) = \frac{1}{4\pi\epsilon_0} \frac{q_1}{|\mathbf{r} - \mathbf{r}_1|}, \tag{2-14}$$

as is readily verified by direct differentiation. With this as a clue it is easy to guess that the potential which gives the electric field of Eq. (2–8) is

$$U(\mathbf{r}) = \frac{1}{4\pi\epsilon_0} \sum_{i=1}^{N} \frac{q_i}{|\mathbf{r} - \mathbf{r}_i|} + \frac{1}{4\pi\epsilon_0} \int_V \frac{\rho(\mathbf{r}')}{|\mathbf{r} - \mathbf{r}'|} \, dv'$$
$$+ \frac{1}{4\pi\epsilon_0} \int_S \frac{\sigma(\mathbf{r}')}{|\mathbf{r} - \mathbf{r}'|} \, da', \tag{2-15}$$

which is also easily verified by direct differentiation. It may seem that Eqs. (2–14) and (2–15) were obtained in a rather arbitrary fashion; however, since all that is required of U is that it satisfy (2–13), and since this has been verified directly, the means by which U was obtained is immaterial.

The electrostatic potential U can be obtained directly as soon as its existence is established. Since U is known to exist, we may write

$$\int_{\text{ref}}^{\mathbf{r}} \mathbf{E}(\mathbf{r}') \cdot d\mathbf{r}' = - \int_{\text{ref}}^{\mathbf{r}} \text{grad} \, U \cdot d\mathbf{r}', \tag{2-16}$$

where ref stands for a reference point at which U is zero. From the definition of the gradient,

$$\text{grad} \, U \cdot d\mathbf{r}' = dU. \tag{2-17}$$

Using (2–17) in Eq. (2–16) converts it into the integral of a perfect differential, which is easily done. The result is

$$-\int_{\text{ref}}^{\mathbf{r}} \mathbf{grad}\; U \cdot d\mathbf{r}' = -U(\mathbf{r}) = \int_{\text{ref}}^{\mathbf{r}} \mathbf{E}(\mathbf{r}') \cdot d\mathbf{r}', \qquad (2\text{–}18)$$

which is really the inverse of Eq. (2–13). If the electric field due to a point charge is used in equation (2–18), and the reference point or lower limit in the integral is taken at infinity, with the potential there zero, the result is

$$U(\mathbf{r}) = \frac{q}{4\pi\epsilon_0 r}. \qquad (2\text{–}19)$$

This, of course, is just a special case of Eq. (2–14), namely, the case where r_1 is zero. This derivation can be extended to obtain Eq. (2–15); however, the procedure is too cumbersome to include here.

Another interesting and useful aspect of the electrostatic potential is its close relation to the potential energy associated with the conservative electrostatic force. The potential energy associated with an arbitrary conservative force is

$$W(\mathbf{r}) = -\int_{\text{ref}}^{\mathbf{r}} \mathbf{F}(\mathbf{r}') \cdot d\mathbf{r}', = \quad \frac{kq_1 q_2}{r} \qquad (2\text{–}20)$$

where $W(\mathbf{r})$ is the potential energy at $\mathbf{r}$ relative to the reference point at which the potential energy is arbitrarily taken to be zero. Since in the electrostatic case $\mathbf{F} = q\mathbf{E}$, it follows that if the same reference point is chosen for the electrostatic potential and for the potential energy, then the electrostatic potential is just the potential energy per unit charge. This idea is sometimes used to introduce the electrostatic potential; we feel, however, that the introduction by means of Eq. (2–13) emphasizes the importance of the electrostatic potential in determining the electrostatic field. There is, of course, no question about the ultimate equivalence of the two approaches.

The utility of the electrostatic potential in calculating electric fields can be seen by contrasting Eqs. (2–8) and (2–15). Equation (2–8) is a vector equation; to obtain the electric field from it, it is necessary to evaluate three sums or three integrals for each term. At best this is a tedious procedure; in some cases it is almost impossible to do the integrals. Equation (2–15), on the other hand, is a scalar equation and involves only one sum or integral per term. Furthermore, the denominators appearing in this equation are all of the form $|\mathbf{r} - \mathbf{r}'|$, which simplifies the integrals compared with those of Eq. (2–8). This simplification is sometimes sufficient to make the difference between doing the integrals and not doing them. It may be objected that after doing the integrals of Eq. (2–15) it is still necessary to differentiate the result; this objection is readily answered by observing that differentiation can always be accomplished if the derivatives exist, and is in fact usually much easier than integration. In Chapter 3 it will be seen that the electrostatic potential is even more important in those problems where the charge distribution is not specified, but must rather be determined in the process of solving the problem.

In the mks system the unit of energy is the newton-meter or joule. The unit of potential is joule/coulomb, but this unit occurs so frequently that it is given a special name, the volt. The unit of the electric field is the newton/coulomb or the volt/meter.

2–5 Conductors and insulators.

So far as their electrical behavior is concerned, materials may be divided into two categories: *conductors* of electricity and *insulators* (*dielectrics*). Conductors are substances, like the metals, which contain large numbers of essentially free charge carriers. These charge carriers (electrons in most cases) are free to wander throughout the conducting material; they respond to almost infinitesimal electric fields, and they continue to move as long as they experience a field. These free carriers carry the electric current when an electric field is maintained in the conductor by an external source of energy.

Dielectrics are substances in which all charged particles are bound rather strongly to constituent molecules. The charged particles may shift their positions slightly in response to an electric field, but they do not leave the vicinity of their molecules. Strictly speaking, this definition applies to an ideal dielectric, one which shows no conductivity in the presence of an externally maintained electric field. Real physical dielectrics may show a feeble conductivity, but in a typical dielectric the conductivity is 10^{20} times smaller than that of a good conductor. Since 10^{20} is a tremendous factor, it is usually sufficient to say that dielectrics are nonconductors.

Certain materials (semiconductors, electrolytes) have electrical properties intermediate between conductors and dielectrics. So far as their behavior in a static electric field is concerned, these materials behave very much like conductors. However, their transient response is somewhat slower; i.e., it takes longer for these materials to reach equilibrium in a static field.

In this and the following four chapters we shall be concerned with materials in *electrostatic* fields. Dielectric polarization, although a basically simple phenomenon, produces some rather complicated effects; hence we shall delay its study until Chapter 4. Conductors, on the other hand, may be treated quite easily in terms of concepts which have already been developed.

Since charge is free to move in a conductor, even under the influence of very small electric fields, the charge carriers (electrons or ions) move until they find positions in which they experience no net force. When they come to rest, the interior of the conductor must be a region devoid of an electric field; this must be so because the charge carrier population in the interior is by no means depleted, and if a field persisted, the carriers would continue to move. *Thus, under static conditions, the electric field in a conductor vanishes.* Furthermore, since $\mathbf{E} = 0$ in a conductor, the potential is the same at all points in the conducting material. In other words, *under static conditions, each conductor forms an equipotential region of space.*

2–6 Gauss' law. An important relationship exists between the integral of the normal component of the electric field over a closed surface and the total charge enclosed by the surface. This relationship, known as Gauss' law, will now be investigated in more detail. The electric field at point $\mathbf{r}$ due to a point charge q located at the origin is

$$\mathbf{E}(\mathbf{r}) = \frac{q}{4\pi\epsilon_0}\frac{\mathbf{r}}{r^3}. \tag{2–21}$$

Consider the surface integral of the normal component of this electric field over a closed surface (such as that shown in Fig. 2–2) which encloses the origin and, consequently, the charge q; this integral is just

$$\oint_S \mathbf{E}\cdot\mathbf{n}\,da = \frac{q}{4\pi\epsilon_0}\oint_S \frac{\mathbf{r}\cdot\mathbf{n}}{r^3}\,da. \tag{2–22}$$

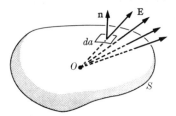

Fig. 2–2. An imaginary closed surface S which encloses a point charge at the origin.

The quantity $(\mathbf{r}/r)\cdot\mathbf{n}\,da$ is the projection of da on a plane perpendicular to r. This projected area divided by r^2 is the solid angle subtended by da, which is written $d\Omega$. It is clear from Fig. 2–3 that the solid angle subtended by da is the same as the solid angle subtended by da', an element of the surface area of the sphere S' whose center is at the origin and whose radius is r'. It is then possible to write

$$\oint_S \frac{\mathbf{r}\cdot\mathbf{n}}{r^3}\,da = \oint_{S'} \frac{\mathbf{r}'\cdot\mathbf{n}}{r'^3}\,da' = 4\pi,$$

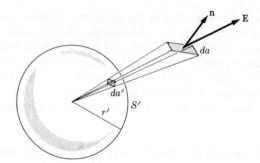

FIG. 2–3. Construction of the spherical surface S' as an aid to evaluation of the solid angle subtended by da.

which shows that

$$\oint_S \mathbf{E} \cdot \mathbf{n} \, da = \frac{q}{4\pi\epsilon_0} 4\pi = \frac{q}{\epsilon_0} \tag{2–23}$$

in the special case described above. If q lies outside of S, it is clear from Fig. 2–4 that S can be divided into two areas S_1 and S_2 each of which subtends the same solid angle at the charge q. For S_2, however, the direction of the normal is towards q, while for S_1 it is away from q. Therefore the contributions of S_1 and S_2 to the surface integral are equal and opposite, and the total integral vanishes. Thus if the surface surrounds a point charge q, the surface integral of the normal component of the electric field is q/ϵ_0, while if q lies outside the surface the surface integral is zero.

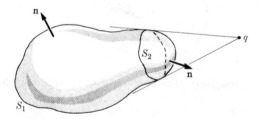

FIG. 2–4. The closed surface S may be divided into two surfaces, S_1 and S_2, each of which subtend the same solid angle at q.

The preceding statement applies to any closed surface, even to so-called re-entrant ones. A study of Fig. 2–5 is sufficient to verify that this is indeed the case.

If several point charges $q_1, q_2, \ldots, q_N$ are enclosed by the surface S, then the total electric field is given by the first term of Eq. (2–8). Each

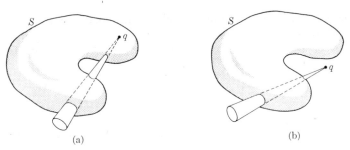

FIG. 2-5. An element of solid angle cutting the surface S more than once.

charge subtends a full solid angle (4π); hence Eq. (2-23) becomes

$$\oint_S \mathbf{E} \cdot \mathbf{n} \, da = \frac{1}{\epsilon_0} \sum_{i=1}^{N} q_i. \tag{2-24}$$

This result can be readily generalized to the case of a continuous distribution of charge characterized by a charge density. If each element of charge $\rho \, dv$ is considered as a point charge, it contributes $\rho \, dv/\epsilon_0$ to the surface integral of the normal component of the electric field provided it is inside the surface over which we integrate. The total surface integral is then the sum of all contributions of this form due to the charge inside the surface. Thus if S is a closed surface which bounds the volume V,

$$\oint_S \mathbf{E} \cdot \mathbf{n} \, da = \frac{1}{\epsilon_0} \int_V \rho \, dv. \tag{2-25}$$

Equations (2-24) and (2-25) are known as Gauss' law. The term on the left, the integral of the normal component of the electric field over the surface S, is sometimes called the *flux* of the electric field through S.

Gauss' law may be expressed in yet another form by using the divergence theorem. The divergence theorem (1-37) states that

$$\oint_S \mathbf{F} \cdot \mathbf{n} \, da = \int_V \operatorname{div} \mathbf{F} \, dv.$$

If this theorem is applied to the surface integral of the normal component of $\mathbf{E}$, it yields

$$\oint_S \mathbf{E} \cdot \mathbf{n} \, da = \int_V \operatorname{div} \mathbf{E} \, dv, \tag{2-26}$$

which, when substituted into Eq. (2-25), gives

$$\int_V \operatorname{div} \mathbf{E} \, dv = \frac{1}{\epsilon_0} \int_V \rho \, dv. \tag{2-27}$$

Equation (2–27) must be valid for all volumes, that is, for any choice of the volume V. The only way in which this can be true is if the integrands appearing on the left and on the right in the equation are equal. Thus the validity of Eq. (2–27) for any choice of V implies that

$$\operatorname{div} \mathbf{E} = \frac{1}{\epsilon_0} \rho. \tag{2–28}$$

This result may be thought of as a differential form of Gauss' law.

2–7 Application of Gauss' law. Equation (2–28) or, more properly, a modified form of this equation which will be derived in Chapter 4, is one of the basic differential equations of electricity and magnetism. In this role it is important, of course; but Gauss' law also has practical utility. This practicality of the law lies largely in providing a very easy way to calculate electric fields in sufficiently symmetric situations. In other words, in certain highly symmetric situations of considerable physical interest, the electric field may be calculated by using Gauss' law instead of by the integrals given above or by the procedures of Chapter 3. When this can be done, it accomplishes a major saving in effort.

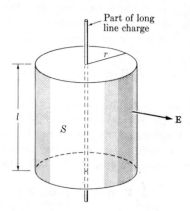

FIG. 2–6. A cylindrical surface to be used with Gauss' law to find the electric field produced by a long line charge.

In order that Gauss' law be useful in calculating the electric field, it must be possible to choose a closed surface such that the electric field has a normal component which is either zero or a single fixed value at every point on the surface. As an example, consider a very long line charge of charge density λ per unit length, as shown in Fig. 2–6. The symmetry of the situation clearly indicates that the electric field is radial and independent of both position along the wire and angular position around the wire. These observations lead us to choose the surface shown in Fig. 2–6. For this surface it is easy to evaluate the integral of the normal component of the electric field. The circular ends contribute nothing, since the electric field is parallel to them. The cylindrical surface contributes $2\pi rlE_r$ since **E** is radial and independent of the position of the cylindrical surface. Gauss' law then takes the form

$$2\pi rlE_r = \frac{\lambda l}{\epsilon_0}.$$ (2–29)

Equation (2–29) can be solved for E_r to give

$$E_r = \frac{\lambda}{2\pi\epsilon_0 r}.$$ (2–30)

The saving of effort accomplished by the use of Gauss' law will be more fully appreciated by solving Problem 2–4, which involves direct application of Eq. (2–8).

Another important result of Gauss' law is that the charge (net charge) of a charged conductor resides on its surface. We saw in Section 2–5 that the electric field inside a conductor vanishes. We may construct a gaussian surface anywhere inside the conductor; by Gauss' law, the net charge enclosed by each of these surfaces is zero. Finally, we construct the gaussian surface S of Fig. 2–7; again the net charge enclosed is zero. The only place left for the charge which is not in contradiction with Gauss' law is for it to reside on the surface of the conductor.

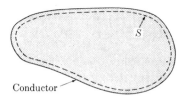

FIG. 2–7. A gaussian surface S constructed inside a charged conductor.

The electric field just outside a charged conductor must be normal to the surface of the conductor. This follows because the surface is an equipotential, and $\mathbf{E} = -\mathbf{grad}\ U$. Let us assume that the charge on a conductor is given by the surface density function σ. If Gauss' law is applied to the small pillbox-shaped surface S of Fig. 2–8, then

$$E\ \Delta S = \left(\frac{\sigma}{\epsilon_0}\right)\Delta S,$$

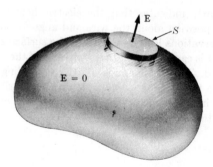

FIG. 2–8. Application of Gauss' law to the closed, pillbox-shaped surface S which intersects the surface of a charged conductor.

where ΔS is the area of one of the pillbox bases. Hence, for the electric field just outside a conductor,

$$E = \frac{\sigma}{\epsilon_0}. \qquad (2\text{–}31)$$

2–8 The electric dipole. Two equal and opposite charges separated by a small distance form an electric dipole. The electric field and potential distribution produced by such a charge configuration can be investigated with the aid of the formulas of Sections 2–3 and 2–4. Suppose that a charge $-q$ is located at the point $\mathbf{r}'$ and a charge q is located at $\mathbf{r}' + \mathbf{l}$, as shown in Fig. 2–9; then the electric field at an arbitrary point $\mathbf{r}$ may be found by direct application of Eq. (2–8). The electric field at $\mathbf{r}$ is found to be

$$\mathbf{E}(\mathbf{r}) = \frac{q}{4\pi\epsilon_0} \left\{ \frac{\mathbf{r} - \mathbf{r}' - \mathbf{l}}{|\mathbf{r} - \mathbf{r}' - \mathbf{l}|^3} - \frac{\mathbf{r} - \mathbf{r}'}{|\mathbf{r} - \mathbf{r}'|^3} \right\}. \qquad (2\text{–}32)$$

This is the correct electric field for any value of q and any value of the separation $\mathbf{l}$; however, it is not easy to interpret. What we want is the dipole field, and in the dipole the separation $\mathbf{l}$ is small compared with $\mathbf{r} - \mathbf{r}'$; hence we may expand Eq. (2–32), keeping only the first non-vanishing term. Since this procedure is of general utility it will be considered in detail. The primary difficulty in making this expansion is caused by the denominator of the first term of Eq. (2–32). The reciprocal of this denominator can be rewritten as

$$|\mathbf{r} - \mathbf{r}' - \mathbf{l}|^{-3} = [(\mathbf{r} - \mathbf{r}')^2 - 2(\mathbf{r} - \mathbf{r}') \cdot \mathbf{l} + l^2]^{-3/2}$$

$$= |\mathbf{r} - \mathbf{r}'|^{-3} \left[1 - \frac{2(\mathbf{r} - \mathbf{r}') \cdot \mathbf{l}}{|\mathbf{r} - \mathbf{r}'|^2} + \frac{l^2}{|\mathbf{r} - \mathbf{r}'|^2} \right]^{-3/2}.$$

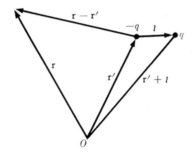

Fig. 2–9. Geometry involved in calculating the electric field $\mathbf{E}(\mathbf{r})$ due to two point charges.

In the last form it is easy to expand by the binomial theorem, keeping only terms linear in l. The result of this expansion is

$$|\mathbf{r} - \mathbf{r}' - \boldsymbol{l}|^{-3} = |\mathbf{r} - \mathbf{r}'|^{-3} \left\{ 1 + \frac{3(\mathbf{r} - \mathbf{r}') \cdot \boldsymbol{l}}{|\mathbf{r} - \mathbf{r}'|^2} + \cdots \right\}, \quad (2\text{–}33)$$

where terms involving l^2 have been dropped. Using Eq. (2–33) in Eq. (2–32) and again keeping only terms linear in l gives

$$\mathbf{E}(\mathbf{r}) = \frac{q}{4\pi\epsilon_0} \left\{ \frac{3(\mathbf{r} - \mathbf{r}') \cdot \boldsymbol{l}}{|\mathbf{r} - \mathbf{r}'|^5} (\mathbf{r} - \mathbf{r}') - \frac{\boldsymbol{l}}{|\mathbf{r} - \mathbf{r}'|^3} + \cdots \right\}. \quad (2\text{–}34)$$

Equation (2–34) gives that part of the electric field, due to a finite electric dipole, which is proportional to the separation of the charges. There are other contributions proportional to the square, the cube, and higher powers of the separation. If, however, the separation is small, these higher powers contribute very little. In the limit as l goes to zero, all of the terms vanish unless the charge becomes infinite. In the limit as l goes to zero while q becomes infinite, in such a way that ql remains constant, all terms except the term linear in l vanish. In this limit a point dipole is formed. A point dipole has no net charge, no extent in space, and is completely characterized by its dipole moment, which is the limit of ql as l goes to zero. We use the symbol $\mathbf{p}$ to represent the electric dipole moment, and write

$$\mathbf{p} = q\boldsymbol{l}. \quad (2\text{–}35)$$

In terms of the dipole moment, Eq. (2–34) may be written

$$\mathbf{E}(\mathbf{r}) = \frac{1}{4\pi\epsilon_0} \left\{ \frac{3(\mathbf{r} - \mathbf{r}') \cdot \mathbf{p}}{|\mathbf{r} - \mathbf{r}'|^5} (\mathbf{r} - \mathbf{r}') - \frac{\mathbf{p}}{|\mathbf{r} - \mathbf{r}'|^3} \right\}. \quad (2\text{–}36)$$

The potential distribution produced by a point dipole is also important. This could be found by looking for a function with gradient equal to the right side of Eq. (2–36). It is, however, easier to apply Eq. (2–15) to the charge distribution consisting of two point charges separated by a small distance. Using the notation of Eq. (2–32), the potential distribution is given by

$$U(\mathbf{r}) = \frac{q}{4\pi\epsilon_0}\left[\frac{1}{|\mathbf{r} - \mathbf{r}' - \boldsymbol{l}|} - \frac{1}{|\mathbf{r} - \mathbf{r}'|}\right]. \tag{2–37}$$

By expanding the first term in exactly the same way as was done for the first term of (2–32) and retaining only the linear term in $\boldsymbol{l}$, Eq. (2–37) can be put in the form

$$U(\mathbf{r}) = \frac{q}{4\pi\epsilon_0}\frac{(\mathbf{r} - \mathbf{r}') \cdot \boldsymbol{l}}{|\mathbf{r} - \mathbf{r}'|^3}. \tag{2–38}$$

This equation is valid to the same approximation as Eq. (2–34); namely, terms proportional to l^2 and to higher powers of l are neglected. For a point dipole, $\mathbf{p}$, Eq. (2–38) is exact; however, it is better written as

$$U(\mathbf{r}) = \frac{1}{4\pi\epsilon_0}\frac{\mathbf{p} \cdot (\mathbf{r} - \mathbf{r}')}{|\mathbf{r} - \mathbf{r}'|^3}. \tag{2–39}$$

Equation (2–39) gives the potential $U(\mathbf{r})$ produced by an electric dipole; from this potential the electric field (Eq. 2–36) may be determined. It is also interesting to inquire about the potential energy of an electric dipole which is placed in an *external electric field*. In the case of two charges, $-q$ at $\mathbf{r}$ and q at $\mathbf{r} + \boldsymbol{l}$, in an electric field described by the potential function $U_{\text{ext}}(\mathbf{r})$, the potential energy is just

$$W = -qU_{\text{ext}}(\mathbf{r}) + qU_{\text{ext}}(\mathbf{r} + \boldsymbol{l}). \tag{2–40}$$

If $\boldsymbol{l}$ is small compared with $\mathbf{r}$, $U_{\text{ext}}(\mathbf{r} + \boldsymbol{l})$ may be expanded in a power series in $\boldsymbol{l}$ and only the first two terms kept. The expansion gives

$$U_{\text{ext}}(\mathbf{r} + \boldsymbol{l}) = U_{\text{ext}}(\mathbf{r}) + \boldsymbol{l} \cdot \mathbf{grad}\, U_{\text{ext}}, \tag{2–41}$$

where the value of the gradient at point $\mathbf{r}$ is to be used. If this expansion is used in Eq. (2–40), the result is

$$W = q\boldsymbol{l} \cdot \mathbf{grad}\, U_{\text{ext}}. \tag{2–42}$$

Going to the limit of a point dipole gives simply

$$W(\mathbf{r}) = \mathbf{p} \cdot \mathbf{grad}\, U_{\text{ext}}, \tag{2–43}$$

which is, of course, exact. Since the electric field is the negative gradient of the electrostatic potential, an alternative form of Eq. (2–43) is

$$W(\mathbf{r}) = -\mathbf{p} \cdot \mathbf{E}_{ext}(\mathbf{r}). \qquad (2\text{–}44)$$

This, then, is the potential energy of a dipole $\mathbf{p}$ in an external electric field $\mathbf{E}_{ext}$, where $\mathbf{E}_{ext}(\mathbf{r})$ is evaluated at the location of the dipole.

It is important to note that two potentials have been discussed in this section. In Eqs. (2–37), (2–38), and (2–39), the electrostatic potential *produced by* an electric dipole is considered. In Eqs. (2–40) through (2–43), the dipole is considered to be in an *existing electric field* described by a potential function $U_{ext}(\mathbf{r})$. This electric field is due to charges other than those comprising the dipole; in fact, the dipole field must be excluded to avoid an infinite result. This statement could lead us to rather complicated questions concerning self-forces and self-energies which we cannot discuss here; however, it may be noted that the potential energy resulting from the interaction of an electric dipole with its own field arises from forces exerted on the dipole by itself. Such forces, known in dynamics as internal forces, do not affect the motion of the dipole as a whole. For our purposes further consideration of this question will be unnecessary.

2–9 Multipole expansion of electric fields. It is apparent from the definition of dipole moments given above that certain aspects of the potential distribution produced by a specified distribution of charge might well be expressed in terms of its electric dipole moment. In order to do this it is necessary, of course, to define the electric dipole moment of an arbitrary charge distribution. Rather than make an unmotivated definition, we shall consider a certain expansion of the electrostatic potential due to an arbitrary charge distribution. To reduce the number of position coordinates, a charge distribution in the neighborhood of the origin of coordinates will be considered. The further restriction will be made that the charge distribution can be entirely enclosed by a sphere of radius a which is small compared with the distance to the point of observation. An arbitrary point within the charge distribution will be designated by $\mathbf{r}'$, the charge density at that point by $\rho(\mathbf{r}')$, and the observation point by $\mathbf{r}$ (see Fig. 2–10). The potential at $\mathbf{r}$ is given by

$$U(\mathbf{r}) = \frac{1}{4\pi\epsilon_0} \int_{V'} \frac{\rho(\mathbf{r}')}{|\mathbf{r} - \mathbf{r}'|} \, dv', \qquad (2\text{–}45)$$

where dv' is used to designate an element of volume in the charge distribution and V' denotes the entire volume occupied by the charge distribution. In view of the restriction made above to points of observation which are remote from the origin, the quantity $|\mathbf{r} - \mathbf{r}'|^{-1}$ can be expanded in a series of ascending powers of $\mathbf{r}'/r$. The result of such an expansion is

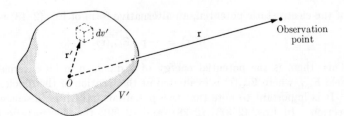

FIG. 2–10. The charge is localized in the volume V with charge density $\rho(\mathbf{r}')$. The electric field is to be calculated at point $\mathbf{r}$.

$$|\mathbf{r} - \mathbf{r}'|^{-1} = (r^2 - 2\mathbf{r} \cdot \mathbf{r}' + r'^2)^{-1/2}$$

$$= \frac{1}{r} \left\{ 1 - \frac{1}{2}\left[-\frac{2\mathbf{r} \cdot \mathbf{r}'}{r^2} + \frac{r'^2}{r^2} \right] + \frac{1}{2}\frac{1}{2}\frac{3}{2}[\quad]^2 + \cdots \right\}, \quad (2\text{–}46)$$

where only the first three terms are explicitly indicated. It should be noted that while $(r'/r)^2$ is negligible compared with $2\mathbf{r}' \cdot \mathbf{r}/r^2$, it may not be dropped in the first set of brackets because it is of the same order as the dominant term in the second set of brackets. Using Eq. (2–46) in Eq. (2–45) and omitting terms involving the cube and higher powers of $\mathbf{r}'$ yields

$$U(\mathbf{r}) = \frac{1}{4\pi\epsilon_0}\int_{V'} \left\{ \frac{1}{r} + \frac{\mathbf{r} \cdot \mathbf{r}'}{r^3} + \frac{1}{2}\left[\frac{3(\mathbf{r} \cdot \mathbf{r}')^2}{r^5} - \frac{r'^2}{r^3} \right] + \cdots \right\} \rho(r')\, dv'.$$

$$(2\text{–}47)$$

Since $\mathbf{r}$ does not involve the variable of integration $\mathbf{r}'$, all of the $\mathbf{r}$ dependence may be taken from under the integral sign, to obtain

$$U(\mathbf{r}) = \frac{1}{4\pi\epsilon_0}\left\{ \frac{1}{r}\int_{V'}\rho(r')\, dv' + \frac{\mathbf{r}}{r^3} \cdot \int_{V'}\mathbf{r}'\rho(r')\, dv' \right.$$

$$\left. + \sum_{i=1}^{3}\sum_{j=1}^{3}\frac{1}{2}\frac{x_i x_j}{r^5}\int_{V'}(3x_i'x_j' - \delta_{ij}r'^2)\rho(\mathbf{r}')\, dv', \right. \quad (2\text{–}48)$$

where x_i, x_j are cartesian components of $\mathbf{r}$, x_i', x_j' are the cartesian components of $\mathbf{r}'$, and δ_{ij} is defined as follows:

$$\delta_{ij} = \begin{Bmatrix} 0, & i \neq j \\ 1, & i = j \end{Bmatrix}.$$

It is easy to interpret Eq. (2–48). The first integral in the equation is clearly the total charge, and the first term is the potential which would result if this total charge were concentrated at the origin. The second integral is very similar to the dipole moment defined in Section 2–7, and so it is called the dipole moment of the charge distribution. As a definition, this represents a generalization of the definition given for two equal and opposite point charges; it is easy to show, however, that both definitions give the same result for two equal and opposite point charges. The second term in Eq. (2–48) is the potential which would result if a point dipole equal to the dipole moment of the charge distribution were located at the origin of coordinates. It is interesting to note that the dipole moment of a charge distribution is independent of the origin of coordinates if the total charge is zero. To verify this, consider a new coordinate system with *origin* at $\mathbf{R}$ in the old system. Denoting a point with respect to the old system by $\mathbf{r}'$ and the same point with respect to the new system by $\mathbf{r}''$, we have

$$\mathbf{r}' = \mathbf{r}'' + \mathbf{R}. \qquad (2\text{–}49)$$

The dipole moment with respect to the old system is

$$\mathbf{p} = \int_{V'} \mathbf{r}'\rho(\mathbf{r}')\, dv' = \int_{V'} (\mathbf{r}'' + \mathbf{R})\rho(\mathbf{r}')\, dv' = \int_{V'} \mathbf{r}''\rho\, dv' + \mathbf{R}Q, \qquad (2\text{–}50)$$

which proves the statement above.

The third term of Eq. (2–48) can be written

$$\sum_{i=1}^{3} \sum_{j=1}^{3} \frac{1}{2} \frac{x_i x_j}{r^5} Q_{ij}, \qquad (2\text{–}51)$$

where Q_{ij} is given by

$$Q_{ij} = \int_{V'} (3x_i' x_j' - \delta_{ij} r'^2)\rho(r')\, dv'. \qquad (2\text{–}52)$$

There are nine components of Q_{ij} corresponding to i, j equal to 1, 2, 3. Of these nine components six are equal in pairs, leaving six distinct components. This set of quantities form the quadrupole moment tensor and represent an extension of the dipole moment concept. There are, of course, higher-order moments which are generated by keeping higher-order terms in the expansion of Eq. (2–48). These higher-order multipoles are important in nuclear physics, but will not be considered further in this book.

The electric multipoles are used, as Eq. (2–48) indicates, to approximate the electric field of a charge distribution. There are, however, many other uses, all in the framework of approximating a real extended charge distribution by point charges, point dipoles, etc. These approximations often make it possible to solve problems which would otherwise be prohibitively difficult.

PROBLEMS

2-1. Two particles, each of mass m and having charge q, are suspended by strings of length l from a common point. Find the angle θ which each string makes with the vertical.

2-2. Two small identical conducting spheres have charges of 2.0×10^{-9} coul and -0.5×10^{-9} coul, respectively. When they are placed 4 cm apart, what is the force between them? If they are brought into contact and then separated by 4 cm, what is the force between them?

2-3. Point charges of 3×10^{-9} coul are situated at each of three corners of a square whose side is 15 cm. Find the magnitude and direction of the electric field at the vacant corner point of the square.

2-4. Given an infinitely long line charge with uniform charge density λ per unit length. Using direct integration, find the electric field at a distance r from the line.

2-5. (a) A circular disk of radius R has a uniform surface charge density σ. Find the electric field at a point on the axis of the disk at a distance z from the plane of the disk. (b) A right circular cylinder of radius R and height L is oriented along the z-axis. It has a nonuniform volume density of charge given by $\rho(z) = \rho_0 + \beta z$ with reference to an origin at the center of the cylinder. Find the force on a point charge q placed at the center of the cylinder.

2-6. A thin, conducting, spherical shell of radius R is charged uniformly with total charge Q. By direct integration, find the potential at an arbitrary point (a) inside the shell, (b) outside the shell.

2-7. Two point charges, $-q$ and $+\frac{1}{2}q$, are situated at the origin and at the point $(a, 0, 0)$ respectively. At what point along the x-axis does the electric field vanish? In the x, y-plane, make a plot of the equipotential surface which goes through the point just referred to. Is this point a true minimum in the potential?

2-8. Show that the $U = 0$ equipotential surface of the preceding problem is spherical in shape. What are the coordinates of the center of this sphere?

2-9. Given a right circular cylinder of radius R and length L containing a uniform charge density ρ. Calculate the electrostatic potential at a point on the cylinder axis but external to the distribution.

2-10. Given a region of space in which the electric field is everywhere directed parallel to the x-axis. Prove that the electric field is independent of the y- and z-coordinates in this region. If there is no charge in this region, prove that the field is also independent of x.

2-11. Given that the dielectric strength of air (i.e., the electric field which produces corona) is 3×10^6 v/m, what is the highest possible potential of an isolated spherical conductor of radius 10 cm?

2-12. A conducting object has a hollow cavity in its interior. If a point charge q is introduced into the cavity, prove that the charge $-q$ is induced on the surface of the cavity. (Use Gauss' law.)

2-13. The electric field in the atmosphere at the earth's surface is approximately 200 v/m, directed downward. At 1400 m above the earth's surface, the electric field in the atmosphere is only 20 v/m, again directed downward. What is the average charge density in the atmosphere below 1400 m? Does this consist predominantly of *positive* or *negative* ions?

2-14. Two infinite parallel conducting plates are separated by the distance d. If the plates have uniform charge densities σ and $-\sigma$, respectively, on their inside surfaces, obtain an expression for the electric field between the plates. Prove that the electric field in the regions external to the plates is zero. [Two charged parallel conducting plates of finite area produce essentially the same electric field in the region between them as was found above provided the dimensions of the plates are large compared with the separation d; such an arrangement is called a *capacitor* (see Chapter 6).]

2-15. A spherical charge distribution has a volume charge density which is a function only of r, the distance from the center of the distribution. In other words, $\rho = \rho(r)$. If $\rho(r)$ is as given below, determine the electric field as a function of r. Integrate the result to obtain an expression for the electrostatic potential $U(r)$, subject to the restriction that $U(\infty) = 0$.

(a) $\rho = A/r$ with A a constant for $0 \leq r \leq R$;
   $\rho = 0$ for $r > R$.

(b) $\rho = \rho_0$ (i.e., constant) for $0 \leq r \leq R$;
   $\rho = 0$ for $r > R$.

2-16. Using Eq. (2-39) for the potential produced by a dipole $\mathbf{p}$, make a plot of the traces of equipotential surfaces in a plane containing the dipole. For convenience, the dipole may be located at the origin. Use the results obtained to sketch in some of the lines of force. Compare the result with Fig. 2-1.

2-17. (a) Show that the force acting on a dipole $\mathbf{p}$ placed in an external electric field $\mathbf{E}_{ext}$ is $\mathbf{p} \cdot \nabla \mathbf{E}_{ext}$. (b) Show that the torque acting on the dipole in this field is

$$\boldsymbol{\tau} = \mathbf{r} \times [\mathbf{p} \cdot \nabla \mathbf{E}_{ext}] + \mathbf{p} \times \mathbf{E}_{ext},$$

where $\mathbf{r}$ is the vector distance to the dipole from the point about which the torque is to be measured. The quantity $\mathbf{p} \times \mathbf{E}_{ext}$, which is independent of the point about which the torque is computed, is called the turning couple acting on the dipole.

2-18. Three charges are arranged in a linear array. The charge $-2q$ is placed at the origin, and two charges, each of $+q$, are placed at $(0, 0, l)$ and $(0, 0, -l)$ respectively. Find a relatively simple expression for the potential $U(\mathbf{r})$ which is valid for distances $|\mathbf{r}| \gg l$. Make a plot of the equipotential surfaces in the x, z-plane.

CHAPTER 3

SOLUTION OF ELECTROSTATIC PROBLEMS

The solution to an electrostatic problem is straightforward for the case in which the charge distribution is everywhere specified, for then, as we have seen, the potential and electric field are given directly as integrals over this charge distribution:

$$U(\mathbf{r}) = \frac{1}{4\pi\epsilon_0} \int \frac{dq'}{|\mathbf{r} - \mathbf{r}'|},$$ (3-1)

$$\mathbf{E}(\mathbf{r}) = \frac{1}{4\pi\epsilon_0} \int \frac{(\mathbf{r} - \mathbf{r}')\,dq'}{|\mathbf{r} - \mathbf{r}'|^3}.$$ (3-2)

However, many of the problems encountered in practice are not of this type. If the charge distribution is not specified in advance, it may be necessary to determine the electric field *first*, before the charge distribution can be calculated. For example, an electrostatic problem may involve several conductors, with either the potential or total charge of each conductor given, but the distribution of surface charge will not be known in general, and cannot be obtained until a complete solution to the problem is effected.

Our aim in this chapter is to develop an alternative approach to electrostatic problems, and to accomplish this we first derive the fundamental differential equation which must be satisfied by the potential U. For the present we shall disregard problems involving dielectric bodies; problems of this type will be solved in Chapter 4.

3-1 Poisson's equation. All of the basic relationships which we shall need here were developed in the preceding chapter. First, we have the differential form of Gauss' law,

$$\text{div } \mathbf{E} = \frac{1}{\epsilon_0}\rho.$$ (3-3)

Furthermore, in a purely electrostatic field, $\mathbf{E}$ may be expressed as minus the gradient of the potential U:

$$\mathbf{E} = -\,\text{grad } U.$$ (3-4)

Combining (3-3) and (3-4), we obtain

$$\text{div grad } U = -\frac{\rho}{\epsilon_0}.$$ (3-5a)

It is convenient to think of div **grad** as a single differential operator, $\nabla \cdot \nabla$ or ∇^2. The latter notation is preferred, and the operator is called the *Laplacian:*

$$\nabla^2 U = -\frac{\rho}{\epsilon_0}.$$ (3-5b)

It is evident that the Laplacian is a pure scalar differential operator, and (3-5b) is a differential equation. This is *Poisson's equation.* The operator ∇^2 involves differentiation with respect to more than one variable; hence Poisson's equation is a *partial differential equation* which may be solved once we know the functional dependence of $\rho(x, y, z)$ and the appropriate boundary conditions.

The operator ∇^2, just like the grad, div, and curl, makes no reference to any particular coordinate system. In order to solve a specific problem, we must write ∇^2 in terms of x, y, z or r, θ, ϕ, or etc. The choice of the particular set of coordinates is arbitrary, but substantial simplification of the problem is usually achieved by choosing a set compatible with the symmetry of the electrostatic problem. The form taken by $\nabla^2 U$ in various coordinate systems is easily found by first taking the gradient of U, and then operating with div, using specific expressions from Chapter 1:

Rectangular coordinates:

$$\nabla^2 U \equiv \frac{\partial^2 U}{\partial x^2} + \frac{\partial^2 U}{\partial y^2} + \frac{\partial^2 U}{\partial z^2}.$$ (3-6)

Spherical coordinates:

$$\nabla^2 U \equiv \frac{1}{r^2} \frac{\partial}{\partial r}\left(r^2 \frac{\partial U}{\partial r}\right) + \frac{1}{r^2 \sin \theta} \frac{\partial}{\partial \theta}\left(\sin \theta \frac{\partial U}{\partial \theta}\right) + \frac{1}{r^2 \sin^2 \theta} \frac{\partial^2 U}{\partial \phi^2}.$$ (3-7)

Cylindrical coordinates:

$$\nabla^2 U \equiv \frac{1}{r} \frac{\partial}{\partial r}\left(r \frac{\partial U}{\partial r}\right) + \frac{1}{r^2} \frac{\partial^2 U}{\partial \theta^2} + \frac{\partial^2 U}{\partial z^2}.$$ (3-8)

For the form of the Laplacian in other, more complicated coordinate systems, the reader is referred to the references at the end of this chapter. It should be noted that r and θ have different meanings in (3-7) and (3-8); in spherical coordinates r is the magnitude of the radius vector from the origin and θ is the polar angle. In cylindrical coordinates, r is the perpendicular distance from the cylinder axis and θ is the azimuthal angle about this axis.

3-2 Laplace's equation. In a certain class of electrostatic problems involving conductors, all of the charge is found either on the surface of the conductors or in the form of fixed point charges. In these cases ρ is zero at most points in space. And where the charge density vanishes, the Poisson equation reduces to the simpler form

$$\nabla^2 U = 0, \qquad (3\text{-}9)$$

which is *Laplace's equation.*

Suppose we have a set of N conductors (one or more of which may be point charges) maintained at the potentials $U_I, U_{II}, \ldots, U_N$. Our problem is to find the potential at all points in space outside of the conductors. This may be accomplished by finding a solution to Laplace's equation which reduces to $U_I, U_{II}, \ldots, U_N$ on the surfaces of the appropriate conductors. Such a solution to Laplace's equation may be shown to be unique, i.e., there is no other solution to Laplace's equation which satisfies the same boundary conditions. A proof of this statement will be given below. The solution to Laplace's equation which we find in this way is not applicable to the interior of the conductors, because the conductors have surface charge, and this implies a discontinuity in the gradient of U across the surface (see Section 2-7). But we have already seen that the interior of each conductor is a region of constant potential, so the solution to our problem is complete.

We shall describe in some detail two methods for solution of Laplace's equation: the first is a method for compounding a general solution to (3-9) from particular solutions in a coordinate system dictated by the symmetry of the problem; the second is the method of images. In addition, a completely general solution to the problem in two dimensions will be found. Before taking up these specific procedures, however, we stop to prove some important properties of the solution to Laplace's equation.

THEOREM I. If $U_1, U_2, \ldots, U_n$ are all solutions of Laplace's equation, then

$$U = C_1 U_1 + C_2 U_2 + \cdots + C_n U_n, \qquad (3\text{-}10)$$

where the C's are arbitrary constants, is also a solution.

The proof of this follows immediately from the fact that

$$\begin{aligned}
\nabla^2 U &= \nabla^2 C_1 U_1 + \nabla^2 C_2 U_2 + \cdots + \nabla^2 C_n U_n \\
&= C_1 \nabla^2 U_1 + C_2 \nabla^2 U_2 + \cdots + C_n \nabla^2 U_n \\
&= 0.
\end{aligned}$$

Through the use of Theorem I we may superimpose two or more solutions of Laplace's equation in such a way that the resulting solution satisfies a given set of boundary conditions. Examples will be given in the following sections.

THEOREM II (Uniqueness theorem). Two solutions of Laplace's equation which satisfy the same boundary conditions differ at most by an additive constant.

To prove this theorem we consider the closed region V_0 exterior to the surfaces $S_I, S_{II}, \ldots, S_N$ of the various conductors in the problem and bounded on the outside by a surface S, the latter being either a surface at infinity or a real physical surface which encloses V_0. Let us assume that U_1 and U_2 are two solutions of Laplace's equation in V_0 which, in addition, have the *same* boundary conditions on $S, S_I, S_{II}, \ldots, S_N$. These boundary conditions may be specified by assigning values of either U or $\partial U/\partial n$ on the bounding surfaces.

We define a new function $\Phi = U_1 - U_2$. Obviously, $\nabla^2\Phi = \nabla^2 U_1 - \nabla^2 U_2 = 0$ in V_0. Furthermore, either Φ or $\mathbf{n} \cdot \mathbf{grad}\ \Phi$ vanishes on the boundaries. Let us apply the divergence theorem to the vector $\Phi\boldsymbol{\nabla}\Phi$:

$$\int_{V_0} \mathrm{div}\ (\Phi\boldsymbol{\nabla}\Phi)\ dV = \int_{S+S_I+\cdots S_N} \Phi\boldsymbol{\nabla}\Phi \cdot \mathbf{n}\ dS$$
$$= 0,$$

since the second integral vanishes. The divergence may be expanded according to Eq. (I–6) of Table 1–1 to give

$$\mathrm{div}\ (\Phi\boldsymbol{\nabla}\Phi) = \Phi\nabla^2\Phi + (\boldsymbol{\nabla}\Phi)^2.$$

But $\nabla^2\Phi$ vanishes at all points in V_0, so that the divergence theorem reduces in this case to

$$\int_{V_0} (\boldsymbol{\nabla}\Phi)^2\ dV = 0.$$

Now $(\boldsymbol{\nabla}\Phi)^2$ must be either positive or zero at each point in V_0, and since its integral is zero, it is evident that $(\boldsymbol{\nabla}\Phi)^2 = 0$ is the only possibility.

The theorem is essentially proved. A function whose gradient is zero at all points cannot change; hence at all points in V_0, Φ has the same value that it has on the bounding surfaces. If the boundary conditions have been given by specifying U_1 and U_2 on the surfaces $S, S_I, \ldots, S_N$, then since $\Phi = 0$ on these surfaces, it vanishes throughout V_0. If the boundary conditions are given in terms of $\partial U_1/\partial n$ and $\partial U_2/\partial n$, then $\boldsymbol{\nabla}\Phi$ equals zero at all points in V_0 and $\boldsymbol{\nabla}\Phi \cdot \mathbf{n} = 0$ on the boundaries. The only solution compatible with the last statement is Φ equal to a constant.

3–3 Laplace's equation in one independent variable. If U is a function of one variable only, Laplace's equation reduces to an ordinary differential equation. Consider the case where U is $U(x)$, a function of the single rectangular coordinate x. Then

$$\frac{d^2U}{dx^2} = 0 \quad \text{and} \quad U(x) = ax + b \quad (3\text{–}11)$$

is the general solution, where a and b are constants chosen to fit the boundary conditions. This is the result already found in the preceding chapter for the potential between two charged conducting plates oriented normal to the x-axis.

The situation is no more complicated in other coordinate systems where U is a function of a single variable. In spherical coordinates where U equals $U(r)$, Laplace's equation and its general solution become

$$\frac{1}{r^2} \frac{d}{dr}\left(r^2 \frac{dU}{dr}\right) = 0, \quad U(r) = -\frac{a}{r} + b. \quad (3\text{–}12)$$

The general solution to Laplace's equation in cylindrical coordinates for a function which is independent of θ and z, that is, for $U(r)$, is left as an exercise for the reader.

3–4 Solutions to Laplace's equation in spherical coordinates. Zonal harmonics. We next turn our attention to solutions of Laplace's equation where U is a function of more than one variable. Many of the problems of interest to us deal with conductors in the shape of spheres or cylinders, and thus solutions of Laplace's equation in either spherical or cylindrical coordinates are called for. We first take up the spherical problem, but we shall find it expedient to *limit the discussion* to cases in which U is independent of the azimuthal angle ϕ. This limitation restricts the class of problems which we shall be able to solve; nevertheless, many interesting physical problems fall into this restricted category, and more complicated problems are really beyond the scope of this book.

For the spherical case, U is $U(r, \theta)$, where r is the radius vector from a fixed origin O and θ is the polar angle (see Fig. 3–1). Using Eq. (3–7), Laplace's equation becomes in this case

$$\frac{1}{r^2} \frac{\partial}{\partial r}\left(r^2 \frac{\partial U}{\partial r}\right) + \frac{1}{r^2 \sin\theta} \frac{\partial}{\partial \theta}\left(\sin\theta \frac{\partial U}{\partial \theta}\right) = 0. \quad (3\text{–}13)$$

This partial differential equation will be solved by a technique known as "separation of variables." A solution of the form $U(r, \theta) = Z(r)P(\theta)$ is substituted into (3–13), yielding

$$\frac{1}{r^2} P(\theta) \frac{d}{dr}\left(r^2 \frac{dZ}{dr}\right) + \frac{Z(r)}{r^2 \sin\theta} \frac{d}{d\theta}\left(\sin\theta \frac{dP}{d\theta}\right) = 0. \quad (3\text{–}14)$$

Note that the partial derivatives have been replaced by total derivatives,

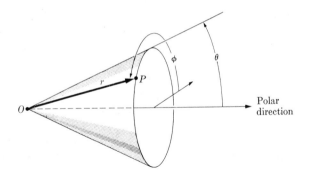

FIG. 3-1. Location of the point P in terms of the spherical coordinates r, θ, ϕ.

since Z and P are each functions of one variable only. Dividing through by $U(r, \theta)$ and multiplying through by r^2, we transform (3-14) into

$$\frac{1}{Z}\frac{d}{dr}\left(r^2 \frac{dZ}{dr}\right) = -\frac{1}{P \sin \theta}\frac{d}{d\theta}\left(\sin \theta \frac{dP}{d\theta}\right). \tag{3-15}$$

The left side of this equation is a function of r only and the right side is a function of θ; the only way in which a function of r can equal a function of θ for all values of r and θ is for both functions to be constant. Hence let each side of (3-15) equal k, where k is the "separation constant."

Not all values of k necessarily yield solutions which are acceptable on physical grounds. Consider the θ equation first:

$$\frac{1}{\sin \theta}\frac{d}{d\theta}\left(\sin \theta \frac{dP}{d\theta}\right) + kP = 0. \tag{3-16}$$

This is Legendre's equation, and the only physically acceptable solutions which are defined over the full range of θ, from 0 to π, correspond to $k = n(n + 1)$, where n is a positive integer. The solution for a particular n will be denoted by $P_n(\theta)$. Solutions of (3-16) for other values of k are ill-behaved in the vicinity of $\theta = 0$ or $\theta = \pi$ radians, becoming infinite or even undefined at these values of θ.* These solutions cannot be made to fit physical boundary conditions and hence must be discarded.†

---

* The discussion here has been all too brief. The interested reader is referred to more mathematical texts for a detailed treatment of Legendre's equation. See, e.g., the book by Margenau and Murphy (p. 61) listed at the end of this chapter. Legendre's equation is usually written in a different form by substituting $x = \cos \theta$, and its solutions are then denoted by $P_n(x)$ or $P_n(\cos \theta)$.

† This statement requires some qualification. In some electrostatic problems the regions around $\theta = 0$ and $\theta = \pi$ may be naturally excluded, for example, by conducting conical surfaces; under these conditions solutions of (3-16) with other values of k could be used. Problems of this type will not be considered here.

The acceptable solutions, the $P_n(\theta)$, are polynomials in $\cos\theta$, and are usually referred to as Legendre polynomials. The first four Legendre functions are given in Table 3–1. It is evident from (3–16) that the P_n may be multiplied by any arbitrary constant.

We now return to the radial equation

$$\frac{d}{dr}\left(r^2\frac{dZ}{dr}\right) = n(n+1)Z, \qquad (3\text{–}17)$$

where we have used the explicit form of k which gave acceptable θ solutions. Inspection of (3–17) shows that two independent solutions are

$$Z_n = r^n \quad \text{and} \quad Z_n = r^{-(n+1)}.$$

Solutions of Laplace's equation are obtained as the product $U_n(r, \theta) = Z_n(r) \times P_n(\theta)$, where particular care must be exercised to have Z and P correspond to the same value of n. This is mandatory, since both sides of Eq. (3–15) are equal to the same constant, namely, $n(n+1)$.

TABLE 3–1

LEGENDRE POLYNOMIALS FOR $n = 0, 1, 2,$ AND 3

n	$P_n(\theta)$
0	1
1	$\cos\theta$
2	$\frac{1}{2}(3\cos^2\theta - 1)$
3	$\frac{1}{2}(5\cos^3\theta - 3\cos\theta)$

As a result of the above discussion we have solved Laplace's equation in spherical coordinates and have obtained the solutions which are known as *zonal harmonics:*

$$U_n = r^n P_n(\theta) \quad \text{or} \quad U_n = r^{-(n+1)}P_n(\theta), \qquad (3\text{–}18)$$

where $P_n(\theta)$ is one of the polynomials listed in Table 3–1, and n is a positive integer or zero. The zonal harmonics form a complete set of functions, i.e., a general solution of Laplace's equation may be constructed as a superposition of these solutions according to Theorem I provided the physical problem shows the appropriate azimuthal symmetry. Several of the zonal harmonics are already well known to us: one of the $n = 0$

solutions, namely $U = $ constant, is a trivial solution of Laplace's equation, valid in any coordinate system; the zonal harmonic r^{-1} is the potential of a point charge; and $r^{-2} \cos \theta$ is the potential of a dipole.

3-5 Conducting sphere in a uniform electric field. We shall illustrate the usefulness of zonal harmonics for electrostatic problems having spherical symmetry by solving the problem of an uncharged conducting sphere placed in an *initially* uniform electric field $\mathbf{E}_0$. The lines of a uniform electric field are parallel, but the presence of the conductor alters the field in such a way that the field lines strike the surface of the conductor, which is an equipotential surface, normally. If we take the direction of the initially uniform electric field as the polar direction (z-direction), and if we make the origin of our coordinate system coincide with the center of the sphere, then from the symmetry of the problem it is clear that the potential will be independent of azimuthal angle ϕ, and may be expressed as a sum of zonal harmonics.

The spherical conductor, of radius a, is an equipotential surface; let us denote its potential by U_0. Our problem is to find a solution to Laplace's equation in the region outside the sphere which reduces to U_0 on the sphere itself, and which has the correct limiting form at large distances away. The solution may be formally written as

$$U(r, \theta) = A_1 + C_1 r^{-1} + A_2 r \cos \theta$$
$$+ C_2 r^{-2} \cos \theta + \tfrac{1}{2} A_3 r^2 (3 \cos^2 \theta - 1)$$
$$+ \tfrac{1}{2} C_3 r^{-3} (3 \cos^2 \theta - 1) + \cdots, \qquad (3\text{-}19)$$

where the A's and C's are arbitrary constants. At large r, the electric field will be only slightly distorted from its initial form, and the potential will be that appropriate to a uniform electric field.

$$[\mathbf{E}(r, \theta)]_{r \to \infty} = \mathbf{E}_0 = E_0 \mathbf{k},$$
$$[U(r, \theta)]_{r \to \infty} = -E_0 z + \text{constant},$$
$$= -E_0 r \cos \theta + \text{constant}. \qquad (3\text{-}20)$$

Hence, in order to make (3-19) and (3-20) agree at large r, $A_2 = -E_0$; furthermore, all the A's from A_3 up must be set equal to zero.

The term $C_1 r^{-1}$ produces a radial field which, as we might expect, is compatible only with a spherical conductor bearing net total charge. Since our problem deals with an uncharged conductor, the constant C_1 must be set equal to zero. At the surface of the sphere $U = U_0$, and the potential must become independent of angle θ. The two terms involving $\cos \theta$ may be made to cancel each other, but the terms with higher inverse powers of r cannot be cancelled one against the other because they contain

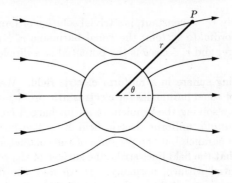

FIG. 3–2. Lines of electric flux for the case of a conducting sphere placed in a uniform electric field.

different Legendre functions. The only possibility is to set all the C_i's with $i \geq 3$ equal to zero. Equation (3–19) now becomes

$$U(r, \theta) = A_1 - E_0 r \cos \theta + C_2 r^{-2} \cos \theta, \qquad \text{for} \quad r \geq a,$$

$$U(a, \theta) = U_0. \tag{3–21}$$

Since the two expressions must be equal at $r = a$, $A_1 = U_0$ and $C_2 = E_0 a^3$.

From the final expression for the potential, we may calculate not only the electric field at all points in space (see Fig. 3–2) but also the surface density of charge on the conducting sphere:

$$\left.\begin{aligned} E_r &= -\frac{\partial U}{\partial r} = E_0 \left(1 + 2\frac{a^3}{r^3}\right) \cos \theta, \\ E_\theta &= -\frac{1}{r}\frac{\partial U}{\partial \theta} = -E_0 \left(1 - \frac{a^3}{r^3}\right) \sin \theta, \end{aligned}\right\} \qquad \text{for} \quad r \geq a, \quad (3\text{–}22)$$

$$\sigma(\theta) = \epsilon_0 E_r \Big|_{r=a} = 3\epsilon_0 E_0 \cos \theta. \tag{3–23}$$

The total charge on the sphere,

$$Q = a^2 \int_0^\pi \sigma(\theta) 2\pi \sin \theta \, d\theta,$$

is obviously zero, which agrees with our initial assumption.

3–6 Cylindrical harmonics. Laplace's equation in cylindrical co-ordinates may also be solved by the method of separation of variables. Here again it will be expedient to work out solutions for only a restricted class of problems, namely, those in which the potential is independent of the coordinate z. These solutions are appropriate for certain problems involving a long straight cylindrical conductor or wire, but *not* for those dealing with a short cylindrical segment.

If the potential is independent of z, Laplace's equation in cylindrical coordinates becomes

$$\frac{1}{r} \frac{\partial}{\partial r} \left(r \frac{\partial U}{\partial r} \right) + \frac{1}{r^2} \frac{\partial^2 U}{\partial \theta^2} = 0. \tag{3-24}$$

Substitution of $U = Y(r)S(\theta)$ reduces the equation to

$$\frac{r}{Y} \frac{d}{dr} \left(r \frac{dY}{dr} \right) = - \frac{1}{S} \frac{d^2 S}{d\theta^2} = k, \tag{3-25}$$

where k again plays the role of a separation constant. The θ-equation is particularly simple; it has the solutions $\cos k^{1/2}\theta$ and $\sin k^{1/2}\theta$. But if these solutions are to make sense physically, each must be a single-valued function of θ; thus

$$\cos k^{1/2}(\theta + 2\pi) = \cos k^{1/2}\theta,$$

$$\sin k^{1/2}(\theta + 2\pi) = \sin k^{1/2}\theta.$$

Or, to put it differently, after θ has gone through its full range from 0 to 2π the function must join *smoothly* to its value at $\theta = 0$. This can be the case only if $k = n^2$, n being an integer. We may further require n to be positive (or zero) without losing any of these solutions.

Returning now to the r-equation, we are able to verify easily that $Y(r)$ is r^n or r^{-n}; unless $n = 0$ when $Y(r) = \ln r$ or $Y(r) = $ constant. Hence the required solutions to Laplace's equation, the so-called *cylindrical harmonics*, are

$$1, \qquad \ln r,$$

$$r^n \cos n\theta, \qquad r^{-n} \cos n\theta,$$

$$r^n \sin n\theta, \qquad r^{-n} \sin n\theta.$$

These functions form a complete set for the variables r, θ in cylindrical coordinates, and the potential $U(r, \theta)$ may be developed as a superposition of cylindrical harmonics in accordance with Theorem I.

*3–7 Laplace's equation in rectangular coordinates. In rectangular co-ordinates, the variables may be separated by making the substitution

$$U(x, y, z) = f_1(x)f_2(y)f_3(z),$$

whereby Laplace's equation reduces to

---

* Starred sections may be omitted without loss of continuity.

$$\frac{1}{f_1(x)} \frac{d^2f_1}{dx^2} + \frac{1}{f_2(y)} \frac{d^2f_2}{dy^2} = -\frac{1}{f_3(z)} \frac{d^2f_3}{dz^2}. \qquad (3\text{--}26\text{a})$$

The left side of this equation is a function of x and y, and the right side is a function of z only; hence both sides must be equal to the same constant, k. This is the first separation constant. The two equations obtained from (3–26a) are

$$\frac{d^2f_3}{dz^2} + kf_3 = 0, \qquad (3\text{--}26\text{b})$$

$$\frac{1}{f_2} \frac{d^2f_2}{dy^2} = k - \frac{1}{f_1} \frac{d^2f_1}{dx^2}.$$

The latter equation has been written such that the variables x and y are separated; each side of this equation is now set equal to $-m$ (the second separation constant). Thus,

$$\frac{d^2f_2}{dy^2} + mf_2 = 0, \qquad (3\text{--}26\text{c})$$

$$\frac{d^2f_1}{dx^2} - (k + m)f_1 = 0. \qquad (3\text{--}26\text{d})$$

Equations (3–26b), (3–26c), and (3–26d) are easily solved. One of the typical solutions for $U(x, y, z)$ is

$$U(x, y, z) = Ae^{-(k+m)^{\frac{1}{2}}x} \cos m^{1/2}y \cos k^{1/2}z. \qquad (3\text{--}27)$$

The other seven independent solutions for a pair of separation constants (k, m) are obtained by making one or more of the following substitutions: $+(k + m)^{1/2}x$ for $-(k + m)^{1/2}x$, $\sin m^{1/2}y$ for $\cos m^{1/2}y$, and $\sin k^{1/2}z$ for $\cos k^{1/2}z$.

Thus far there are no restrictions on k or m, but boundary conditions on the problem usually restrict k (or m) to a discrete set of positive or negative values. It is worth while making the point that it is the boundary conditions which really pick out the *pertinent solutions* to a partial differential equation; the function

$$U(x, y, z) = \sum_p \sum_q A_{pq} e^{-(p^2+q^2)^{\frac{1}{2}}x} \cos py \cos qz$$

for fixed x and y is just the Fourier series expansion for an *arbitrary* even function of z.

The individual solutions, (3–27), do not represent particularly simple potentials, and we shall not try to correlate them with physical situations. The case where both separation constants are zero is more interesting; hence we turn our attention to this case. From (3–26d), it is evident that

$f_1(x) = a_1x$, or $f_1(x) =$ constant, is a solution; from (3–26c), we obtain $f_2(y)$, etc. Thus,

$$U(x, y, z) = A_1xyz + A_2xy + A_3yz + A_4xz$$
$$+ A_5x + A_6y + A_7z + A_8, \quad (3\text{–}28a)$$

where the A's are arbitrary constants. This solution may be applied to the case where three conducting planes intersect at right angles. If these planes are the coordinate planes xy, yz, and zx, and are all at the same potential, then

$$U(x, y, z) = A_1xyz + A_8. \qquad (3\text{–}28b)$$

It is left as an exercise for the reader to determine the surface charge density on the coordinate planes that is compatible with (3–28b).

*3–8 Laplace's equation in two dimensions. General solution. If the potential is a function of only two rectangular coordinates, Laplace's equation is written

$$\frac{\partial^2 U}{\partial x^2} + \frac{\partial^2 U}{\partial y^2} = 0. \qquad (3\text{–}29a)$$

It is possible to obtain the general solution to this equation by means of a transformation to a new set of independent variables; nevertheless, it should be emphasized that such a transformation leads to a simplification of the original equation only in the two-dimensional case. Let

$$\xi = x + jy, \qquad \eta = x - jy,$$

where $j = \sqrt{-1}$ is the unit imaginary number. In terms of these relationships,

$$\frac{\partial^2}{\partial x^2} = \frac{\partial^2}{\partial \xi^2} + 2\frac{\partial^2}{\partial \xi\, \partial \eta} + \frac{\partial^2}{\partial \eta^2},$$

$$\frac{\partial^2}{\partial y^2} = -\frac{\partial^2}{\partial \xi^2} + 2\frac{\partial^2}{\partial \xi\, \partial \eta} - \frac{\partial^2}{\partial \eta^2},$$

and

$$\nabla^2 U = 4\frac{\partial^2 U}{\partial \xi\, \partial \eta} = 0. \qquad (3\text{–}29b)$$

It is evident that the general solution to (3–29b) is

$$U = F_1(\xi) + F_2(\eta) = F_1(x + jy) + F_2(x - jy), \qquad (3\text{–}30)$$

where F_1 and F_2 are *arbitrary* functions. The functions F_1 and F_2 are complex quantities in general, but two real functions may be constructed in the following way. First let $F_2(x - jy) = F_1(x - jy)$, that is, let the two functions F_1 and F_2 have the same dependence on their arguments; then

$$U_1 = F_1(x + jy) + F_1(x - jy) = 2 \operatorname{Re} [F_1(x + jy)],$$

where Re stands for "real part of." Furthermore, the second real potential function is

$$U_2 = -j[F_1(x + jy) - F_1(x - jy)] = 2 \operatorname{Im} [F_1(x + jy)],$$

where Im stands for "imaginary part of." Thus the real and imaginary parts of any complex function $F(x + jy)$ are both solutions of Laplace's equation.

The solutions found in this way are not restricted to any particular coordinate system. For example, the cylindrical harmonics of Section 3–7 are obtained from the complex functions* $(x + jy)^n = r^n e^{jn\theta}$, and $\ln (x + jy) = \ln r + j\theta$. On the other hand, when it comes to solving a particular two-dimensional problem, there is no standard procedure for finding the appropriate complex function. This method generates so many solutions that it is not possible to enumerate them all and cast out those which do not agree with boundary conditions on the problem. In simple cases, the required functions may be found by trial and error; in other cases, the method of *conformal mapping* (which is beyond the scope of this book) may be useful.

3–9 Electrostatic images. For a given set of boundary conditions the solution to Laplace's equation is unique, so that if one obtains a solution $U(x, y, z)$ by any means whatever, and if this U satisfies all boundary conditions, then a complete solution to the problem has been effected. The method of images is a procedure for accomplishing this result without specifically solving a differential equation. It is not universally applicable to all types of electrostatic problems, but enough interesting problems fall into this category to make it worth while discussing the method here.

Suppose the potential may be written in the following way:

$$U(\mathbf{r}) = U_1(\mathbf{r}) + \frac{1}{4\pi\epsilon_0} \int_S \frac{\sigma(r') \, da'}{|\mathbf{r} - \mathbf{r}'|}, \tag{3-31}$$

where U_1 is either a specified function or easily calculable, and the integral represents the contribution to the potential from surface charge on all conductors appearing in the problem. The function σ is not known. It may happen, and this is the essence of the image-charge method, that the last term in (3–31) can be replaced by a potential U_2 which is due to

---

* The cylindrical and rectangular coordinates are related in the usual way: $x = r \cos \theta$, $y = r \sin \theta$.

a *specified* charge distribution. This is possible so long as the surfaces of all conductors coincide with equipotential surfaces of the combined $U_1 + U_2$. The specified charges producing U_2 are called *image charges*. They do not really exist, of course. Their apparent location is "inside" the various conductors, and the potential $U = U_1 + U_2$ is a valid solution to the problem only in the exterior region.

As an example of this method, we shall solve the problem of a point charge q placed near a conducting plane of infinite extent. To formulate the problem mathematically, let the conducting plane coincide with the yz-plane, and let the point charge lie on the x-axis at $x = d$ (see Fig. 3–3a).

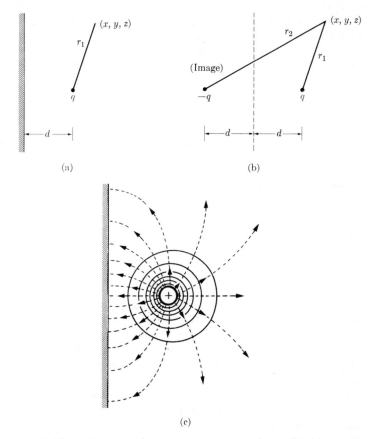

(a)   (b)

(c)

Fig. 3–3. Problem of a point charge and conducting plane solved by means of the image-charge method: (a) original problem, (b) location of image charge, (c) lines of force (dotted) and equipotential surfaces (solid).

The potential fits the prescription (3–31), with

$$U_1(x, y, z) = \frac{q}{4\pi\epsilon_0 r_1} = \frac{q}{4\pi\epsilon_0 \sqrt{(x - d)^2 + y^2 + z^2}}. \qquad (3\text{--}32)$$

Consider now a different problem, that of two point charges (q and $-q$) a distance $2d$ apart, as shown in Fig. 3–3(b). The potential of these two charges,

$$U(x, y, z) = \frac{q}{4\pi\epsilon_0 r_1} - \frac{q}{4\pi\epsilon_0 r_2}, \qquad (3\text{--}33)$$

not only satisfies Laplace's equation at all points exterior to the charges, but also reduces to a constant (namely, zero) on the plane which perpendicularly bisects the segment joining the two charges. Thus (3–33) satisfies the boundary conditions of the original problem. Because solutions to Laplace's equation are unique, (3–33) is the correct potential in the entire half-space exterior to the conducting plane. The charge $-q$ which gives rise to the potential

$$U_2(x, y, z) = -\frac{q}{4\pi\epsilon_0 r_2} = -\frac{q}{4\pi\epsilon_0 \sqrt{(x + d)^2 + y^2 + z^2}} \qquad (3\text{--}34)$$

is called the *image* of the point charge q. Naturally, the image does not really exist, and (3–32) does *not* give correctly the potential inside or to the left of the conducting plane in Fig. 3–3(a).

The electric field **E** in the exterior region may be obtained as the negative gradient of (3–33). Since the surface of the conducting plane represents an interface joining two solutions of Laplace's equation, namely, $U = 0$ and (3–33), the discontinuity in the electric field is accommodated by a surface charge density σ on the plane:

$$\sigma(y, z) = \epsilon_0 E_x|_{x=0} = -\frac{qd}{2\pi(d^2 + y^2 + z^2)^{3/2}}. \qquad (3\text{--}35)$$

The lines of force and equipotential surfaces appropriate to the original problem are shown in Fig. 3–3(c). These are the same lines of force and equipotential surfaces appropriate to the two point charge problem in Fig. 3–3(b) except that in the latter case the flux lines would continue into the left half-plane. It is evident from the figure that *all* of the electric flux lines which would normally converge on the image charge are intercepted by the plane in Fig. 3–3(c). Hence the total charge on the plane is equal to that of the image charge, $-q$. This same result may be obtained mathematically by integrating (3–35) over the entire surface (see Problem 3–10).

It is evident that the point charge q exerts an attractive force on the plane, because the induced surface charge is of the opposite sign. By

Newton's law of action and reaction, this force is equal in magnitude to the force exerted on q by the plane. Since the point charge experiences no force due to its own field,

$$\mathbf{F} = -q \, \mathbf{grad} \, U_2, \qquad (3\text{–}36)$$

which is just the force exerted on it by the image charge.

Another problem which may be solved simply in terms of images is that of determining the electric field of a point charge q in the vicinity of a right-angle intersection of two conducting planes (see Fig. 3–4a). The positions of the necessary image charges are shown in Fig. 3–4(b). It is readily seen that the two planes shown dotted in the figure are surfaces of zero potential due to the combined potentials of q and the three image charges.

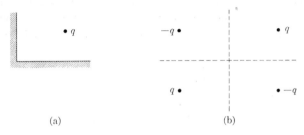

(a)   (b)

Fig. 3–4. Point charge in a right-angle corner.

3–10 Point charge and conducting sphere. The principal difficulty in solving a problem by image technique is that of finding a group of image charges which, together with the originally specified charges, produce equipotential surfaces at the conductors. The problem is straightforward only in cases where the geometry is simple. Such is the case, however, for a point charge q in the vicinity of a conducting sphere; it requires a single image charge to make the sphere a surface of *zero potential*. An additional image charge is needed to change the potential of the sphere to some other constant value.

We shall first determine the magnitude and location of the image q' which together with the point charge q produces zero potential at all points on the sphere. The geometry of the situation is shown in Fig. 3–5. The point charge q is a distance d from the center of the sphere, and the radius of the sphere is a. It is apparent from the symmetry of the problem that the image charge q' will lie on the line passing through q and the center of the sphere.

The desired results are most easily obtained by means of spherical coordinates, with the origin of coordinates at the center of the sphere.

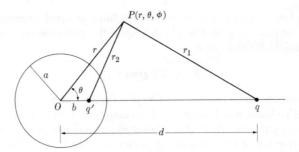

FIG. 3–5. Point charge q in the vicinity of a conducting sphere; q' is the image charge.

Let the polar axis be taken as the line joining q to the origin. The distance b and the magnitude of q' are to be determined in terms of the specified quantities: q, d, a. The potential at an arbitrary point P due to q and q' is given by

$$U(r, \theta, \phi) = \frac{q}{4\pi\epsilon_0 r_1} + \frac{q'}{4\pi\epsilon_0 r_2}$$

$$= \frac{1}{4\pi\epsilon_0}\left[\frac{q}{\sqrt{r^2 + d^2 - 2rd\cos\theta}} + \frac{q'}{\sqrt{r^2 + b^2 - 2rb\cos\theta}}\right].$$

(3–37)

On the surface of the sphere, $r = a$, and $U(a, \theta, \phi) = 0$ for all θ and ϕ. But from expression (3–37), $U(a, \theta, \phi)$ can equal zero for all θ *only* if the two square roots are proportional to each other. This is the case if $b = a^2/d$, for then

$$\sqrt{a^2 + b^2 - 2ab\cos\theta} = \frac{a}{d}\sqrt{d^2 + a^2 - 2ad\cos\theta}.$$

Hence,

$$b = \frac{a^2}{d},$$

(3–38)

and furthermore,

$$q' = -\frac{a}{d}q.$$

(3–39)

These equations serve to specify the location and magnitude of the first image charge.

A second image charge q'' may be placed at the center of the sphere without destroying the equipotential nature of the spherical surface. The magnitude of q'' is arbitrary; it may be adjusted to fit the boundary conditions on the problem. Thus a complete solution to the point charge-conducting sphere problem has been effected; the potential at all points exterior to the sphere is

$$U(r, \theta, \phi) = \frac{1}{4\pi\epsilon_0}\left[\frac{q}{r_1} + \frac{q'}{r_2} + \frac{q''}{r}\right]. \tag{3-40}$$

The potential of the spherical conductor itself is

$$U(a, \theta, \phi) = \frac{q''}{4\pi\epsilon_0 a}; \tag{3-41}$$

and the surface density of charge on the sphere is

$$\sigma(\theta, \phi) = -\epsilon_0 \frac{\partial U}{\partial r}\bigg|_{r=a}. \tag{3-42}$$

All the lines of force which would normally converge on the image charges are intercepted by the sphere; hence the total charge on the sphere, Q, is equal to the sum of the image charges:

$$Q = q' + q''. \tag{3-43}$$

This result may be verified by direct integration of (3-42).

Special cases of interest are the *grounded* sphere: $U(a) = 0$, $q'' = 0$; and the *uncharged spherical conductor*: $q'' = -q'$.

3-11 Line charges and line images. Thus far, our image technique has been limited to problems involving point charges, and hence point images. In this section we shall take up several problems which may be solved by means of line image charges. Consider two infinitely long, parallel, line charges, with charges λ and $-\lambda$ per unit length, respectively, as shown in Fig. 3-6. The potential at any point is given by

$$U = -\frac{\lambda}{2\pi\epsilon_0}[\ln r_1 - \ln r_2] = -\frac{\lambda}{2\pi\epsilon_0}\ln\frac{r_1}{r_2}, \tag{3-44}$$

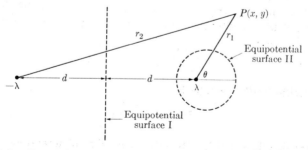

FIG. 3-6. Two infinitely long, parallel line charges (of charge λ and $-\lambda$ per unit length) are shown cutting the plane of the paper.

where r_1 and r_2 are the perpendicular distances from the point to the two line charges. The equipotentials are obtained by setting (3–44) equal to a constant, a procedure which is equivalent to requiring that

$$\frac{r_1}{r_2} = M, \tag{3-45}$$

where M is constant. Hence the equipotentials may be specified by (3–45).

The equipotential corresponding to $M = 1$ is the plane located halfway between the two line charges, shown as equipotential surface I in the figure. The potential of the plane is zero. Hence the problem of a long line charge oriented parallel to a conducting plane has been effectively solved. The potential in the half-space is given correctly by (3–44). Let us assume that the line charge shown on the right side of the figure is the specified charge, which is at a distance d from the conducting plane. Then the line charge on the left side of the figure plays the role of an image. Again, the total charge on the plane is equal to that of the image charge.

Let us next consider equipotential surfaces corresponding to other values of M. The general form of the surface may be found by expressing r_1 and r_2 in rectangular coordinates. For convenience, we choose the origin of the coordinate system on the positive line charge, and make this charge coincide with the z-axis; we let the second line charge be located at $x = -2d, y = 0$. Now

$$r_1^2 = x^2 + y^2$$

and

$$r_2^2 = (x + 2d)^2 + y^2,$$

so that (3–45) becomes, after a little algebraic manipulation,

$$x^2 + y^2 - \frac{4M^2 xd}{1 - M^2} = \frac{4M^2 d^2}{1 - M^2}. \tag{3-46}$$

This is the equation of a circular cylinder extending parallel to the z-axis. If M is less than one, the cylinder surrounds the positive line charge, as does equipotential surface II of the figure. The axis of the cylinder goes through the point

$$x = \frac{2M^2 d}{1 - M^2}, \qquad y = 0; \tag{3-47}$$

and the radius of the cylinder is

$$R_c = \left| \frac{2Md}{1 - M^2} \right|. \tag{3-48}$$

We are now in a position to solve a number of interesting problems involving cylindrical conductors, but only one of this type will be discussed. Consider the problem of a long cylindrical conductor in the vicinity of a conducting plane, and oriented parallel to it. The cylinder bears the charge λ per unit length. Figure 3–6 may serve to illustrate the problem, the two conductors coinciding with the dotted surfaces. Both of the line charges are images in this case, and the potential in the region surrounding the cylinder and to the right of the plane is given by (3–44). It is evident that the charge induced on the plane is equal to $-\lambda$ per unit distance in the z-direction.

3–12 System of conductors. Coefficients of potential. In the preceding sections several important methods for obtaining solutions to Laplace's equation have been discussed. Although general in scope, these methods are limited by practical considerations to problems in which the conductors have rather simple shapes. When their shapes are complicated, complete mathematical solution is out of the question; nevertheless, certain conclusions can be drawn about the system just because the potential satisfies Laplace's equation. In fact, we shall prove here that a linear relationship exists between the potential of one of the conductors and the charges on the various conductors in the system. The coefficients in this relationship, the so-called *coefficients of potential*, are functions only of the geometry and, although not always calculable, may be determined directly from experiment.

Suppose there are N conductors in fixed geometry. Let all of the conductors be uncharged except conductor j, which bears the charge Q_{j0}. The appropriate solution to Laplace's equation in the space exterior to the conductors will be given the symbol $U^{(j)}(x, y, z)$, and the potential of each of the conductors will be indicated by $U_1^{(j)}, U_2^{(j)}, \ldots, U_j^{(j)}, \ldots, U_n^{(j)}$. Now let us change the charge of the jth conductor to λQ_{j0}. The function $\lambda U^{(j)}(x, y, z)$ satisfies Laplace's equation, since λ is a constant; that the new boundary conditions are satisfied by this function may be seen from the following argument. The potential at all points in space is multiplied by λ; thus all derivatives (and in particular the gradient) of the potential are multiplied by λ. Because $\sigma = \epsilon_0 E_n$, it follows that all charge densities are multiplied by λ. Thus the charge of the jth conductor is λQ_{j0} and all other conductors remain uncharged.

A solution of Laplace's equation which fits a particular set of boundary conditions is unique; therefore we have found *the correct solution*, $\lambda U^{(j)}(x, y, z)$, to our modified problem. The interesting conclusion we draw from this discussion is that the potential of each conductor is proportional to the charge Q_j of conductor j, that is,

$$U_i^{(j)} = p_{ij}Q_j, \qquad (i = 1, 2, \ldots, N), \qquad (3\text{--}49)$$

where p_{ij} is a constant which depends only on the geometry.

The same argument may be applied to the case where conductor k is charged: $Q_k = \nu Q_{k0}$, all other conductors being uncharged. Here the appropriate solution to Laplace's equation is $\nu U^{(k)}(x, y, z)$, where $U^{(k)}$ is the solution for $\nu = 1$. It is apparent, then, that

$$\lambda U^{(j)}(x, y, z) + \nu U^{(k)}(x, y, z) \tag{3–50}$$

is a solution appropriate to the case where both conductors are charged. Again we appeal to the uniqueness of a solution for a given set of boundary conditions. Thus (3–50) is *the solution* for this case, and the potential of each conductor may be written as

$$U_i = p_{ij}Q_j + p_{ik}Q_k, \qquad (i = 1, 2, \ldots, N). \tag{3–51}$$

This result may be generalized immediately to the case where all N conductors are charged:

$$U_i = \sum_{j=1}^{N} p_{ij}Q_j. \tag{3–52}$$

This is the linear relationship between potential and charge which we have been seeking; the coefficients p_{ij} are called the *coefficients of potential*. In Chapter 6 it will be shown that the array of these coefficients is symmetrical, i.e., that $p_{ij} = p_{ji}$.

3–13 Solutions of Poisson's equation. In the preceding sections, we have dealt exclusively with Laplace's equation and its solution. Laplace's equation is applicable to those electrostatic problems in which all the charge resides on surfaces of conductors or is concentrated in the form of point or line charges. We shall see in the next chapter that it is necessary for only the *free charge* (i.e., the charge which is free to move or to be transferred from one object to another) to be distributed in this manner; if the region between the conductors is filled with one or more simple dielectric media, then Laplace's equation still holds in these media.

Let us consider, now, an electrostatic problem in which part of the charge (the prescribed charge) is given by $\rho(x, y, z)$, a known function, and the rest of the charge (the induced charge) resides on the surfaces of conductors. Such a problem requires the solution of Poisson's equation. The general solution to this problem may be written as an integral of the type (3–1) over the *prescribed charge* plus a general solution to Laplace's equation. The solution to Laplace's equation must be chosen, however, so that the entire potential satisfies all boundary conditions.

When all of the charge is prescribed, i.e., when $dq = \rho(x, y, z)\, dv$ is known at all points in space, then Eq. (3–1) represents the entire solution to Poisson's equation, and this integral may be performed (either analytically or numerically). There is one case, however, where the solution to Poisson's equation may be obtained more direcly than by means of the formal solution (3-1); this occurs when both ρ and U are functions of only one independent variable. As an example of this case, let ρ be a function of the spherical coordinate, r, only, and let the entire charge be distributed in a spherically symmetric way. Then (3-5b) becomes

$$\frac{1}{r^2}\frac{d}{dr}\left(r^2\frac{dU}{dr}\right) = -\frac{1}{\epsilon_0}\rho(r). \qquad (3\text{-}53)$$

We shall assume that the total charge is bounded, i.e., that either the charge does not extend to infinity or the charge density drops off sufficiently rapidly at large radii. Equation (3-53) may then be integrated directly, assuming the function $\rho(r)$ given, and the two constants of integration may be determined (1) from Gauss' Law for the electric field at some radius, and (2) from the fact that $U \to 0$ as $r \to \infty$.

References

The following texts are recommended for (1) a more complete discussion of Legendre's equation, (2) the general form of Laplace's equation in orthogonal, curvilinear coordinates, and (3) a more complete discussion of the solution to Laplace's equation:

H. Margenau and G. M. Murphy, *The Mathematics of Physics and Chemistry*, D. Van Nostrand Co., Inc., New York, 1943.

J. A. Stratton, *Electromagnetic Theory*, McGraw-Hill Book Co., Inc., New York, 1941.

W. Panofsky and M. Phillips, *Classical Electricity and Magnetism*, Addison-Wesley, 1955.

PROBLEMS

3-1. Two spherical conducting shells of radii r_a and r_b are arranged concentrically and are charged to the potentials U_a and U_b, respectively. If $r_b > r_a$, find the potential at points between the shells, and at points $r > r_b$.

3-2. Two long cylindrical shells of radii r_a and r_b are arranged coaxially and are charged to the potentials U_a and U_b, respectively. Find the potential at points between the cylindrical shells.

3-3. If U_1 is a solution to Laplace's equation, prove that the partial derivative of U_1 with respect to one or more of the rectangular coordinates (e.g., $\partial U_1/\partial x$, $\partial^2 U_1/\partial x^2$, $\partial^2 U_1/\partial x \partial y$, etc.) is also a solution.

3-4. Show that half the zonal harmonics are generated by differentiating r^{-1} successively with respect to the rectangular coordinate z ($z = r \cos \theta$).

3-5. Obtain $\nabla^2 U$ in cylindrical coordinates (Eq. 3-8), from the rectangular form, (3-6), by direct substitution: $x = r \cos \theta$, $y = r \sin \theta$.

3-6. Find the potential of an axial quadrupole: point charges q, $-2q$, q placed on the z-axis at distances l, 0, $-l$ from the origin. Find the potential only at distances $r \gg l$, and show that this potential is proportional to one of the zonal harmonics.

3-7. A conducting sphere of radius a bearing total charge Q is placed in an initially uniform electric field E_0. Find the potential at all points exterior to the sphere.

3-8. A long cylindrical conductor of radius a bearing no net charge is placed in an initially uniform electric field $\mathbf{E}_0$. The direction of $\mathbf{E}_0$ is perpendicular to the cylinder axis. Find the potential at points exterior to the cylinder, and find also the charge density on the cylindrical surface.

*3-9. Show that Im $A[(x + jy)]^{1/2} = Ar^{1/2} \sin \frac{1}{2}\theta$ satisfies Laplace's equation, but that the electric field derived from this function has a discontinuity at $\theta = 0$. (Note that r and θ are cylindrical coordinates here.) The function may be used to describe the potential at the edge of a charged conducting plane. The conducting plane coincides with the xz-plane, but only for positive values of x. Find the charge density on the plane. Make a sketch showing several equipotential surfaces and several lines of force.

3-10. A point charge q is situated a distance d from a grounded conducting plane of infinite extent. Obtain the total charge induced on the plane by direct integration of the surface charge density.

3-11. Two point charges, q_1 and q_2, are located near a conducting plane of infinite extent. Find the image charges which are needed to make the plane a surface of constant potential. From the result just obtained, can you predict the image charge distribution required for the case of a body of arbitrary shape with charge density ρ situated near a conducting plane of infinite extent?

3-12. Find the force between a point charge q and an *uncharged* conducting sphere of radius a. The point charge is located a distance r from the center of the sphere, where $r > a$.

---

* Starred problems are more difficult.

3-13. Show that the problem of an uncharged conducting sphere in an initially uniform electric field $\mathbf{E}_0$ may be solved by means of images. [*Hint:* A uniform electric field in the vicinity of the origin may be approximated by the field of two point charges Q and $-Q$ placed on the z-axis at $z = -L$ and $z = +L$, respectively. The field becomes more nearly uniform as $L \to \infty$. It is evident that $Q/2\pi\epsilon_0 L^2 = E_0$.]

3-14. A point charge q is located inside and at distance r from the center of a spherical conducting shell. The inner radius of the shell is a. Show that this problem can be solved by the image technique, and find the charge density σ induced on the inside surface of the shell. (The potential of the spherical shell cannot be completely specified in terms of q and its image, because exterior fixed charges can also contribute. Nevertheless, these exterior charges will add only a constant term to the potential.) Find the total charge induced on the inside surface of the shell (a) by physical arguments, and (b) by integration of σ over the surface.

3-15. A long conducting cylinder bearing a charge λ per unit length is oriented parallel to a grounded conducting plane of infinite extent. The axis of the cylinder is at distance x_0 from the plane, and the radius of the cylinder is a. Find the location of the line image, and find also the constant M (which determines the potential of the cylinder) in terms of a and x_0.

3-16. A spherical distribution of charge is characterized by a constant charge density ρ for $r \leq R$. For radii greater than R, the charge density is zero. Find the potential $U(r)$ by integrating Poisson's equation. Check this result by evaluating the integral (3-1). [*Hint:* To perform (3-1), divide the charge region into spherical concentric shells of thickness dr.]

3-17. A dipole $\mathbf{p}$ is oriented normal to and at distance d from an infinite conducting plane. The plane is grounded (i.e., at zero potential). Calculate the force exerted on the plane by the dipole.

3-18. A thunderstorm contains a charge $+Q$ at altitude h_1 and, directly below this, a charge $-Q$ at altitude h_2. Find an expression for the vertical electric field E_v at the earth's surface at distance d from the storm. For $h_1 = 5000m$, $h_2 = 3000m$, and $Q = 15\,coul$, make a graph showing how E_v varies, from $d = 0$ to $d = 20$ km.

CHAPTER 4

THE ELECTROSTATIC FIELD IN DIELECTRIC MEDIA

Thus far, we have ignored problems involving dielectric media, and have dealt with cases in which the electric field is produced exclusively by free charges: either by a specified distribution of them or by free charge on the surface of conductors. We now wish to remedy this situation and take up the more general case.

An ideal dielectric material is one which has no free charges. Nevertheless, all material media are composed of molecules, these in turn being composed of charged entities (atomic nuclei and electrons), and the molecules of the dielectric are certainly affected by the presence of an electric field. The electric field causes a force to be exerted on each charged particle, positive particles being pushed in the direction of the field, negative particles oppositely, so that the positive and negative parts of each molecule are displaced from their equilibrium positions in opposite directions. These displacements, however, are limited (in most cases to very small fractions of a molecular diameter) by strong restoring forces which are set up by the changing charge configuration in the molecule. The overall effect from the macroscopic point of view is most easily visualized as a displacement of the entire positive charge in the dielectric relative to the negative charge. The dielectric is said to be *polarized*.

A polarized dielectric, even though it is electrically neutral on the average, produces an electric field, both at exterior points and inside the dielectric as well. As a result, we are confronted with what appears to be an awkward situation: the polarization of the dielectric depends on the total electric field in the medium, but a part of the electric field is produced by the dielectric itself. Furthermore, the distant electric field of the dielectric may modify the free charge distribution on conducting bodies, and this in turn will change the electric field *in the dielectric*. It is the main purpose of this chapter to develop general methods for handling this curious situation.

4–1 Polarization. Consider a small volume element Δv of a dielectric medium which, as a whole, is electrically neutral. If the medium is polarized, then a separation of positive and negative charge has been effected, and the volume element is characterized by an electric dipole moment

$$\Delta \mathbf{p} = \int_{\Delta v} \mathbf{r} \, dq. \tag{4–1}$$

According to Section 2–9, this quantity determines the electric field produced by Δv at distant points (i.e., at distances from Δv large compared with the dimensions of the volume element).

Since $\Delta \mathbf{p}$ depends on the size of the volume element, it is more convenient to work with $\mathbf{P}$, the electric dipole moment per unit volume:

$$\mathbf{P} = \frac{\Delta \mathbf{p}}{\Delta v}. \tag{4-2}$$

Strictly speaking, $\mathbf{P}$ must be defined as the limit of this quantity as Δv becomes very small from the macroscopic viewpoint. In this way $\mathbf{P}$ becomes a point function, $\mathbf{P}(x, y, z)$. $\mathbf{P}$ is usually called the *electric polarization*, or simply the *polarization*, of the medium. Its dimensions are charge per unit area; in mks units, coul/m^2.

It is apparent that $\mathbf{P}(x, y, z)$ is a vector quantity which, in each volume element, has the direction of $\Delta \mathbf{p}$. This, in turn, has the direction of displacement of positive charge relative to negative charge (see Fig. 4-1).

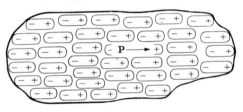

FIG. 4-1. A piece of polarized dielectric material. Each volume element is represented as a dipole $\Delta \mathbf{p}$.

Although Δv is assumed very small from the macroscopic point of view, it still contains many molecules. It is sometimes desirable to speak about the electric dipole moment of a single molecule, that is,

$$\mathbf{p}_m = \int_{\text{molecule}} \mathbf{r}\, dq, \tag{4-3}$$

since a molecule is one of the small, electrically neutral entities which make up the dielectric material. It is evident from (4-1) that the dipole moment associated with Δv is given by $\Delta \mathbf{p} = \sum \mathbf{p}_m$, where the summation extends over all molecules inside the element Δv. Hence,

$$\mathbf{P} = \frac{1}{\Delta v} \sum_m \mathbf{p}_m. \tag{4-4}$$

This approach will be developed further in Chapter 5.

Although Fig. 4-1 represents each volume element of the polarized dielectric as a small dipole, it may be more instructive to visualize the dielectric in terms of its molecules, and to imagine that each dipole of Fig. 4-1 represents a single molecule.

4–2 External field of a dielectric medium. Consider now a finite piece of dielectric material which is polarized, i.e., which is characterized at each point $\mathbf{r}'$ by a polarization, $\mathbf{P}(\mathbf{r}')$. The polarization gives rise to an electric field, and our problem is to calculate this field at point $\mathbf{r}$, which is outside of the dielectric body (see Fig. 4–2). As in Chapter 2, we shall find it more convenient to calculate first the potential $U(\mathbf{r})$, and obtain the electric field as minus the gradient of U.

Each volume element $\Delta v'$ of the dielectric medium is characterized by a dipole moment $\Delta \mathbf{p} = \mathbf{P} \, \Delta v'$, and since the distance between (x, y, z) and $\Delta v'$ is large compared with the dimensions of $\Delta v'$, this quantity (the dipole moment) completely determines $\Delta v'$'s contribution to the potential:

$$\Delta U(\mathbf{r}) = \frac{\Delta \mathbf{p} \cdot (\mathbf{r} - \mathbf{r}')}{4\pi\epsilon_0 |\mathbf{r} - \mathbf{r}'|^3} = \frac{\mathbf{P}(\mathbf{r}') \cdot (\mathbf{r} - \mathbf{r}') \, \Delta v'}{4\pi\epsilon_0 |\mathbf{r} - \mathbf{r}'|^3}. \tag{4–5}$$

Here $\mathbf{r} - \mathbf{r}'$ is the vector, directed out from $\Delta v'$, whose magnitude is given by

$$|\mathbf{r} - \mathbf{r}'| = \sqrt{(x - x')^2 + (y - y')^2 + (z - z')^2}. \tag{4–6}$$

The entire potential at point $\mathbf{r}$ is obtained by summing the contributions from all parts of the dielectric:

$$U(\mathbf{r}) = \frac{1}{4\pi\epsilon_0} \int_{V_0} \frac{\mathbf{P}(\mathbf{r}') \cdot (\mathbf{r} - \mathbf{r}') \, dv'}{|\mathbf{r} - \mathbf{r}'|^3}. \tag{4–7}$$

This result is correct, and U may be evaluated directly from (4–7) if the functional form of $\mathbf{P}$ is known. It will be to our advantage, however, to express (4–7) in a rather different way by means of a simple mathematical transformation.

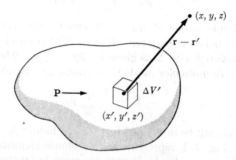

FIG. 4–2. The electric field at (x, y, z) may be calculated by summing up the contributions due to the various volume elements $\Delta V'$ in V_0. The surface of V_0 is denoted by S_0.

If $|\mathbf{r} - \mathbf{r}'|$ is given by (4-6), then

$$\nabla'\left(\frac{1}{|\mathbf{r} - \mathbf{r}'|}\right) = +\frac{\mathbf{r} - \mathbf{r}'}{|\mathbf{r} - \mathbf{r}'|^3}, \qquad (4\text{-}8)$$

as may be seen by direct application of the gradient operator in cartesian coordinates. The ∇' operator involves derivatives with respect to the primed coordinates. In certain circumstances it may be desirable to perform a gradient operation with respect to the unprimed coordinates; this will be indicated in the usual way by ∇. Evidently, ∇' operating on a function of $|\mathbf{r} - \mathbf{r}'|$ is equal to $-\nabla$ operating on the same function. We shall require the ∇ operator later in order to get the electric field at point $\mathbf{r}$. However, in performing the integral (4-7) over the dielectric volume V_0, the point $\mathbf{r}$ is held fixed; hence the integrand of (4-7) may be transformed by means of (4-8):

$$\frac{\mathbf{P} \cdot (\mathbf{r} - \mathbf{r}')}{|\mathbf{r} - \mathbf{r}'|^3} = \mathbf{P} \cdot \nabla'\left(\frac{1}{|\mathbf{r} - \mathbf{r}'|}\right). \qquad (4\text{-}9)$$

Equation (4-9) may be further transformed by means of the vector identity (I-6) of Table 1-1:

$$\mathrm{div}'\,(f\mathbf{A}) = f\,\mathrm{div}'\,\mathbf{A} + \mathbf{A} \cdot \nabla' f, \qquad (4\text{-}10)$$

where f is any scalar point function and $\mathbf{A}$ is an arbitrary vector point function. Here again the prime indicates differentiation with respect to the primed coordinates. Letting $f = (1/|\mathbf{r} - \mathbf{r}'|)$ and $\mathbf{A} = \mathbf{P}$, the integrand, (4-9), becomes

$$\frac{\mathbf{P} \cdot (\mathbf{r} - \mathbf{r}')}{|\mathbf{r} - \mathbf{r}'|^3} = \mathrm{div}'\left(\frac{\mathbf{P}}{|\mathbf{r} - \mathbf{r}'|}\right) - \frac{1}{|\mathbf{r} - \mathbf{r}'|}\,\mathrm{div}'\,\mathbf{P}. \qquad (4\text{-}11)$$

Finally, the potential, (4-7), may be written as

$$U(\mathbf{r}) = \frac{1}{4\pi\epsilon_0} \oint_{S_0} \frac{\mathbf{P} \cdot \mathbf{n}\,da'}{|\mathbf{r} - \mathbf{r}'|} + \frac{1}{4\pi\epsilon_0} \int_{V_0} \frac{(-\mathrm{div}'\,\mathbf{P})\,dv'}{|\mathbf{r} - \mathbf{r}'|}, \qquad (4\text{-}12)$$

where the volume integral of $\mathrm{div}'\,(\mathbf{P}/|\mathbf{r} - \mathbf{r}'|)$ has been replaced by a surface integral through application of the divergence theorem, and $\mathbf{n}$, of course, is the outward normal to the surface element da' (outward means out of the dielectric).

The quantities $\mathbf{P} \cdot \mathbf{n}$ and $-\mathrm{div}\,\mathbf{P}$ which appear in the integrals of (4-12) are two scalar functions obtained from the polarization $\mathbf{P}$. It seems expedient to give these quantities special symbols, and since they have the dimensions charge per unit area and charge per unit volume, respectively, we write

$$\sigma_P \equiv \mathbf{P} \cdot \mathbf{n} = P_n, \tag{4-13}$$

and

$$\rho_P \equiv -\operatorname{div} \mathbf{P}, \tag{4-14}$$

and call σ_P and ρ_P *polarization charge densities* or *bound charge densities*. The term "bound charge" is used to emphasize that the charges are not free to move around or be extracted from the dielectric material. The surface density of bound charge is given by the component of polarization normal to the surface, and the volume density of bound charge is a measure of the nonuniformity of the polarization inside the material.

The potential due to the dielectric material,

$$U(\mathbf{r}) = \frac{1}{4\pi\epsilon_0} \left[\oint_{S_0} \frac{\sigma_P \, da'}{|\mathbf{r} - \mathbf{r}'|} + \int_{V_0} \frac{\rho_P \, dv'}{|\mathbf{r} - \mathbf{r}'|} \right],$$

$$= \frac{1}{4\pi\epsilon_0} \int \frac{dq'_P}{|\mathbf{r} - \mathbf{r}'|}, \tag{4-15}$$

is now written in such a way that it is evident that it arises from a charge distribution. In other words, the dielectric material has been replaced by an appropriate distribution of bound charge.

Although (4-15) has been obtained by means of a mathematical transformation, it should be possible to understand σ_P and ρ_P on purely physical grounds. That a surface charge density σ_P exists is evident from Fig. 4–1, where it is seen that this charge is made up from the ends of similarly oriented dipoles. In this way a charge density is developed on every surface which is not parallel to the polarization vector. Turning now to ρ_P, we expect that $\rho_P \, \Delta v'$ represents the *excess* or *net charge* in the volume element $\Delta v'$. That this is truly the case may be seen in the following way: let us define two charge densities ρ^+ and ρ^- as representing the total positive charge and the total negative charge per unit volume, respectively. That is, ρ^+ represents all the atomic nuclei in unit volume of the dielectric and, similarly, ρ^- counts all the electrons. In the unpolarized state, each volume element of the dielectric is electrically neutral; hence

$$\rho_0^+(x', y', z') + \rho_0^-(x', y', z') = 0, \tag{4-16}$$

where the subscript zero denotes densities in the unpolarized configuration. Let us assume that as a consequence of polarization the positive charge is displaced by $\boldsymbol{\delta}^+(x, y, z)$ and the negative charge by $\boldsymbol{\delta}^-(x, y, z)$. The positive charge crossing an element of area da' is $\rho_0^+ \, \boldsymbol{\delta}^+ \cdot \mathbf{n} \, da'$, and thus the *gain of positive charge* by the volume element $\Delta v'$ during the polarization process is

$$- \oint_{\Delta S} \rho_0^+ \, \boldsymbol{\delta}^+ \cdot \mathbf{n} \, da', \tag{4-17}$$

where ΔS is the surface bounding $\Delta v'$. Similarly, the displacement of negative charge increases the charge (decreases the negative charge) in $\Delta v'$ by

$$\oint_{\Delta S} (-\rho_0^-) \, \boldsymbol{\delta}^- \cdot \mathbf{n} \, da. \qquad (4\text{–}18)$$

The total gain in charge by the volume element $\Delta v'$ is the sum of (4–17) and (4–18), and as a consequence of (4–16) may be written as

$$-\oint_{\Delta S} \rho_0^+ (\boldsymbol{\delta}^+ - \boldsymbol{\delta}^-) \cdot \mathbf{n} \, da' = -\text{div} \, [\rho_0^+ (\boldsymbol{\delta}^+ - \boldsymbol{\delta}^-)] \, \Delta v'. \qquad (4\text{–}19)$$

But $\boldsymbol{\delta}^+ - \boldsymbol{\delta}^-$ is just the relative displacement of positive and negative charge densities, and $\rho_0^+ (\boldsymbol{\delta}^+ - \boldsymbol{\delta}^-)$ is equivalent, therefore, to what we have called the polarization $\mathbf{P}$. Thus $\rho_P \, \Delta v'$ is the net charge in a volume element of the polarized dielectric.

At first sight it may seem rather strange that having started with electrically neutral volume elements of dielectric material, we end up with volume elements which bear a net charge. According to our original point of view, the dielectric is composed of elemental dipoles $\Delta \mathbf{p}$, and it was essential that each $\Delta \mathbf{p}$ be electrically neutral in order that Eq. (4–5) give the potential correctly. Now we find that so long as div $\mathbf{P}$ does not vanish, the individual volume elements appear to be charged. The origin of this seeming paradox is found in the mathematical transformation (4–11); the contribution from each volume element is transformed to a different volume term and a surface term. The total charge in the volume and surface of the element is still zero; but when we stack various volume elements together to form a macroscopic piece of dielectric material, we find that the contributions to the potential from the various "internal surfaces" cancel out. We are left with effectively charged volume elements and a surface contribution from the external boundary.

The total polarization charge of a dielectric body,

$$Q_P = \int_{V_0} (-\text{div}' \, \mathbf{P}) \, dv' + \oint_{S_0} \mathbf{P} \cdot \mathbf{n} \, da', \qquad (4\text{–}20)$$

must equal zero, since it was our premise that the dielectric, as a whole, is electrically neutral. This result is immediately obvious from the form of (4–20), which clearly vanishes as a consequence of the divergence theorem.

We now have two distinct expressions for the electrostatic potential $U(\mathbf{r})$ due to a polarized dielectric specimen, namely, (4–7) and (4–15). Both are correct, but we shall find the latter expression more convenient in most cases. The electric field $\mathbf{E}$ may be obtained as minus the gradient of (4–15). Since U is a function of the coordinates (x, y, z), the appropriate gradient is $-\nabla$. The unprimed coordinates appear only in the function $1/|\mathbf{r} - \mathbf{r}'|$. Hence, noting that $\nabla(1/|\mathbf{r} - \mathbf{r}'|) = -\nabla'(1/|\mathbf{r} - \mathbf{r}'|)$ and using (4–8), we obtain

$$\mathbf{E}(\mathbf{r}) = \frac{1}{4\pi\epsilon_0}\left[\int_{S_0} \frac{\sigma_P(\mathbf{r} - \mathbf{r}')\, da'}{|\mathbf{r} - \mathbf{r}'|^3} + \int_{V_0} \frac{\rho_P(\mathbf{r} - \mathbf{r}')\, dv'}{|\mathbf{r} - \mathbf{r}'|^3}\right]. \quad (4\text{–}21)$$

4–3 The electric field inside a dielectric. Before we can write an expression for the electric field inside a polarized medium, it is necessary to define this electric field precisely. What we are interested in, of course, is the *macroscopic electric field*, i.e., the average electric field in a small region of the dielectric which, nevertheless, contains a large number of molecules. An alternative and perhaps preferable approach is to define the electric field directly in terms of a macroscopic experiment: *the (macroscopic) electric field is the force per unit charge on a test charge embedded in the dielectric, in the limit where the test charge is so small that it does not itself affect the charge distribution.* This test charge must be dimensionally small from the macroscopic point of view (what we shall call a "point" charge), but it will be large compared with the size of a molecule.

Although the above statement is the fundamental definition of the macroscopic electric field $\mathbf{E}$, it is difficult to use this definition directly to obtain an expression for the field, since we would have to calculate the force on a charged body of extended size, and then go to the limit as the size of the object decreased. Hence we find it expedient to use another property of the electric field to help us obtain the analytic expression we are seeking, and in this way we shall get $\mathbf{E}$ in terms of the polarization charges of the medium. Later, in Section 4–10, it will be shown that the quantity we have called $\mathbf{E}$ is indeed in agreement with the fundamental "force definition."

The electrostatic field in a dielectric must have the same basic properties which we found applied to $\mathbf{E}$ in vacuum; in particular, $\mathbf{E}$ is a conservative field, and hence derivable from a scalar potential. Thus,

$$\mathbf{curl}\ \mathbf{E} = 0$$

or, equivalently,

$$\oint \mathbf{E} \cdot d\mathbf{l} = 0.$$

Let us apply the last equation to the path $ABCD$ shown in Fig. 4–3, where the segment AB lies in a needle-shaped cavity cut out of the dielectric, and the segment CD lies in the dielectric proper. Since the segments AD and BC may be made arbitrarily small, the line integral reduces to

$$\mathbf{E}_v \cdot 1 - \mathbf{E}_d \cdot 1 = 0$$

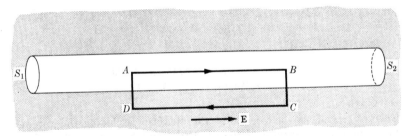

FIG. 4–3. The path $ABCD$ lies partly in the needle-shaped cavity, and partly in the dielectric. In an isotropic dielectric (see Section 4–5) the polarization $\mathbf{P}$ has the direction of $\mathbf{E}$, so that, for the orientation of the needle shown, $\sigma_P = 0$ on the cylindrical walls. In an anisotropic dielectric, σ_P is not necessarily zero, but its value does not affect the longitudinal component of electric field in the cavity.

or, equivalently,

$$E_{vt} = E_{dt}, \qquad (4\text{–}22)$$

where the subscripts v and d refer to vacuum and dielectric respectively, and the subscript t stands for tangential component.

Equation (4–22) is valid regardless of the orientation of the needle-shaped cavity. If the "needle" is oriented along the direction of $\mathbf{E}$, then $E_{dt} = E_d$; furthermore, by symmetry, the field in the cavity is along the direction of the needle, that is, $E_{vt} = E_v$. We are thus led to an important conclusion:*

> The electric field in a dielectric is equal to the electric field inside a needle-shaped cavity in the dielectric provided the cavity axis is oriented parallel to the direction of the electric field.

Evidently, the problem of calculating the electric field inside a dielectric reduces to calculating the electric field inside a needle-shaped cavity in the dielectric. But the electric field in the cavity is an external field, and hence may be determined by means of the results of Section 4–2. Just as in Section 4–2, we assume here that the polarization of the dielectric is a given function $\mathbf{P}(x', y', z')$, and we calculate the potential and electric field arising from this polarization. Taking the field point $\mathbf{r}$ at the center of the cavity and using Eq. (4–15), we obtain for the potential

---

* This statement is strictly true only for isotropic dielectrics (see Section 4–5). For anisotropic dielectrics the symmetry argument fails, and our conclusion must be generalized: the electric field in a dielectric is equal to the longitudinal component of the electric field inside a needle-shaped cavity in the dielectric provided the cavity axis is oriented parallel to the direction of the electric field in the dielectric.

$$U(\mathbf{r}) = \frac{1}{4\pi\epsilon_0} \int_{V_0 - V_1} \frac{\rho_P(x', y', z')\, dv'}{|\mathbf{r} - \mathbf{r}'|}$$

$$+ \frac{1}{4\pi\epsilon_0} \int_{S_0 + S'} \frac{\sigma_P(x', y', z')\, da'}{|\mathbf{r} - \mathbf{r}'|}, \qquad (4\text{-}23)$$

where $V_0 - V_1$ is the volume of the dielectric excluding the "needle," S_0 is the exterior surface of the dielectric, and $S' = S_1 + S_2 + S_c$ are the needle surfaces. But from Fig. 4–3 it is seen that $\sigma_P = 0$ on the cylindrical surface S_c of the needle; furthermore, the needle may be made arbitrarily thin so that the surfaces S_1 and S_2 have negligible area. Thus only the exterior surfaces of the dielectric contribute, and the surface integral of Eq. (4–23) becomes identical in form to the surface integral of Eq. (4–15). The volume integral of Eq. (4–23) excludes the cavity; however, the contribution of the cavity to this integral is negligible, as may readily be seen. The charge density ρ_P is bounded; the quantity $dv'/|\mathbf{r} - \mathbf{r}'|$ does not diverge at the field point (i.e., when $\mathbf{r}' = \mathbf{r}$) because the volume of a point is a higher-order zero than the lim $|\mathbf{r} - \mathbf{r}'|$; and finally volume V_1 of the needle may be made arbitrarily small by making the cavity thin. Thus we need not exclude the volume V_1, and Eq. (4–23) becomes similar in form to Eq. (4–15). In other words, Eq. (4–15) gives the potential $U(\mathbf{r})$ regardless of whether the point $\mathbf{r}$ is located inside or external to the dielectric.

The electric field $\mathbf{E}(\mathbf{r})$ may be calculated as minus the gradient of Eq. (4–23). But this differs only by a negligible amount from Eq. (4–21). *Thus (4–21) gives the medium's contribution to the electric field at $\mathbf{r}$, independently of whether $\mathbf{r}$ is inside or outside the medium.*

The calculations indicated in Eqs. (4–15) and (4–21) are straightforward for cases in which $\mathbf{P}(x, y, z)$ is a known function of position. (Some examples of this type are to be found among the problems at the end of this chapter.) In most cases, however, the polarization arises in response to an electric field which has been imposed on the dielectric medium [that is, $\mathbf{P}(x', y', z')$ is a function of the *total macroscopic electric field* $\mathbf{E}(x', y', z')$], and under these conditions the situation is much more complicated. First, it is necessary to know the functional form of $\mathbf{P}(\mathbf{E})$; but this is known experimentally in most cases and hence is not a source of difficulty. The real complication arises because $\mathbf{P}$ depends on the *total electric field*, including the contribution from the dielectric itself, and it is this contribution which we are in the process of evaluating. Thus we cannot determine $\mathbf{P}$ because we don't know $\mathbf{E}$, and vice versa.

It is evident that a different approach to the problem is needed, and this will be provided in the following sections.

4-4 Gauss' law in a dielectric. The electric displacement. In Chapter 2 we derived an important relationship between electric flux and charge, namely, Gauss' law. This law states that the electric flux across an arbitrary closed surface is proportional to the total charge enclosed by the surface. In applying Gauss' law to a region containing free charges embedded in a dielectric, we must be careful to include all of the charge inside the gaussian surface, bound charge as well as free charge.

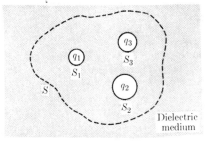

FIG. 4-4. Construction of a gaussian surface S in a dielectric medium.

In Fig. 4-4 the dashed surface S is an imaginary closed surface located inside a dielectric medium. There is a certain amount of free charge, Q, in the volume bounded by S, and we shall assume that this free charge exists on the surfaces of three conductors in amounts q_1, q_2, and q_3. By Gauss' law,

$$\oint_S \mathbf{E} \cdot \mathbf{n} \, da = \frac{1}{\epsilon_0} (Q + Q_P), \qquad (4\text{-}24)$$

where Q is the total free charge, i.e.,

$$Q = q_1 + q_2 + q_3,$$

and Q_P is the polarization charge:

$$Q_P = \int_{S_1+S_2+S_3} \mathbf{P} \cdot \mathbf{n} \, da + \int_V (-\text{div } \mathbf{P}) \, dv. \qquad (4\text{-}25a)$$

Here V is volume of the dielectric enclosed by S. There is no boundary of the dielectric at S, so that the surface integral in (4-25a) *does not* contain a contribution from S.

If we transform the volume integral in (4-25a) to a surface integral by means of the divergence theorem, we must be careful to include contributions from all surfaces bounding V, namely, S, S_1, S_2, and S_3. It is evident that the last three contributions will cancel the first term of (4-25a), so that

$$Q_P = -\oint_S \mathbf{P} \cdot \mathbf{n} \, da. \qquad (4\text{-}25b)$$

Combining this result with (4–24), we obtain

$$\oint_S (\epsilon_0 \mathbf{E} + \mathbf{P}) \cdot \mathbf{n}\, da = Q. \tag{4–26}$$

Equation (4–26) states that the flux of the vector $\epsilon_0\mathbf{E} + \mathbf{P}$ through a closed surface is equal to the *total free charge* enclosed by the surface. This vector quantity is important enough to warrant a name and a separate symbol. We define, therefore a, new macroscopic field vector $\mathbf{D}$, the *electric displacement:*

$$\mathbf{D} = \epsilon_0 \mathbf{E} + \mathbf{P}, \tag{4–27}$$

which evidently has the same units as $\mathbf{P}$, charge per unit area.

In terms of $\mathbf{D}$, Eq. (4–26) becomes

$$\oint_S \mathbf{D} \cdot \mathbf{n}\, da = Q, \tag{4–28}$$

and this result is usually referred to as Gauss' law for the electric displacement, or simply Gauss' law. Equation (4–28) is applicable to a region of space bounded by any closed surface S; if we apply it to a small region in which all of the free charge enclosed is distributed as a charge density ρ, then Gauss' law becomes

$$\oint_S \mathbf{D} \cdot \mathbf{n}\, da = \rho\, \Delta V.$$

Dividing this equation by ΔV and proceeding to the limit, we obtain

$$\operatorname{div} \mathbf{D} = \rho, \tag{4–29}$$

a result which is sometimes called the differential form of Gauss' law.

The advantage of the procedure just followed is that the total electrostatic field at each point in the dielectric medium is expressed as the sum of two parts,

$$\mathbf{E}(x, y, z) = \frac{1}{\epsilon_0} \mathbf{D}(x, y, z) - \frac{1}{\epsilon_0} \mathbf{P}(x, y, z), \tag{4–30}$$

where the first term, $(1/\epsilon_0)\mathbf{D}$, is related to the free charge density through its divergence, and the second term, $(-1/\epsilon_0)\mathbf{P}$, is proportional to the polarization of the medium. In a vacuum the electric field is given entirely by the first term in (4–30).

4–5 Electric susceptibility and dielectric constant. In the introduction to this chapter it was stated that the polarization of a dielectric medium occurs in response to the electric field in the medium. The degree of polarization depends not only on the electric field, but also on the properties of the molecules which make up the dielectric material. From the macroscopic point of view, the behavior of the material is completely specified by an experimentally determined relationship, $\mathbf{P} = \mathbf{P}(\mathbf{E})$, where $\mathbf{E}$ is the macroscopic electric field. This is a point relationship, and if $\mathbf{E}$ varies from point to point in the material, then $\mathbf{P}$ will vary accordingly.

For most materials, $\mathbf{P}$ vanishes when $\mathbf{E}$ vanishes. Since this is the usual behavior, we shall limit our discussion here to materials of this type. (Dielectrics with a permanent polarization will be discussed briefly in Section 5–4.) Furthermore, if the material is isotropic, then the polarization should have the same direction as the electric field which is causing it. These results are summarized by the equation

$$\mathbf{P} = \chi(E)\mathbf{E}, \tag{4–31}$$

where the scalar quantity $\chi(E)$ is called the *electric susceptibility* of the material. A great many materials are electrically isotropic; this category includes fluids, polycrystalline and amorphous solids, and some crystals. A treatment of the electrical properties of anisotropic materials is beyond the scope of this text.

Combining (4–31) with (4–27), we obtain an expression for $\mathbf{D}$ in isotropic media:

$$\mathbf{D} = \epsilon(E)\mathbf{E}, \tag{4–32}$$

$$\epsilon(E) = \epsilon_0 + \chi(E), \tag{4–33}$$

where $\epsilon(E)$ is the *permittivity* of the material. It is evident that ϵ, ϵ_0, and χ all have the same units.

Although we have been careful to write χ and ϵ in the form $\chi(E)$ and $\epsilon(E)$, nevertheless it is found experimentally that χ and ϵ are frequently independent of the electric field, except perhaps for very intense fields. In other words, χ and ϵ are constants characteristic of the material. Materials of this type will be called *linear dielectrics*, and they obey the relations

$$\mathbf{P} = \chi\mathbf{E}, \tag{4–31a}$$

$$\mathbf{D} = \epsilon\mathbf{E}. \tag{4–32a}$$

The electrical behavior of a material is now completely specified by either the permittivity ϵ or the susceptibility χ. It is more convenient, however, to work with a dimensionless quantity K defined by

$$\epsilon = K\epsilon_0. \tag{4–34}$$

K is called the dielectric coefficient, or simply the *dielectric constant*. From (4–33) it is evident that

$$K = \frac{\epsilon}{\epsilon_0} = 1 + \frac{\chi}{\epsilon_0}. \tag{4–35}$$

The dielectric constants for a few commonly encountered materials are given in Table 4–1. Except for a few examples in which the polarization **P** of the material is specified, the problems in this book deal with linear dielectrics.

If the electric field in a dielectric is made very intense, it will begin to pull electrons completely out of the molecules, and the material will become conducting. The maximum electric field which a dielectric can withstand without breakdown is called its dielectric strength. The dielectric strengths E_{max}, of a few substances are also given in Table 4–1.

TABLE 4–1

PROPERTIES OF DIELECTRIC MATERIALS*

(Dielectric constant K and dielectric strength E_{max})

Material	K	E_{max}, volts/m
Glass†	5–10	9×10^6
Mica	6.0	5–20×10^6
Nylon	3.5	16×10^6
Rubber†	2–3.5	16–40×10^6
Sulfur	4.0	
Wood†	2.5–8.0	
Alcohol, ethyl (0°C)	28.4	
Benzene (0°C)	2.3	
Petroleum oil	2.1	12×10^6
Water (distilled, 0°C)	88.0	
Water (distilled, 20°C)	80.0	
Air (1 atm)	1.00059	3×10^6
Air (100 atm)	1.0548	
CO_2 (1 atm)	1.000985	

* Data from the Handbook of Chemistry and Physics, 33rd edition, Chemical Rubber Publishing Co., Cleveland, Ohio.

† For materials such as glass, rubber, and wood, the chemical composition varies; hence the range of dielectric constants. It is not to be inferred that the material is nonlinear.

4–6 Point charge in a dielectric fluid. One of the simplest problems involving a dielectric which we might consider is that of a point charge q in a homogeneous isotropic medium of infinite extent. The dielectric medium will be assumed to be linear and characterized by a dielectric constant K. Although this problem is quite simple, it will nevertheless prove instructive.

If the point charge q were situated in a vacuum, the electric field would be a pure radial field. But since $\mathbf{E}$, $\mathbf{D}$, and $\mathbf{P}$ are all parallel to one another at each point, the radial nature of the field is not changed by the presence of the medium. Furthermore, from the symmetry of the problem, $\mathbf{E}$, $\mathbf{D}$, and $\mathbf{P}$ can depend only on the distance from the point charge, not on any angular coordinate. Let us apply Gauss' law, Eq. (4–28), to a spherical surface of radius r which is located concentrically about q. For convenience, q will be located at the origin. Then

$$4\pi r^2 D = q$$

and

$$D = \frac{q}{4\pi r^2},$$

or

$$\mathbf{D} = \frac{q}{4\pi r^3}\,\mathbf{r}. \tag{4–36}$$

The electric field and polarization may now be evaluated quite easily:

$$\mathbf{E} = \frac{q}{4\pi K \epsilon_0 r^3}\,\mathbf{r}, \tag{4–37}$$

$$\mathbf{P} = \frac{(K-1)q}{4\pi K r^3}\,\mathbf{r}. \tag{4–38}$$

Thus the electric field is smaller by the factor K than would be the case if the medium were absent.

At this point, it will be instructive to look at the problem in more detail, and try to see why the dielectric has weakened the electric field. The electric field has its origin in all of the charge, bound and free. The free charge is just the point charge q. The bound charge, however, is made up from two contributions, a volume density $\rho_P = -\operatorname{div}\mathbf{P}$, and a surface density $\sigma_P = \mathbf{P}\cdot\mathbf{n}$ on the surface of the dielectric in contact with the point charge. Using Eq. (4–38), we find that $\operatorname{div}\mathbf{P}$ vanishes, so there is no volume density of bound charge in this case.

Our point charge q is a point in the macroscopic sense. Actually, it is large on a molecular scale, and we can assign to it a radius b which eventually will be made to approach zero. The total surface bound charge is then given by

$$Q_P = \lim_{b\to 0} 4\pi b^2 (\mathbf{P}\cdot\mathbf{n})_{r=b} = -\frac{(K-1)q}{K}. \tag{4–39}$$

The total charge,

$$Q_P + q = \frac{1}{K}\,q, \tag{4–40}$$

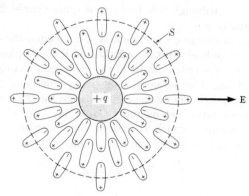

Fig. 4–5. Schematic diagram showing the orientation of polarized molecules in a dielectric medium surrounding a "point charge" q.

appears as a point charge from the macroscopic point of view, and it is now clear why the electric field is a factor K smaller than it would be if the medium were absent. A schematic diagram of the point charge q in a dielectric medium is shown in Fig. 4–5.

4–7 Boundary conditions on the field vectors. Before we can solve more complicated problems, we must know how the field vectors **E** and **D** change in passing an interface between two media. The two media may be two dielectrics with different properties, or a dielectric and a conductor. Vacuum may be treated as a dielectric with permittivity ϵ_0.

Consider two media, 1 and 2, in contact as shown in Fig. 4–6. We shall assume that there is a surface density of free charge, σ, which may vary from point to point on the interface. Let us construct the small pillbox-shaped surface S which intersects the interface and encloses an area ΔS of the interface, the height of the pillbox being negligibly small in comparison with the diameter of the bases. The free charge enclosed by S is

$$\sigma \, \Delta S + \tfrac{1}{2}(\rho_1 + \rho_2) \times \text{volume},$$

but the volume of the pillbox is negligibly small, so that the last term may be neglected. Applying Gauss' law to S, we find

$$\mathbf{D}_2 \cdot \mathbf{n}_2 \, \Delta S + \mathbf{D}_1 \cdot \mathbf{n}_1 \, \Delta S = \sigma \, \Delta S,$$

or

$$(\mathbf{D}_2 - \mathbf{D}_1) \cdot \mathbf{n}_2 = \sigma. \tag{4–41a}$$

Since $\mathbf{n}_2$ may serve as the normal to the interface,

$$D_{2n} - D_{1n} = \sigma. \tag{4–41b(}$$

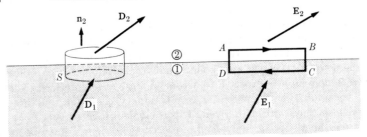

FIG. 4-6. Boundary conditions on the field vectors at the interface between two media may be obtained by applying Gauss' law to S, and integrating $\mathbf{E} \cdot d\mathbf{l}$ around the path $ABCDA$.

Thus, the discontinuity in the normal component of $\mathbf{D}$ is given by the surface density of free charge on the interface. Or, to put it another way, if there is no free charge on the interface between two media, the normal component of $\mathbf{D}$ is continuous.

Because the electrostatic field $\mathbf{E}$ may be obtained as minus the gradient of a potential, the line integral of $\mathbf{E} \cdot d\mathbf{l}$ around any closed path vanishes. Let us apply this result to the rectangular path $ABCD$ of Fig. 4-6. On this path, the lengths AB and CD will be taken equal to Δl and the segments AD and BC will be assumed to be negligibly small. Therefore

$$\mathbf{E}_2 \cdot \Delta \mathbf{l} + \mathbf{E}_1 \cdot (-\Delta \mathbf{l}) = 0,$$

or

$$(\mathbf{E}_2 - \mathbf{E}_1) \cdot \Delta \mathbf{l} = 0. \tag{4-42a}$$

Hence, the desired result:

$$E_{2t} = E_{1t}, \tag{4-42b}$$

that is, the tangential component of the electric field is continuous across an interface.

The above results have been obtained for two arbitrary media, but it is worth our while to specialize the equations for the case where one of the media is a conductor. If medium 1 is taken as the conductor, then $\mathbf{E}_1 = 0$. Since $\mathbf{E}_1$ vanishes, there is no polarization, and by Eq. (4-27) $\mathbf{D}_1$ also vanishes. Thus (4-41b) and (4-42b) become

$$D_{2n} = \sigma, \tag{4-43}$$

$$E_{2t} = 0, \tag{4-44}$$

for the displacement and electric field in a dielectric just outside of a conductor.

It is evident on purely physical grounds that the potential U must be continuous across an interface. This follows because the difference in potential, ΔU, between two closely spaced points is $-\mathbf{E} \cdot \Delta \mathbf{l}$, where $\Delta \mathbf{l}$ is the separation of the two points, and from what has been said above there is no reason to expect $\mathbf{E}$ to become infinite at an interface. Actually, the continuity of the potential is a boundary condition, but not independent of those already derived. It is equivalent in most cases to (4–42b).

From the discussion above and in preceding sections, it may be inferred that the electric displacement $\mathbf{D}$ is closely related to free charge. We should now like to prove an important property of $\mathbf{D}$, namely, that the flux of $\mathbf{D}$ is continuous in regions containing no free charge. To do so, we again resort to Gauss' law. Let us focus our attention on a region of space and construct *lines of displacement*, which are imaginary lines drawn in such a way that the direction of a line at any point is the direction of $\mathbf{D}$ at that point. Next we imagine a tube of displacement, a volume bounded on the sides by lines of $\mathbf{D}$ but not cut by them (see Fig. 4–7). The tube is terminated at its ends by the surfaces S_1 and S_2. Applying Gauss' law, we obtain

$$\int_{S_2} \mathbf{D} \cdot \mathbf{n}\, da - \int_{S_1} \mathbf{D} \cdot \mathbf{n}'\, da = Q. \tag{4–45}$$

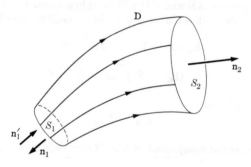

Fig. 4–7. A tube of displacement flux.

If there is no free charge in the region, then $Q = 0$, and the same amount of flux enters the tube through S_1 as leaves through S_2. When free charge is present, it determines the discontinuity in displacement flux; thus lines of displacement terminate on free charges. The lines of force, on the other hand, may terminate on free or bound charges.

4–8 Boundary-value problems involving dielectrics. The fundamental equation which has been developed in this chapter is

$$\operatorname{div} \mathbf{D} = \rho, \tag{4–46}$$

where ρ is the free charge density. If the dielectrics with which we are concerned are linear, isotropic, and homogeneous, then $\mathbf{D} = \epsilon\mathbf{E}$, where ϵ is a constant characteristic of the material, and we may write

$$\text{div } \mathbf{E} = \frac{1}{\epsilon}\rho. \tag{4-47}$$

But the electrostatic field $\mathbf{E}$ is derivable from a scalar potential U, i.e.,

$$\mathbf{E} = -\mathbf{grad}\ U;$$

so that

$$\nabla^2 U = -\frac{1}{\epsilon}\rho. \tag{4-48}$$

Thus the potential in the dielectric satisfies Poisson's equation; the only difference between (4-48) and the corresponding equation for the potential in vacuum is that ϵ replaces ϵ_0.

In most cases of interest the dielectric contains no free charge distributed throughout its volume, that is, $\rho = 0$ inside the dielectric material. The free charge exists on the surfaces of conductors or is concentrated in the form of point charges which may, to be sure, be embedded in the dielectric. In these circumstances, the potential satisfies Laplace's equation throughout the body of the dielectric:

$$\nabla^2 U = 0. \tag{4-49}$$

In some problems there may be a surface density of free charge, σ, on the surface of a dielectric body or on the interface between two dielectric materials, but this does not alter the situation, and Eq. (4-49) still applies so long as $\rho = 0$.

An electrostatic problem involving linear, isotropic, and homogeneous dielectrics reduces, therefore, to finding solutions of Laplace's equation in each medium, and joining the solutions in the various media by means of the boundary conditions of the preceding section. There are many problems which may be solved by this method; one example will be discussed here and additional examples will be found in the problems at the end of the chapter.

4–9 Dielectric sphere in a uniform electric field. We should like to determine how the lines of force are modified when a dielectric sphere of radius a is placed in a region of space containing an *initially* uniform electric field, $\mathbf{E}_0$. Let us assume the dielectric to be linear, isotropic, and homogeneous, and to be characterized by the dielectric constant K. Furthermore, it bears no free charge. The origin of our coordinate system may be taken at the center of the sphere, and the direction of $\mathbf{E}_0$ as the polar direction (z-direction); the potential may then be expressed as a sum of zonal harmonics. Just as in Section 3–5, all boundary conditions can be satisfied by means of the two lowest-order harmonics, and we write

$$U_1(r, \theta) = A_1 r \cos \theta + C_1 r^{-2} \cos \theta \qquad (4\text{–}50)$$

for the vacuum region (1) outside the sphere, and

$$U_2(r, \theta) = A_2 r \cos \theta + C_2 r^{-2} \cos \theta \qquad (4\text{–}51)$$

for the dielectric region (2). The constants A_1, A_2, C_1, and C_2 are unknown and must be determined from the boundary conditions. The harmonic r^{-1} is not required, since its presence implies a net charge on the sphere. A constant term may be added to (4–50) and to (4–51), but since the same constant is required in both equations, we may, without loss of generality, take it to be zero.

At distances far from the sphere, the electric field will retain its uniform character, and $U_1 \rightarrow -E_0 r \cos \theta$. Hence $A_1 = -E_0$. Furthermore, unless $C_2 = 0$, the potential and associated electric field would become infinite at the center of the sphere, and this would imply the existence of a macroscopic dipole at the center, i.e., a dipole whose moment is not proportional to ΔV. Certainly, this is not the case; as has already been discussed in Section 4–3, the potential and macroscopic field do not become infinite in a dielectric devoid of free charges. Hence $C_2 = 0$, and the remaining constants, A_2 and C_1, may be obtained from the boundary conditions of Section 4–7.

Continuity of the potential across the interface between the dielectric and vacuum requires that $U_1 = U_2$ at $r = a$, or

$$-E_0 a + C_1 a^{-2} = A_2 a. \qquad (4\text{–}52)$$

Since the normal component of **D** at the interface is $D_r = -\epsilon(\partial U/\partial r)$, the continuity of D_r (there is no free charge on the surface of the dielectric) requires that $D_{1r} = D_{2r}$ at $r = a$, or

$$E_0 + 2C_1 a^{-3} = -KA_2. \qquad (4\text{–}53)$$

Continuity of E_t at $r = a$ is equivalent to (4–52).

Combining Eqs. (4–52) and (4–53), we obtain

$$A_2 = -\frac{3E_0}{K + 2} \qquad (4\text{–}54)$$

and

$$C_1 = \frac{(K - 1)a^3 E_0}{K + 2}. \qquad (4\text{–}55)$$

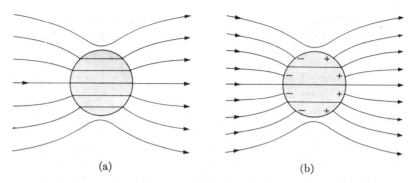

(a)   (b)

FIG. 4–8. A uniform electric field is distorted by the presence of a dielectric sphere: (a) lines of electric displacement, (b) lines of the electric field.

Thus the problem has been solved. The potential is given by (4–50) or (4–51), and the constants A_1, C_1, A_2, and C_2 are all known. The components of $\mathbf{E}$ and $\mathbf{D}$ may be obtained at any point (r, θ, ϕ) by differentiation. It is evident from (4–54) and because $C_2 = 0$ that the electric field inside the sphere has the direction of $\mathbf{E}_0$ and is given by

$$\mathbf{E}_2 = \frac{3}{K + 2} \mathbf{E}_0. \qquad (4\text{–}56)$$

The lines of displacement and the lines of force are shown in Fig. 4–8.

4–10 Force on a point charge embedded in a dielectric. We are now in a position to determine the force on a small, spherical, charged conductor embedded in a linear, isotropic dielectric. In the limit in which the conductor is negligibly small from the macroscopic viewpoint, this calculation gives the force on a point charge.

The electric field and surface charge density at a representative point of the conductor surface will be obtained by the boundary-value procedure of the preceding section, and the force $\mathbf{F}$ may then be obtained from the integral over the surface:

$$\mathbf{F} = \oint_S \mathbf{E}'\sigma \, da. \qquad (4\text{–}57)$$

Here $\mathbf{E}'$ stands for the electric field at the surface element da minus that part of the field produced by the element itself. In other words,

$$\mathbf{E}' = \mathbf{E} - \mathbf{E}_s, \qquad (4\text{–}58)$$

where $\mathbf{E}_s$ is the electric field produced by the surface element of charge, $\sigma \, da$. It is important that $\mathbf{E}_s$ not be included in the field $\mathbf{E}'$, because the quantity $\mathbf{E}_s\sigma\,da$ represents the interaction of the charge element $\sigma\,da$ with its *own* field; this self-interaction clearly produces no net force on the element, but gives rise to a surface stress

$$\mathfrak{F}_s = \sigma E_s, \tag{4–59}$$

which is due to the mutual repulsion of the electrons (or of the excess positive ions) in the surface layer. This stress is balanced by strong cohesive forces in the material of which the element is composed. It should be pointed out that when calculating forces on charged objects in Chapters 2 and 3, we implicitly subtracted the self field $\mathbf{E}_s$; thus, when calculating the force on a point charge, the field produced *by* the point charge was not included. A further discussion of the forces on charged objects will be taken up in Section 6–8.

It may appear that the self field of the charged surface element $\sigma\,da$ is negligible because the element is of infinitesimal size. This, however, is not the case. The element is small from the macroscopic point of view, to be sure, but one never quite goes to the limit. At a point directly on its surface, the element appears to be an infinite plane, i.e., the element subtends an angle of 2π; hence,

$$\mathbf{E}_s = \frac{\sigma}{2\epsilon}\,\mathbf{n}, \tag{4–60}$$

where $\mathbf{n}$ is a normal to the element and ϵ is the permittivity of the dielectric in contact with it. Thus the stress $\mathfrak{F}_s$ is proportional to σ^2, and is always a tension regardless of the sign of σ.

It is our purpose here to calculate the force on a *conductor*. Using the boundary conditions of Section 4–7, the total electric field at the conductor is given by

$$\mathbf{E} = \frac{\sigma}{\epsilon}\,\mathbf{n}. \tag{4–61}$$

Combining (4–58), (4–60), and (4–61), we obtain

$$\mathbf{E}' = \tfrac{1}{2}\mathbf{E},$$

and the force on the conductor becomes

$$\mathbf{F} = \tfrac{1}{2}\oint_S \mathbf{E}\sigma\,da. \tag{4–57a}$$

Let us now fix our attention on a small spherical conductor embedded in a dielectric of infinite extent. The total charge on the conductor is Q; its radius is a. Since we shall eventually go to the limit in which a becomes very small, and since variations in the electric field (if they exist) are on a macroscopic scale, it is sufficient to consider the case in which the electric field is initially uniform in the neighborhood of the conductor. Let us denote this uniform field by the symbol $\mathbf{E}_0$. The picture is similar to that of the boundary-value problem we solved in Section 3–5, except that here the conducting sphere is embedded (or immersed) in a dielectric of permittivity ϵ, and in addition bears a net charge Q.

By analogy with Section 3–5 we easily determine:

the potential,

$$U(r, \theta) = U_0 - E_0 r \cos \theta + \frac{E_0 a^3}{r^2} \cos \theta + \frac{Q}{4\pi \epsilon r} ; \qquad (4\text{–}62)$$

the electric field,

$$E_r = E_0(1 + 2a^3/r^3) \cos \theta + Q/4\pi \epsilon r^2, \qquad (4\text{–}63)$$

$$E_\theta = -E_0(1 - a^3/r^3) \sin \theta;$$

and the surface charge density on the surface of the sphere,

$$\sigma(\theta) = \epsilon E_r \Big|_{r = a} = 3\epsilon E_0 \cos \theta + Q/4\pi a^2. \qquad (4\text{–}64)$$

The force may now be determined from Eq. (4–57a). By symmetry, the only nonzero component of force is that in the direction $\theta = 0$, i.e., in the z-direction:

$$F_z = \tfrac{1}{2}\int_0^\pi (E_r)_{r=a} \cos \theta \sigma(\theta) 2\pi a^2 \sin \theta \, d\theta$$

$$= E_0 Q, \qquad (4\text{–}65a)$$

or

$$\mathbf{F} = Q\mathbf{E}_0. \qquad (4\text{–}65b)$$

This result is unchanged as we go to the limit of small a. Thus the electric field in the dielectric, $\mathbf{E}_0$, is in agreement with the fundamental definition, namely, the force on a small test charge Q divided by the magnitude of Q.

PROBLEMS

4-1. A thin dielectric rod of cross section A extends along the x-axis from $x = 0$ to $x = L$. The polarization of the rod is along its length, and is given by $P_x = ax^2 + b$. Find the volume density of polarization charge and the surface polarization charge on each end. Show *explicitly* that the total bound charge vanishes in this case.

4-2. A dielectric cube of side L has a radial polarization given by $\mathbf{P} = A\mathbf{r}$, where A is a constant, and $\mathbf{r} = \mathbf{i}x + \mathbf{j}y + \mathbf{k}z$. The origin of coordinates is at the center of the cube. Find all bound charge densities, and show *explicitly* that the total bound charge vanishes.

4-3. A dielectric rod in the shape of a right circular cylinder of length L and radius R is polarized in the direction of its length. If the polarization is uniform and of magnitude P, calculate the electric field resulting from this polarization at a point on the axis of the rod.

4-4. Prove the following relationship between the polarization, $\mathbf{P}$, and the bound charge densities ρ_P and σ_P, for a dielectric specimen of volume V and surface S.

$$\int_V \mathbf{P}\, dv = \int_V \rho_P \mathbf{r}\, dv + \int_S \sigma_P \mathbf{r}\, da.$$

Here, $\mathbf{r} = \mathbf{i}x + \mathbf{j}y + \mathbf{k}z$ is the position vector from any fixed origin. [*Hint:* Expand div $(x\mathbf{P})$ according to Eq. (4–10).]

4-5. Two semi-infinite blocks of dielectric are placed almost in contact so that there exists a narrow gap of constant separation between them. The polarization $\mathbf{P}$ is constant throughout all of the dielectric material, and it makes the angle γ with the normal to the planes bounding the gap. Determine the electric field in the gap.

4-6. A long cylindrical conductor of radius a, bearing the charge λ per unit length, is immersed in a dielectric medium of constant permittivity ϵ. Find the electric field at distance $r > a$ from the axis of the cylinder.

4-7. Two dielectric media with dielectric constants K_1 and K_2 are separated by a plane interface. There is no free charge on the interface. Find a relationship between the angles θ_1 and θ_2, where these are the angles which an arbitrary line of displacement makes with the normal to the interface: θ_1 in medium 1, θ_2 in medium 2.

4-8. A coaxial cable of circular cross section has a compound dielectric. The inner conductor has an outside radius a; this is surrounded by a dielectric sheath of dielectric constant K_1 and of outer radius b. Next comes another dielectric sheath of dielectric constant K_2 and outer radius c. If a potential difference U_0 is imposed between the conductors, calculate the polarization at each point in the two dielectric media.

*4-9. Two dielectric media with constant permittivities ϵ_1 and ϵ_2 are separated by a plane interface. There is no free charge on the interface. A point charge q is embedded in the medium characterized by ϵ_1, at a distance d from the interface. For convenience, we may take the yz-plane through the origin to be the interface, and we locate q on the x-axis at $x = -d$. If

$$r = \sqrt{(x+d)^2 + y^2 + z^2}, \qquad \text{and} \qquad r' = \sqrt{(x-d)^2 + y^2 + z^2},$$

then it is easily demonstrated that $(1/4\pi\epsilon_1)[(q/r) + (q'/r')]$ satisfies Laplace's equation at all points in medium 1 except at the position of q. Furthermore, $q''/4\pi\epsilon_2 r$ satisfies Laplace's equation in medium 2. Show that all boundary conditions can be satisfied by these potentials, and in so doing determine q' and q''. (Refer to Fig. 4–9.)

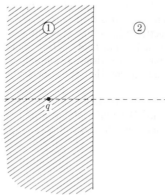

FIGURE 4–9

4–10. A long dielectric cylinder of radius a and dielectric constant K is placed in a uniform electric field $\mathbf{E}_0$. The axis of the cylinder is oriented at right angles to the direction of $\mathbf{E}_0$. The cylinder contains no free charge. Determine the electric field at points inside and outside the cylinder.

4–11. Two parallel conducting plates are separated by the distance d and maintained at the potential difference ΔU. A dielectric slab, of dielectric constant K and of uniform thickness $t < d$, is inserted between the plates. Determine the field vectors $\mathbf{E}$ and $\mathbf{D}$ in the dielectric and also in the vacuum between dielectric and one plate. Neglect edge effects due to the finite size of the plates.

4–12. Two parallel conducting plates are separated by the distance d and maintained at the potential difference ΔU. A dielectric slab, of dielectric constant K and of uniform thickness d, is inserted snugly between the plates; however, the slab does not completely fill the volume between the plates. Find the electric field (a) in the dielectric, and (b) in the vacuum region between the plates. Find the charge density σ on that part of the plate (c) in contact with the dielectric, and (d) in contact with vacuum. (e) Find σ_P on the surface of the dielectric slab.

4–13. A conducting sphere of radius R floats half submerged in a liquid dielectric medium of permittivity ϵ_1. The region above the liquid is a gas of permittivity ϵ_2. The total free charge on the sphere is Q. Find a radial inverse-square electric field satisfying all boundary conditions, and determine the free, bound, and total charge densities at all points on the surface of the sphere. Formulate an argument to show that this electric field is the actual one.

4–14. A uniform electric field $\mathbf{E}_0$ is set up in a medium of dielectric constant K. Prove that the field inside a spherical cavity in the medium is

$$\mathbf{E} = \frac{3K\mathbf{E}_0}{2K + 1}.$$

*4–15. A dielectric sphere of radius R has a permanent polarization $\mathbf{P}$ which is uniform in direction and magnitude. The polarized sphere gives rise to an electric field. Determine this field both inside and outside the sphere. Inside the sphere the electric field, which is in the opposite direction to the polarization, is called a depolarizing field. [*Hint:* Since div $\mathbf{P}$ vanishes at all points, the electrostatic potential satisfies Laplace's equation both inside and outside the sphere. Do *not* assume that the dielectric is characterized by a dielectric constant.]

4–16. In the text, it was shown that the polarization $\mathbf{P} = \rho_0^+ (\, (\boldsymbol{\delta}^+ - \boldsymbol{\delta}^-)$. Use this relation for the uniformly polarized sphere of Problem 4–15 to determine the external dipole field directly.

CHAPTER 5

MICROSCOPIC THEORY OF DIELECTRICS

In the preceding chapter we were concerned with the macroscopic aspects of dielectric polarization, and it was shown how in many cases the polarization could be taken into account through the introduction of a dielectric constant. In this way the electric field could be computed directly from a consideration of the free charge distribution. Although reference was made to the molecules of the dielectric several times in Chapter 4, a microscopic treatment of the material was not carried through in detail, and the over-all picture which was presented was certainly from the macroscopic point of view. We should now like to examine the molecular nature of the dielectric, and see how the electric field responsible for polarizing the molecule is related to the macroscopic electric field. Furthermore, on the basis of a simple molecular model it is possible to understand the linear behavior which is characteristic of a large class of dielectric materials.

5–1 Molecular field in a dielectric. The electric field which is responsible for polarizing a molecule of the dielectric is called the molecular field, $\mathbf{E}_m$. This is the electric field at a molecular position in the dielectric; it is produced by all external sources and by all polarized molecules in the dielectric *with the exception* of the one molecule at the point under consideration. It is evident that $\mathbf{E}_m$ need not be the same as the macroscopic electric field because, as was discussed in Section 4–3, the latter quantity is related to the force on a test charge which is large in comparison with molecular dimensions.

The molecular field may be calculated in the following way. Let us cut out a small piece of the dielectric, leaving a spherical cavity surrounding the point at which the molecular field is to be computed. The dielectric which is left will be treated as a continuum, i.e., from the macroscopic point of view. Now we put the dielectric back into the cavity, molecule by molecule, except for the molecule at the center of the cavity where we wish to compute the molecular field. The molecules which have just been replaced are to be treated, not as a continuum, but as individual dipoles. The procedure just outlined can be justified only if the result of the calculation is independent of the size of the cavity; we shall see that under certain conditions this is indeed the case.

Let us suppose that the thin dielectric sample has been polarized by placing it in the uniform electric field between two parallel plates which are oppositely charged, as shown in Fig. 5–1(a). It will be assumed that

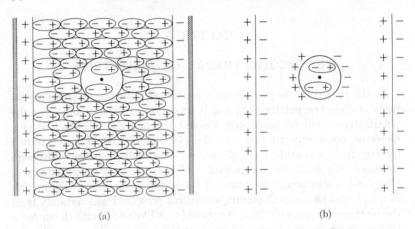

(a)   (b)

FIG. 5-1. Replacement of the dielectric outside the "cavity" by a system of bound charges.

the polarization is uniform on a macroscopic scale (i.e., div $\mathbf{P} = 0$), and that $\mathbf{P}$ is parallel to the field producing it. The part of the dielectric external to the cavity may be replaced by a system of bound charges as shown in Fig. 5-1(b), whence the electric field at the center of the cavity may be written as

$$\mathbf{E}_m = \mathbf{E}_x + \mathbf{E}_d + \mathbf{E}_s + \mathbf{E}'. \qquad (5\text{-}1)$$

Here, $\mathbf{E}_x$ is the primary electric field due to the charged parallel plates, $\mathbf{E}_d$ is the depolarizing field due to bound charge on the outside surfaces of the dielectric, $\mathbf{E}_s$ is due to bound charge on the cavity surface S, and $\mathbf{E}'$ is due to all of the dipoles inside of S. Although we are not concerned with the explicit form of $\mathbf{E}_x$, it is evident that if the dimensions of the plates are large compared with their separation, $E_x = (1/\epsilon_0)\sigma$, where σ is the surface charge density. The depolarizing field is also produced by two parallel planes of charge, this time with the density σ_P. Since $\sigma_P = P_n = \pm P$,

$$\mathbf{E}_d = -\frac{1}{\epsilon_0}\mathbf{P}. \qquad (5\text{-}2)$$

Let us write the macroscopic electric field *in the dielectric* without a subscript, that is, $\mathbf{E}$. Since the normal component of the electric displacement $\mathbf{D}$ is continuous across the vacuum-dielectric interface, and since $\mathbf{D} = \epsilon_0\mathbf{E}_x$ in the vacuum just outside the dielectric slab,

$$\epsilon_0\mathbf{E}_x = \epsilon_0\mathbf{E} + \mathbf{P}. \qquad (5\text{-}3)$$

Combining Eqs. (5-1), (5-2), and (5-3) yields

$$\mathbf{E}_m = \mathbf{E} + \mathbf{E}_s + \mathbf{E}', \qquad (5\text{-}4)$$

which is an equation relating the molecular field to the macroscopic electric field in the dielectric material. This result is quite general, and not restricted to the geometry of Fig. 5–1; nevertheless, the above derivation is instructive and will be useful to the subject discussed in Section 5–4.

The field $\mathbf{E}_s$ arises from bound charge density, $\sigma_P = P_n$, on the spherical surface S. Using spherical coordinates, and taking the polar direction along the direction of $\mathbf{P}$, as in Fig. 5–2, we obtain

$$dE_s = \frac{(-P \cos \theta)}{4\pi\epsilon_0 r^3} \, \mathbf{r} \, da, \tag{5–5}$$

where $\mathbf{r}$ is the vector from the surface to the center of the sphere. From symmetry, it is evident that only the component of $d\mathbf{E}_s$ along the direction of $\mathbf{P}$ will contribute to the integral of (5–5) over the complete surface. Since $da = r^2 \sin \theta \, d\theta \, d\phi$,

$$\mathbf{E}_s = \frac{1}{4\pi\epsilon_0} \, \mathbf{P} \int_0^{2\pi} d\phi \int_0^{\pi} \cos^2 \theta \sin \theta \, d\theta$$

$$= \frac{1}{3\epsilon_0} \, \mathbf{P}. \tag{5–6}$$

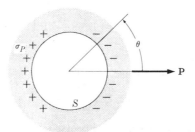

Fig. 5–2. Calculation of the "cavity" surface contribution to $\mathbf{E}_m$.

Finally, we come to the last term in (5–4), that due to the electric dipoles inside S. There are a number of important cases for which this term vanishes. If there are a great many dipoles in the cavity, if they are oriented parallel but randomly distributed in position, and if there are no correlations between the positions of the dipoles, then $\mathbf{E}' = 0$. This is the situation which might prevail in a gas or a liquid. Similarly, if the dipoles in the cavity are located at the regular atomic positions of a cubic crystal,* then again $\mathbf{E}' = 0$. In this connection, the reader is referred to Problem 5–2.

---

* Crystals with the highest symmetry belong to the cubic system.

In the general case, $\mathbf{E}'$ is not zero, and if the material contains several species of molecule, $\mathbf{E}'$ may differ at the various molecular positions. It is this term which gives rise to the anisotropic electrical behavior of calcite, for example. It is not our purpose, however, to develop a theory of anisotropic materials; hence we restrict further discussion to the rather large class of materials in which $\mathbf{E}' = 0$. Thus, Eq. (5–4) reduces to

$$\mathbf{E}_m = \mathbf{E} + \frac{1}{3\epsilon_0}\,\mathbf{P}. \qquad (5\text{–}7)$$

It is interesting to note that this result would be obtained directly by the above method if the spherical "cavity" were created by removing just one molecule. But under these conditions the cavity would be so small that the replacement of the rest of the dielectric by a system of bound charges could not be justified.

The dipole moment of a molecule per unit polarizing field is called its polarizability, α. In other words,

$$\mathbf{p}_m = \alpha\mathbf{E}_m. \qquad (5\text{–}8)$$

If there are N molecules per unit volume, then the polarization $\mathbf{P} = N\mathbf{p}_m$, and combining this result with (5–7) and (5–8), we obtain

$$\mathbf{P} = N\alpha\left(\mathbf{E} + \frac{1}{3\epsilon_0}\,\mathbf{P}\right). \qquad (5\text{–}9)$$

This equation may be rewritten in terms of the dielectric constant, K, since $\mathbf{P} = (K - 1)\epsilon_0\mathbf{E}$. In this way, Eq. (5–9) becomes

$$\alpha = \frac{3\epsilon_0}{N}\,\frac{(K - 1)}{(K + 2)}, \qquad (5\text{–}10)$$

which is known as the Clausius-Mossotti equation. It is evident that (5–10) defines a molecular property, namely, the molecular polarizability, in terms of quantities which can be determined on a macroscopic basis.

5–2 Induced dipoles. A simple model. The molecules of a dielectric may be classified as *polar* or *nonpolar*. A polar molecule is one which has a permanent dipole moment, even in the absence of a polarizing field $\mathbf{E}_m$. In the next section the response of a polar dielectric to an external electric field will be studied, but here we deal with the somewhat simpler problem involving nonpolar molecules, in which the "centers of gravity" of the positive and negative charge distributions normally coincide. Symmetrical molecules such as H_2, N_2, and O_2, or monatomic molecules such as He, Ne, and A, fall into this category.

The application of an electric field causes a relative displacement of the positive and negative charges in nonpolar molecules, and the molecular dipoles so created are called *induced dipoles*. The simplest type of molecule which can be envisaged is that composed of a single neutral atom. It is possible to construct a simple classical model for the atom and from this model derive an expression for the induced dipole moment, and hence for its polarizability. Although specifically designed to treat monatomic molecules, the model may be used for symmetrical diatomic molecules by applying it separately to each of the atoms in the molecule to obtain the atomic polarizabilities. The molecular polarizability is then the sum of these, or twice the atomic polarizability.

An atom consists of an extremely small positively charged nucleus surrounded by orbital electrons which are in a state of continual motion. Since the electrons traverse their orbits in an exceedingly short time, of the order of 10^{-15} second, it is evident that in the equivalent "static" atom each electronic charge is smeared over its orbit. Quantum mechanics tells us that although this picture is essentially correct, it is somewhat naive; the electrons are not really localized on orbits, but have a finite probability of being situated in any part of the atom. Thus the response of the atom to an electrostatic field or to slowly varying electric fields may be treated by considering the electron to be distributed over its orbit in the atom, and each orbit to be smeared over a substantial part of the atomic volume. In short, a simple classical model of the atom consistent with this picture is a point positive charge (the nucleus) surrounded by a spherically symmetric cloud of negative charge in which the density is essentially uniform out to the atomic radius R_0, and zero at larger radii.

We are now in a position to compute the polarizability of this "atom." The nucleus will be assigned the charge Ze, where e is the absolute value of the electronic charge and Z is the atomic number. Since the atom is electrically neutral, the total charge in the electron cloud is $-Ze$. If the atom is placed in a polarizing field $\mathbf{E}_m$, the nucleus will be displaced *relative* to the center of the charge cloud by a distance which we shall call x. This displacement will be in the direction of $\mathbf{E}_m$. We shall assume that the charge cloud moves rigidly during this displacement, i.e., there is no distortion of the cloud by the polarizing field. The displacement x may be determined from the equilibrium of forces on the nucleus; the force ZeE_m acts in the direction of the field, whereas an electrostatic force between the nucleus and charge cloud tends to restore the initial configuration. By Gauss' law, the negative charge attracting the nucleus is that part of the cloud within the sphere of radius x, and if the electronic density in the cloud is uniform, then this charge is Zex^3/R_0^3. Hence

$$\frac{(Ze)(Zex^3/R_0^3)}{4\pi\epsilon_0 x^2} = ZeE_m, \tag{5-11}$$

or

$$Zex = 4\pi\epsilon_0 R_0^3 E_m. \tag{5-12}$$

Since the atomic dipole created in this process is $\mathbf{p}_m = Ze\mathbf{x}$, the last equation may be compared with (5–8), whence

$$\alpha = 4\pi\epsilon_0 R_0^3. \tag{5–13}$$

The atomic model just described may be tested by comparing results obtained from it with results derived from other sources. For example, Eq. (5–13) may be combined with the Clausius-Mossotti equation (5–10) to eliminate α; the resulting equation predicts the atomic radius R_0 in terms of experimentally determined quantities. R_0 obtained in this way agrees reasonably well with results from other experiments in those cases for which the model is particularly suited; R_0 is of the order of magnitude of 1 angstrom unit, i.e., 10^{-10} m. (See Problem 5–1.)

The polarizability derived in (5–13) is a constant, independent of the polarizing field. Hence (5–13) leads to a constant value of K, and the dielectric so described is linear.

*5–3 Polar molecules. The Langevin-Debye formula. As mentioned in the preceding section, a polar molecule has a permanent dipole moment. A polar molecule consists of at least two different species of atoms; during molecule formation some of the electrons may be completely or partially transferred from one atomic species to the other, the resulting electronic arrangement being such that positive and negative charge centers do not coincide in the molecule. In the absence of an electric field a macroscopic piece of the polar dielectric is not polarized, since the individual dipoles are randomly oriented, as shown in Fig. 5–3. The polarization has been defined as

$$\mathbf{P} = \frac{1}{\Delta v} \sum \mathbf{p}_m, \tag{5–14}$$

where the summation extends over all molecules in the volume element Δv. When the $\mathbf{p}_m$ are oriented at random, the summation vanishes.

If the polar dielectric is subjected to an electric field, the individual dipoles experience torques which tend to align them with the field. If the

Fig. 5–3. A random distribution of permanent dipoles.

field is strong enough, the dipoles may be completely aligned, and the polarization achieves the saturation value

$$\mathbf{P}_s = N\mathbf{p}_m, \tag{5-15}$$

where N is the number of molecules per unit volume. This orientation effect is in addition to the induced dipole effects which are usually present also. For the moment, we shall ignore the induced dipole contribution, but its effect will be added in later.

At field strengths normally encountered, the polarization of a polar dielectric is usually far from its saturation value, and if the temperature of the specimen is raised the polarization becomes even smaller. The lack of complete dipole alignment is due to the thermal energy of the molecules, which tends to produce random dipole orientations. The average effective dipole moment per molecule may be calculated by means of a principle from statistical mechanics which states that at temperature T the probability of finding a particular molecular energy W is proportional to

$$e^{-W/kT}, \tag{5-16}$$

where k is Boltzmann's constant and T is the absolute temperature. A complete discussion of the basis for this principle will not be given here; the reader familiar with the Maxwell velocity distribution in a perfect gas has already encountered the principle. According to the Maxwell distribution law, the probability of a molecular velocity v is proportional to $e^{-mv^2/2kT}$. But in Maxwell's perfect gas the molecules have only kinetic energy, $\frac{1}{2}mv^2$; in the general case W in (5–16) must include both kinetic energy W_k and potential energy W_p, and the factor becomes

$$e^{-W_k/kT}e^{-W_p/kT}. \tag{5-17}$$

The potential energy of a permanent dipole p_0 in an electric field $\mathbf{E}_m$ is

$$W_p = -\mathbf{p}_0 \cdot \mathbf{E}_m = -p_0 E_m \cos\theta, \tag{5-18}$$

where θ is the angle between $\mathbf{p}_0$ and the electric field. Since the molecular kinetic energies do not depend on the electric field, we can ignore the velocity distribution completely in the following calculation. The effective dipole moment of a molecular dipole is its component along the field direction, i.e., $p_0 \cos\theta$. Using the above principle, the average value of this quantity is found to be

$$\langle p_0 \cos\theta \rangle = \frac{\int p_0 \cos\theta\, e^{+p_0 E_m \cos\theta/kT}\, d\Omega}{\int e^{+p_0 E_m \cos\theta/kT}\, d\Omega}, \tag{5-19}$$

where $d\Omega$ is an element of solid angle that may be replaced by $2\pi \sin\theta\, d\theta$ where the limits on θ are 0 and π. Since p_0, E_m, and kT are constants in

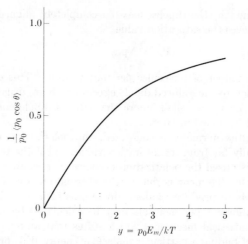

FIG. 5–4. Plot of the Langevin function. The asymptotic value as $y \to \infty$ is one.

the integration, the integrals may be readily performed. It is convenient to define

$$y = \frac{p_0 E_m}{kT}.$$ (5–20)

Equation (5–19) then yields:

$$\langle p_0 \cos \theta \rangle = p_0 \left[\coth y - \frac{1}{y} \right],$$ (5–21)

which is known as the Langevin formula. A plot of this function is given in Fig. 5–4.

It can be seen from the figure that Eq. (5–21) does indeed give a saturation effect at large field strengths. At small values of y, however, the curve is linear, and it is this linear region which is important at ordinary temperatures. The molecular dipole moment p_0 of most polar materials is such that $y \ll 1$ for a full range of field strengths, even for those approaching the dielectric strength of the material, so long as the temperature is above about 250°K. Thus a dielectric material containing polar molecules is, in general, *linear*.

Since it is the linear region of (5–21) which is important, it is appropriate to expand $\coth y$ in a power series and keep only leading terms (see Problem 5–4). The first term cancels the last term in (5–21), with the result that

$$\langle p_0 \cos \theta \rangle \approx \frac{1}{3} p_0 y = \frac{p_0^2 E_m}{3kT}.$$ (5–22a)

The term $\langle p_0 \cos \theta \rangle$ is the average effective dipole moment; therefore the polarization $P = N \langle p_0 \cos \theta \rangle$ and has the direction of $\mathbf{E}_m$. Hence (5–22a) may be written in the form

$$\frac{1}{N} \mathbf{P} = \frac{p_0^2}{3kT} \mathbf{E}_m. \tag{5–22b}$$

From a comparison of this equation with (5–8), it is evident that the polarizability α (i.e., the molecular dipole moment per unit polarizing field) is

$$\alpha = \frac{p_0^2}{3kT}. \tag{5–23}$$

This result has been derived by neglecting induced dipole moments, and represents what we might call an *orientational* polarizability. Induced dipoles effects, such as have been considered in the previous section, give rise to what might be termed a *deformation* polarizability, α_0. In the general case, then, the total molecular polarizability is

$$\alpha = \alpha_0 + \frac{p_0^2}{3kT}, \tag{5–24}$$

an expression which is known as the Langevin-Debye equation, and which has been of great importance in interpreting molecular structures.

*5–4 Permanent polarization.   Ferroelectricity.   It was seen in Section 5–1 that it is the molecular field $\mathbf{E}_m$ which is responsible for polarizing the individual molecules. The relationship between $\mathbf{E}_m$ and the macroscopic electric field $\mathbf{E}$ was given in Eq. (5–7). In most cases the polarization is proportional to $\mathbf{E}$, so that $\mathbf{E}_m$ vanishes when $\mathbf{E}$ goes to zero. But under certain conditions (5–7) is also compatible with a permanent (or spontaneous) polarization. When $\mathbf{E}$ is set equal to zero,

$$\mathbf{E}_m = \frac{1}{3\epsilon_0} \mathbf{P}_0, \tag{5–25}$$

or, in words, if a polarization $\mathbf{P}_0$ exists, it will create an electric field at the molecule which tends to polarize the molecule. To be sure, a polarizing field exists; but if this field gives rise to a polarization different from $\mathbf{P}_0$, then the solution is not self-consistent. Therefore, if N is the number of molecules per unit volume,

$$\mathbf{P}_0 = N\alpha \mathbf{E}_m = \frac{N\alpha}{3\epsilon_0} \mathbf{P}_0, \tag{5–26}$$

which is satisfied when either

$$\mathbf{P}_0 = 0$$

or

$$\frac{N\alpha}{3\epsilon_0} = 1. \tag{5–27}$$

Thus the condition for a permanent polarization is Eq. (5–27).*

For most materials $N\alpha/3\epsilon_0$ is less than one, and ordinary dielectric behavior results. In a few crystalline solids, however, condition (5–27) is met. Such materials are called *ferroelectric* because their electrical properties are analogous to the magnetic properties of ferromagnetic materials. The best known example of a ferroelectric material is barium titanate, $BaTiO_3$, which exhibits a spontaneous dipole moment at temperatures below 120°C. This temperature is called the *Curie point* of the material.

The polarized state of a ferroelectric material is a relatively stable one, and one which can persist for long periods of time. This statement may surprise us to some extent because a polarized specimen is subjected to its own depolarizing field and, depending on the geometry of the specimen, this depolarizing field may be rather large. The depolarizing field is largest for a specimen in the shape of a flat slab, polarized in a direction normal to its faces. As was seen in Section 5–1, if the dimensions of the slab face are large compared with the slab thickness, then

$$\mathbf{E}_d = -\frac{1}{\epsilon_0}\mathbf{P}. \tag{5–28}$$

Actually, the high stability of a polarized ferroelectric is due to the fact that there is *no* depolarizing field on the specimen, even for the case of slab geometry. The specimen is polarized by placing it between parallel conducting plates which subsequently have a large potential difference applied to them. In this process the *free* charge from the plates will, to a large extent, be neutralized by surface bound charge, as is also the case during polarization of a conventional dielectric. If the parallel plates are now brought to the same potential by short-circuiting them, the polarized state of the ferroelectric is still energetically favorable, so the *free charge stays in place*, still neutralizing the bound charge. The situation is something like that shown in Fig. 5–5; the *free charge* is held in place by the surface bound charge. The macroscopic field inside the ferroelectric is zero; furthermore, the external electric field is zero, and it is difficult to distinguish the polarized specimen from a conventional unpolarized dielectric material.

If a large potential difference of the opposite sign is now applied to the plates surrounding the polarized ferroelectric, the specimen will change

---

* Strictly speaking, Eq. (5–27) has been derived for materials which are composed of only one species of molecule, and for which the term $\mathbf{E}'$ of Section 5–1 vanishes. In a quantitative theory applicable to the general case, Eq. (5–27) is replaced by a set of simultaneous equations. Such complications are not necessary for a fundamental understanding of the origin of ferroelectricity, and consequently will not be discussed here.

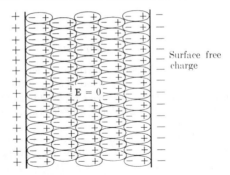

FIG. 5–5. A polarized piece of ferroelectric material.

its polarization, and free charge of the opposite sign will flow to the plates from the external circuit, sufficient not only to neutralize the free charge already there, but also to neutralize the new bound charge. Thus a ferroelectric slab between two parallel plates may serve as the basic element of a memory device; it is capable of storing $\pm$ or $\mp$, and its polarization persists in the absence of an external electric field. The number $\pm$ or $\mp$ may be read by applying a potential difference across the specimen. If the applied field is in the direction of the original polarization, no charge will pass through the external circuit; if the potential difference is opposite to the original polarization, a charge will flow through the external circuit as the polarization of the ferroelectric changes its direction.

A polarized ferroelectric is stable against a reversed electric field provided this electric field is not too large. Figure 5–6 shows the complete curve of polarization versus electric field; it is evident that for low fields there are two values of P for each value of E. A curve such as that in Fig. 5–6 is called a *hysteresis loop*. Hysteresis means "to lag behind," and it is apparent that the polarization vector lags the electric field vector. Points b and a are the stable configurations at $E = 0$; they represent the polarizations $\pm$ and $\mp$, respectively. Point c is the electric field which must be exceeded in order to reverse the polarization.

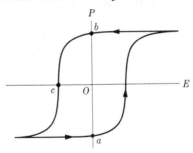

FIG. 5–6. Hysteresis curve for a ferroelectric specimen.

PROBLEMS

5–1. Use the Clausius-Mossotti equation to determine the polarizability of *atoms* in the air molecules: N_2, O_2. [Note that only the weighted average of the polarizabilities for nitrogen and oxygen may be obtained from (5–10).] Combine this result with the theory of Section 5–2 to determine the average radius of the atom in an air molecule.

5–2. Figure 5–7 shows a simple cubic lattice of molecules all of which have the same (in direction and magnitude) dipole moment $\mathbf{p}_m$. Let us fix our attention on one particular molecule, call it j. It is evident that j has six nearest neighbors at distance a, twelve next-nearest neighbors at distance $\sqrt{2}\,a$, etc. Find the electric field at j due to the six $\mathbf{p}_m$ on nearest-neighbor molecules for an arbitrary orientation of $\mathbf{p}_m$. (Let the lines joining j to its nearest neighbors define the x-, y-, and z-axes. For simplicity, take $\mathbf{p}_m$ in the xz-plane, making an angle θ with the x-axis.)

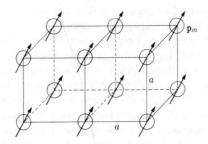

Fig. 5–7. Part of a simple cubic array of molecules, each with dipole moment $\mathbf{p}_m$.

5–3. Using the result of Problem 5–1 for the atomic polarizability of nitrogen, compute the relative displacement of the nitrogen nucleus and electron cloud at a field strength $E_m = 3 \times 10^6$ volts/m. Compare this displacement with the radius of the atom found in Problem 5–1.

5–4. By using the well-known series expansions for e^y, expand $\coth y$, and obtain Eq. (5–22a) from (5–21). Go one step further and obtain another term in the series (5–22a).

5–5. Water is a polar molecule for which the Clausius-Mossotti equation is, strictly speaking, not applicable. Assume its validity, however, and determine p_0 for the water molecule.

CHAPTER 6

ELECTROSTATIC ENERGY

Many problems in mechanics are greatly simplified by means of energy considerations. Hence, when the mechanical behavior of an electrical system is to be studied, it may prove advantageous to use energy methods. In general, the energy of a system of charges, just like that of any other mechanical system, may be divided into its potential and kinetic contributions. Under static conditions, however, the entire energy of the charge system exists as potential energy, and we are particularly concerned with that potential energy which arises from electrical interaction of the charges, the so-called *electrostatic energy*.

In Section 2–4, it was shown that the electrostatic energy of a point charge is closely related to the electrostatic potential U at the position of the point charge. In fact, if q is the magnitude of a particular point charge, then the work done *on* the charge in moving it from position A to position B is

$$\text{Work} = \int_A^B \mathbf{F}_m \cdot d\mathbf{l} = -q \int_A^B \mathbf{E} \cdot d\mathbf{l}$$

$$= q \int_A^B \operatorname{grad} U \cdot d\mathbf{l} = q(U_B - U_A). \tag{6-1}$$

Here, the mechanical force $\mathbf{F}_m$ has been chosen so as to balance exactly the electric force $q\mathbf{E}$ at each point along the path. Under these conditions the charged particle does not accelerate, and Eq. (6–1) represents the change in electrostatic energy of the charge over the path interval $A \to B$.

Similar considerations may be applied to more complicated systems of charges; in fact, the electrostatic energy of an arbitrary charge distribution may be calculated as the work required to assemble this distribution of charge without imparting to it other forms of energy.

6–1 Potential energy of a group of point charges. By the electrostatic energy of a group of m point charges, we mean the potential energy of the system relative to the state in which all point charges are infinitely separated from one another. This energy may be obtained rather easily by calculating the work to assemble the charges, bringing in one at a time. The first charge q_1 may be placed in position without the expenditure of energy; to place the second, q_2, requires

$$\Delta W_2 = \frac{q_2 q_1}{4\pi\epsilon_0 r_{12}}, \tag{6-2}$$

where $r_{12} = |\mathbf{r}_1 - \mathbf{r}_2|$. For the third charge, q_3,

$$\Delta W_3 = q_3 \left[\frac{q_1}{4\pi\epsilon_0 r_{13}} + \frac{q_2}{4\pi\epsilon_0 r_{23}} \right]. \tag{6-3}$$

The work required to bring in the fourth charge, fifth charge, etc., may be written down in a similar fashion. The total electrostatic energy of the assembled m-charge system is the sum of the ΔW's, namely,

$$W = \frac{1}{2} \sum_{j=1}^{m} \sum_{k=1}^{m}{}' \frac{q_k q_j}{4\pi\epsilon_0 r_{kj}}, \tag{6-4}$$

where the prime on the second summation means that the term $k = j$ is specifically excluded.

Equation (6–4) may be written in a somewhat different way by noting that the final value of the potential U at the jth point charge is

$$U_j = \sum_{k=1}^{m}{}' \frac{q_k}{4\pi\epsilon_0 r_{kj}}. \tag{6-5}$$

Thus the electrostatic energy of the system is

$$W = \frac{1}{2} \sum_{j=1}^{m} q_j U_j. \tag{6-6}$$

If the point charges had been assembled in a linear dielectric medium of infinite extent, instead of in vacuum, then the permittivity ϵ would replace ϵ_0 in Eqs. (6–2), (6–3), and (6–4), but Eq. (6–6) would remain unchanged. In the following section it will be shown that this last equation has rather general validity. It applies to a group of point charges which are located in more than one dielectric medium; it even applies to conductors of finite size. The only limitation on the validity of Eq. (6–6) is that all dielectrics in the electrical system be linear.

6–2 Electrostatic energy of a charge distribution. In this section we shall calculate the electrostatic energy of an arbitrary charge distribution with volume density ρ and surface density σ. Some of the charge may reside on the surfaces of conductors; in fact, it will be explicitly assumed that there are conductors in the system. In addition, it will be assumed that the dielectrics in the system are *linear;* this restriction is necessary in order that the work expended in bringing the system to its final charged state shall be independent of the way in which this final state is reached.

Suppose we assemble the charge distribution by bringing in charge increments δq from a reference potential $U_A = 0$. If the charge distribution is partly assembled and the potential at a particular point in the system is $U'(x, y, z)$, then, from Eq. (6–1), the work required to place δq at this point is

$$\delta W = U'(x, y, z)\,\delta q. \tag{6–7}$$

The charge increment δq may be added to a volume element located at (x, y, z), such that $\delta q = \delta\rho\,\Delta v$, or δq may be added to a surface element at the point in question, whereby $\delta q = \delta\sigma\,\Delta a$. The total electrostatic energy of the assembled charge distribution is obtained by summing contributions of the form (6–7).

Since the work required to assemble the charges is independent of the order in which things are done, we may choose a particular assembly procedure for which the summation of the δW's is conveniently calculated. This procedure is one in which all parts of the system are brought to their final charge values in concert, i.e., at any instant of time during the charging process all charge densities will be at the same fraction of their final values. Let us call this fraction α. If the final values of the charge densities are given by the functions, $\rho(x, y, z)$ and $\sigma(x, y, z)$, then the charge densities at an arbitrary time are $\alpha\rho(x, y, z)$ and $\alpha\sigma(x, y, z)$. Furthermore, the increments in these densities are $\delta\rho = \rho(x, y, z)\,\delta\alpha$ and $\delta\sigma = \sigma(x, y, z)\,\delta\alpha$. The total electrostatic energy, which is obtained by summing (6–7), is

$$W = \int_0^1 \delta\alpha \int_V \rho(x, y, z)\,U'(\alpha; x, y, z)\,dv$$

$$+ \int_0^1 \delta\alpha \int_S \sigma(x, y, z)\,U'(\alpha; x, y, z)\,da. \tag{6–8}$$

But since all charges are at the same fraction, α, of their final values, the potential $U'(\alpha; x, y, z) = \alpha U(x, y, z)$, where U is the final value of the potential at (x, y, z). Making this substitution, we find that the integration over α is readily done, and yields

$$W = \tfrac{1}{2}\int_V \rho U\,dv + \tfrac{1}{2}\int_S \sigma U\,da, \tag{6–9}$$

the desired result for the energy of a charge distribution.

It was stipulated that conductors are present in the system. Although (6–9) covers this case very well, it is convenient to separate out the contribution from the conductors explicitly. The last integral involves, in part, integrations over the surface of these conductors; since a conductor is an equipotential region, each of these integrations may be done:

$$\tfrac{1}{2}\int_{\text{conductor } j} \sigma U\,da = \tfrac{1}{2}Q_j U_j, \tag{6–10}$$

where Q_j is the charge on the jth conductor. Hence Eq. (6–9) becomes

$$W = \tfrac{1}{2}\int_V \rho U\,dv + \tfrac{1}{2}\int_{S'} \sigma U\,da + \tfrac{1}{2}\sum_j Q_j U_j, \tag{6–11}$$

where the last summation is over all conductors, and the surface integral is restricted to nonconducting surfaces. As we have seen in Chapter 3, in many problems of practical interest all of the free charge resides on the surfaces of conductors. In these circumstances Eq. (6–11) reduces to

$$W = \tfrac{1}{2} \sum_j Q_j U_j. \tag{6–12}$$

We shall have occasion to develop this equation in a later section of this chapter.

For the present, we should like to compare (6–12) with Eq. (6–6), which was derived for an assembly of point charges. It appears at first sight that the two equations are identical; however, there is an important difference. Equation (6–12) was derived by starting with uncharged conductors which were gradually charged by bringing in charge increments; thus the energy depicted by (6–12) includes both interaction energy and self-energies. In deriving (6–6), each point charge was brought in as a unit; hence the energy to assemble the "point" charge from smaller charge increments, the so-called self-energy of the charge, is not included. The two methods really do give the same result for an assembly of "point" charges, however, as may be seen from a more detailed examination of (6–12). The potential of the jth conductor may be written as the sum of two terms,

$$U_j = U_{j1} + U_{j2}, \tag{6–13}$$

where U_{j1} is the contribution to the potential due to the charge on conductor j itself, and U_{j2} is the contribution from charge on other conductors. Thus Eq. (6–12) becomes

$$W = \tfrac{1}{2} \sum_j Q_j U_{j1} + \tfrac{1}{2} \sum_j Q_j U_{j2}. \tag{6–14}$$

The first term of this equation represents the various self-energies of the conductors. Each self-energy, $\tfrac{1}{2} Q_j U_{j1}$, depends on the environment of the conductor (since the charge distribution on each conductor adjusts itself to its environment); furthermore, the only physically meaningful potential associated with conductor j is the total potential U_j. Thus the decomposition, Eq. (6–14), does *not* make a great deal of sense in general. However, if the conductors are so small that they may be treated as point charges from the macroscopic point of view, then redistribution of charge on the "point" cannot be important, and each self-energy may be taken to be independent of its environment. In addition, since by potential at the point charge j we mean U_{j2}, the energy required to place a group of *previously charged, very small conductors* in position is the second summation in (6–14), and this is equivalent to Eq. (6–6).

6–3 Energy density of an electrostatic field. In the preceding section an expression was developed for the electrostatic energy of an arbitrary distribution of free charge. This expression, Eq. (6–9), involves an explicit integration over the charge distribution. It is possible, however, to express the electrostatic energy of the system in a different way, and this alternate form is frequently rather useful. By means of a mathematical transformation, therefore, we convert (6–9) to an integral involving the field vectors **E** and **D** of the system.

We again consider an arbitrary distribution of free charge characterized by the densities ρ and σ. For convenience, it will be assumed that the charge system is bounded, i.e., it is possible to construct a closed surface of finite dimensions which encloses all of the free charge. In addition, all surface densities of free charge, σ, will be assumed to reside on conductor surfaces. The last statement is really no restriction at all, since a surface charge density on a dielectric-dielectric interface may be spread out slightly and then treated as a volume density, ρ. The densities ρ and σ are related to the electric displacement;

$$\rho = \operatorname{div} \mathbf{D}$$

throughout the dielectric regions, and

$$\sigma = \mathbf{D} \cdot \mathbf{n}$$

on the conductor surfaces. Hence Eq. (6–9) becomes

$$W = \tfrac{1}{2} \int_V U \operatorname{div} \mathbf{D} \, dv + \tfrac{1}{2} \int_S U\mathbf{D} \cdot \mathbf{n} \, da. \tag{6–15}$$

The volume integral here refers to the region where div **D** is different from zero, and this is the region external to the conductors. The surface integral is over the conductors.

The integrand in the first integral of (6–15) may be transformed by means of a vector identity which we have had occasion to use several times before, Eq. (I–6) of Table 1–1:

$$U \operatorname{div} \mathbf{D} = \operatorname{div} U\mathbf{D} - \mathbf{D} \cdot \mathbf{grad} \, U.$$

Of the two volume integrals resulting from this transformation, the first may be converted to a surface integral through the use of the divergence theorem. Finally, using the fact that $\mathbf{E} = -\mathbf{grad}\, U$, we may write (6–15) as

$$W = \tfrac{1}{2} \int_{S+S'} U\mathbf{D} \cdot \mathbf{n}' \, da + \tfrac{1}{2} \int_V \mathbf{D} \cdot \mathbf{E} \, dv + \tfrac{1}{2} \int_S U\mathbf{D} \cdot \mathbf{n} \, da. \tag{6–16}$$

This equation may be simplified substantially. The surface $S + S'$ over which the first integral of (6–16) is to be evaluated is the entire surface bounding the volume V. It consists, in part, of S (the surfaces of all conductors in the system), and also of S' (a surface which bounds our system from the outside, and which we may choose to locate at infinity). In both cases the normal $\mathbf{n}'$ is directed *out of* the volume V. In the last integral the normal $\mathbf{n}$ is directed out of the conductor, hence *into* V. Thus the two surface integrals over S cancel each other. It remains to show that the integral over S' vanishes.

If our charge distribution, which is arbitrary but bounded, bears a net charge, then at large distances from the charge system the potential falls off inversely as the distance, i.e., as r^{-1}. $\mathbf{D}$ falls off as r^{-2}. The area of a closed surface which passes through a point at distance r is proportional to r^2. Hence the value of the integral over S' which bounds our system at distance r is proportional to r^{-1}, and when S' is moved out to infinity, its contribution vanishes.

If the charge distribution bears zero net charge, then the potential at large distances acts like some multipole and falls off *more* rapidly than r^{-1}. Again the contribution from S' may be seen to vanish. Thus, for the electrostatic energy, we have

$$W = \tfrac{1}{2} \int_V \mathbf{D} \cdot \mathbf{E} \, dv, \qquad (6\text{--}17)$$

where the integration is over the volume of the system external to the conductors, i.e., over the various dielectrics in the system. The integration may, of course, be extended to include all space, since the electric field $\mathbf{E}$ equals zero inside a conductor.

Where is the electrostatic energy of the electrical system located? This is a question which has no precise meaning; nevertheless, it is convenient to imagine the energy to be stored in the electric field. Equation (6–17) shows that such a procedure is at least not unreasonable, and in addition it prescribes that the energy be distributed with a density $\tfrac{1}{2}\mathbf{D} \cdot \mathbf{E}$ per unit volume. Hence we are led to the concept of *energy density* in an electrostatic field:

$$w = \tfrac{1}{2}\mathbf{D} \cdot \mathbf{E}. \qquad (6\text{--}18a)$$

Since Eq. (6–17) was derived on the basis of linear dielectrics, each dielectric is characterized by a constant permittivity ϵ. Furthermore, the discussion in preceding chapters has been limited to isotropic dielectrics. Thus (6–18a) is equivalent to

$$w = \tfrac{1}{2}\epsilon E^2. \qquad (6\text{--}18b)$$

6–4 Energy of a system of charged conductors. Coefficients of potential.
In Section 3–12 it was shown that a linear relationship exists between the potentials and charges on a set of conductors. In fact, in a system composed of N conductors, the potential of one of them is given by

$$U_i = \sum_{j=1}^{N} p_{ij} Q_j. \tag{3-51}$$

The derivation of (3–51) was carried out for N conductors in vacuum; however, it is clear that this derivation also holds when dielectrics are present in the system, so long as these dielectrics are both linear and devoid of free charge. The coefficient p_{ij} is the potential of the ith conductor due to a unit charge on conductor j. These coefficients are usually referred to as *coefficients of potential*.

In Section 6–2 an expression was developed for the electrostatic energy of a set of N charged conductors, namely, Eq. (6–12). Combining this result with Eq. (3–51), we obtain

$$W = \tfrac{1}{2} \sum_{i=1}^{N} \sum_{j=1}^{N} p_{ij} Q_i Q_j. \tag{6-19}$$

Thus the energy is a quadratic function of the charges on the various conductors.

A number of general statements can be made about the coefficients p_{ij}, the most important being that (1) $p_{ij} = p_{ji}$, (2) all of the p_{ij} are positive, and (3) $p_{ii} - p_{ij} \geq 0$ for all j. The first of these statements follows from Eq. (6–19), which expresses W as $W(Q_1 \cdots Q_N)$; thus

$$dW = \left(\frac{\partial W}{\partial Q_1}\right) dQ_1 + \cdots + \left(\frac{\partial W}{\partial Q_N}\right) dQ_N.$$

If dQ_1 only is changed, then

$$dW = \left(\frac{\partial W}{\partial Q_1}\right) dQ_1 = \tfrac{1}{2} \sum_{j=1}^{N} (p_{1j} + p_{j1}) Q_j \, dQ_1. \tag{6-20}$$

This increment in the electrostatic energy may also be calculated directly from Eq. (6–1). Bringing in dQ_1 from a zero potential reservoir, we obtain

$$dW = U_1 \, dQ_1 = \sum_{j=1}^{N} p_{1j} Q_j \, dQ_1. \tag{6-21}$$

Equations (6–20) and (6–21) must be equivalent for all possible values of the Q_j, which implies that

$$\tfrac{1}{2}(p_{1j} + p_{j1}) = p_{1j},$$

or

$$p_{j1} = p_{1j}. \tag{6-22}$$

The second statement above, that the potential produced by a net positive charge is positive, is almost intuitively obvious but difficult to prove in a rigorous way. That the third statement is true may be seen from the following argument: let conductor i bear a positive charge Q_i, all other conductors being uncharged. Since conductor j ($j \neq i$) is uncharged, the net number of lines of displacement leaving this conductor is zero. We distinguish two cases: (a) there are no lines of displacement leaving or impinging upon conductor j, whence we infer that the conductor is in an equipotential region, i.e., it is shielded by another conductor. For example, it could be located inside conductor i, and its potential might be U_i. In this circumstance, $p_{ij} = p_{ii}$. If conductor j is inside conductor k, then $p_{ik} = p_{ij}$; we immediately transfer our attention to conductor k.   (b) Lines of displacement flux leaving conductor j are balanced in number by lines impinging on it. The origin of the displacement flux is the charge on i; hence it must be possible to trace a flux line, which impinges on j, back (perhaps via other conductors) to i. Thus i is at a higher potential than j:

$$U_i > U_j, \qquad (Q_i \text{ is positive})$$

or

$$p_{ii} > p_{ij}. \tag{6-23}$$

We must, however, add the equality sign to cover case (a).

The usefulness of the coefficients p_{ij} may be illustrated by means of a simple example. Problem: to find the potential of an *uncharged* spherical conductor in the presence of a point charge q at distance r, where $r > R$, and R is the radius of the spherical conductor. The point charge and sphere are taken to be a system of two conductors, and use is made of the equality $p_{12} = p_{21}$. If the sphere is charged (Q) and the "point" uncharged, then the potential of the "point" is $Q/4\pi\epsilon_0 r$; thus

$$p_{12} = p_{21} = \frac{1}{4\pi\epsilon_0 r}.$$

Evidently, when the "point" has charge q and the sphere is uncharged, the potential of the latter is $q/4\pi\epsilon_0 r$.

6-5 Coefficients of capacitance and induction. Equation (3-51), which was derived in Chapter 3 and discussed again in Section 6-4, is a set of N linear equations giving the potentials of the conductors in terms of their charges. This set of equations may be solved for the Q_i's, yielding

$$Q_i = \sum_{j=1}^{N} c_{ij} U_j, \tag{6-24}$$

where c_{ii} is called a *coefficient of capacitance* and c_{ij} ($i \neq j$) is a *coefficient of induction*. The actual inversion of Eq. (3-51), expressing each c in terms of the p_{ij}, is most easily done by using determinants.

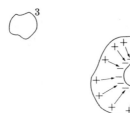

Fig. 6-1. Conductors 1 and 2 form a capacitor. $p_{31} = p_{32}$ since, by Gauss' law, when 1 and 2 are uncharged they must be at the same potential, independently of the charge on 3. Similarly, $p_{41} = p_{42}$.

Properties of the c's follow from those of the p's, which we have already discussed. Thus: (1) $c_{ij} = c_{ji}$, (2) $c_{ii} > 0$, (3) the coefficients of induction are negative or zero.

Equation (6-24) may be combined with Eq. (6-12) to give an alternative expression for the electrostatic energy of an N-conductor system:

$$W = \tfrac{1}{2} \sum_{i=1}^{N} \sum_{j=1}^{N} c_{ij} U_i U_j. \tag{6-25}$$

6-6 Capacitors. Two conductors which can store equal and opposite charges ($\pm Q$), independently of whether other conductors in the system are charged, form what is called a *capacitor*. This independence of other charges implies that one of the pair of conductors is shielded by the other; in other words, the potential contributed to *each* of the pair by external charges must be the same. Such a situation is depicted in Fig. 6-1 where conductors 1 and 2 form a device of this type. In general, if two conductors, 1 and 2, form a capacitor, we may write

$$U_1 = p_{11}Q + p_{12}(-Q) + U_x,$$
$$U_2 = p_{12}Q + p_{22}(-Q) + U_x, \tag{6-26}$$

where $\pm Q$ are the charges stored and U_x is the common potential contributed by other (external) charges.

If Eqs. (6-26) are subtracted, we find

$$\Delta U = U_1 - U_2 = (p_{11} + p_{22} - 2p_{12})Q. \tag{6-27}$$

Thus the difference in potential between the conductors of a capacitor is proportional to the charge stored, Q. (Obviously, the total charge stored is zero but, by convention, the absolute value of the charge on one of the two conductors is called the *charge* on the capacitor.) Equation (6–27) may be written

$$Q = C \, \Delta U, \tag{6–28}$$

where $C = (p_{11} + p_{22} - 2p_{12})^{-1}$ is called the *capacitance* of the capacitor. Evidently C is the charge stored per unit of potential difference; in the mks system C is measured in coulombs/volt, or farads (1 farad $\equiv$ 1 coulomb/volt).

Using the results of previous sections in this chapter, the energy of a charged capacitor may be written as

$$W = \frac{1}{2} C \, (\Delta U)^2 = \frac{1}{2} Q \, \Delta U = \frac{1}{2} \frac{Q^2}{C} . \tag{6–29}$$

If the two conductors making up the capacitor have simple geometrical shapes, the capacitance may be obtained analytically. Thus, for example, it is easy to calculate the capacitance of two parallel plates, two coaxial cylinders, two concentric spheres, or that of a cylinder and a plane. The capacitance of a parallel-plate capacitor (Fig. 6–2) will be derived here; other simple cases are taken up in the exercises at the end of the chapter.

Except for the fringing field at the edge of the parallel plates, the electric field between them is uniform. An ideal parallel-plate capacitor is one in which the plate separation d is very small compared with dimensions of the plate; thus the fringing field may be neglected in the ideal case. If the region between the plates is filled with dielectric of permittivity ϵ, then the electric field between the plates is

$$E = \frac{1}{\epsilon} \sigma = \frac{Q}{\epsilon A} , \tag{6–29}$$

where A is the area of one plate. The potential difference $\Delta U = Ed$.

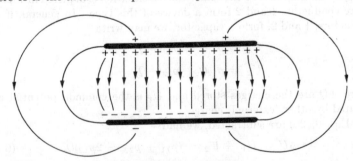

Fig. 6–2. The electric field between oppositely charged parallel plates of finite area.

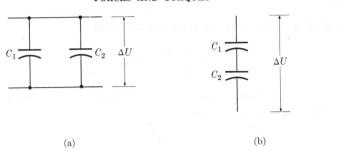

(a)　　　　　　　　　　　　　　　　　(b)

FIG. 6–3. (a) Parallel and (b) series connection of two capacitors.

Therefore

$$C = \frac{Q}{\Delta U} = \frac{\epsilon A}{d} \tag{6–30}$$

is the capacitance of this capacitor.

When a capacitor is depicted as part of an electric circuit, it is usually indicated by the symbol ⊣⊢ . Two or more capacitors may be joined together by connecting one of the conductors of the first capacitor to a conductor of the second, etc. Possible ways of joining two capacitors are by parallel connection (Fig. 6–3a), or by series connection (Fig. 6–3b). After the capacitors are joined, it is usually desirable to talk about the equivalent capacitance of the combination. In the parallel case, the same voltage ΔU which appears across each capacitor also appears across the combination; hence the equivalent capacitance is given by

$$C = \frac{Q_{\text{total}}}{\Delta U} = C_1 + C_2. \tag{6–31a}$$

If two uncharged capacitors are connected in series and subsequently charged, *conservation of charge* requires that each capacitor acquire the same charge. Thus the equivalent capacitance C of the combination is related to C_1 and C_2 by the expression

$$\frac{1}{C} = \frac{1}{C_1} + \frac{1}{C_2}. \tag{6–31b}$$

6–7 Forces and torques. Thus far in this chapter we have developed a number of alternative procedures for calculating the electrostatic energy of a charge system. We shall now show how the force on one of the objects in the charge system may be calculated from a knowledge of this electrostatic energy. Let us suppose we are dealing with an isolated system composed of a number of parts (conductors, point charges, dielectrics), and we allow one of these parts to make a small displacement $d\mathbf{r}$ under the influence of the electrical forces acting upon it. The mechanical work performed *by* the system in these circumstances is

$$dW_m = \mathbf{F} \cdot d\mathbf{r}$$
$$= F_x\, dx + F_y\, dy + F_z\, dz. \qquad (6\text{–}32)$$

Because the system is isolated, this work is done at the expense of the electrostatic energy W; in other words,

$$dW + dW_m = 0. \qquad (6\text{–}33)$$

Combining (6–32) and (6–33) yields

$$-dW = F_x\, dx + F_y\, dy + F_z\, dz$$

and

$$F_x = -\,\frac{\partial W}{\partial x}, \qquad (6\text{–}34)$$

with similar expressions for F_y and F_z.

If the object under consideration is constrained to move in such a way that it rotates about an axis, then Eq. (6–32) may be replaced by

$$dW_m = \boldsymbol{\tau} \cdot d\boldsymbol{\theta}, \qquad (6\text{–}35)$$

where $\boldsymbol{\tau}$ is the electrical torque and $d\boldsymbol{\theta}$ is the angular displacement. Writing $\boldsymbol{\tau}$ and $d\boldsymbol{\theta}$ in terms of their components (τ_1, τ_2, τ_3), $(d\theta_1, d\theta_2, d\theta_3)$, and combining Eqs. (6–33) and (6–35), we obtain

$$\tau_1 = -\,\frac{\partial W}{\partial \theta_1}, \qquad (6\text{–}36)$$

etc.

Thus our goal has been achieved:

$$F_x = -\left(\frac{\partial W}{\partial x}\right)_Q, \qquad (6\text{–}34a)$$

$$\tau_1 = -\left(\frac{\partial W}{\partial \theta_1}\right)_Q, \qquad (6\text{–}36a)$$

where the subscript Q has been added to denote that the system is isolated, and hence its total charge remains constant during the displacement $d\mathbf{r}$ or $d\boldsymbol{\theta}$. To exploit this method it is necessary to express W in analytic form, and the specific dependence of W on the coordinate x, or θ_1, must be given. An example showing the usefulness of the method will be presented shortly.

Equations (6–34a) and (6–36a) do not, however, cover all cases of interest because, as was mentioned in their derivation, they are limited to isolated systems in which the charge in the system remains constant.

In another important class of problems all of the free charge exists on the surfaces of conductors, and these are maintained at fixed potentials by means of external sources of energy (e.g., by means of batteries). Here again we may allow one of the parts of the system to move under the influence of electrical forces acting upon it, and the mechanical work performed (this time by the system and the batteries) will still be given by Eq. (6–32). But the energy conservation equation becomes, in this instance,

$$dW + dW_m = dW_b, \tag{6–37}$$

where dW_b is the energy supplied by the batteries. Before we can proceed to an expression linking W and the force on some part of the system for this case it will be necessary to eliminate dW_b from Eq. (6–37).

The electrostatic energy W of a system of charged conductors has been given earlier, in Eq. (6–12). If, now, some part of the system is displaced while at the same time the potentials of all conductors remain fixed,

$$dW = \tfrac{1}{2} \sum_j U_j \, dQ_j. \tag{6–38}$$

Furthermore, the energy supplied by the batteries, dW_b, is the work required to move each of the charge increments dQ_j from zero potential to the potential of the appropriate conductor; by (6–1) this is

$$dW_b = \sum_j U_j \, dQ_j. \tag{6–39}$$

Thus

$$dW_b = 2 \, dW. \tag{6–40}$$

Using this equation to eliminate dW_b from (6–37) and combining the result with (6–32), we obtain

$$dW = F_x \, dx + F_y \, dy + F_z \, dz$$

or

$$F_x = \left(\frac{\partial W}{\partial x} \right)_U. \tag{6–41}$$

Here the subscript U is used to denote the fact that all potentials are maintained constant during the virtual displacement $d\mathbf{r}$. In a similar fashion, we may derive

$$\tau_1 = \left(\frac{\partial W}{\partial \theta_1} \right)_U. \tag{6–42}$$

As an example of the energy method, let us consider the following problem. A parallel-plate capacitor of plate separation d has the region between its plates filled by a block of solid dielectric of permittivity ϵ.

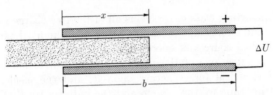

F<small>IG</small>. 6–4. Dielectric slab partially withdrawn from between two charged plates.

The dimensions of each plate are length b, width w. The plates are maintained at the constant potential difference ΔU. If the dielectric block is withdrawn along the b dimension until only the length x remains between the plates (see Fig. 6–4), calculate the force tending to pull the block back into place.

Solution. The energy of the system may be calculated by any of several methods. Thus, for example,

$$W = \tfrac{1}{2}\int_V \epsilon E^2\, dv$$

where the region of integration need include only those parts of space where $E \neq 0$. Neglecting fringing effects at the edge of the capacitor, we find

$$W = \tfrac{1}{2}\epsilon\left(\frac{\Delta U}{d}\right)^2 dwx + \tfrac{1}{2}\epsilon_0\left(\frac{\Delta U}{d}\right)^2 dw(b - x).$$

The force may be calculated from Eq. (6–41):

$$F_x = \tfrac{1}{2}(\epsilon - \epsilon_0)w\,\frac{(\Delta U)^2}{d}$$

in the direction of increasing x.

6–8 Force on a charge distribution. This chapter would not be complete without a brief discussion of the calculation of electrical force from first principles, i.e., by direct integration, although this procedure has been discussed at some length in an earlier chapter (see Section 4–10). The important thing to remember is that when calculating the force on a charge element dq, the electric field produced by this element, $\mathbf{E}_s$, must be subtracted from the total electric field:

$$d\mathbf{F} = (\mathbf{E} - \mathbf{E}_s)\, dq. \tag{6–43}$$

Thus, for example, when we calculate the force on a point charge, the infinite electric field produced *by* the point charge itself must be excluded from the effective electric field acting at the point. The effect of the charge interacting with its own electric field is such as to produce internal stresses in the charge, but these stresses can never combine in such a way that they would tend to produce a rigid displacement of the charge.

The force on an object bearing the surface charge $\sigma(x, y, z)$ is obtained by combining Eqs. (4–57) and (4–58):

$$\mathbf{F} = \oint_S (\mathbf{E} - \mathbf{E}_s)\sigma \, da, \tag{6–44}$$

where the integral is taken over the entire surface of the object. The field $\mathbf{E}_s$ is given by Eq. (4–60):

$$\mathbf{E}_s = \frac{\sigma}{2\epsilon} \mathbf{n}. \tag{6–45}$$

If the object is a conductor, there is a simple relationship between the total electric field at the surface, $\mathbf{E}$, and $\mathbf{E}_s$. Thus the force on a conductor, as we have already found in Section 4–10, is

$$\mathbf{F} = \tfrac{1}{2}\oint_S \sigma\mathbf{E} \, da, \tag{6–46a}$$

or

$$\mathbf{F} = \oint_S \frac{\sigma^2}{2\epsilon} \mathbf{n} \, da. \tag{6–46b}$$

Finally, let us determine the force on a volume charge distribution. The force on a charge element $\rho \, dv$ is

$$d\mathbf{F} = (\mathbf{E} - \mathbf{E}_s)\rho \, dv. \tag{6–47}$$

But the field $\mathbf{E}_s$ produced by the volume element dv is proportional to the volume divided by the square of some relevant dimension of the element, and this ratio approaches zero in the limit where $dv \to 0$. Thus $\mathbf{E}_s$ is a negligible fraction of $\mathbf{E}$, and we may write

$$\mathbf{F} = \int_{V_0} \rho\mathbf{E} \, dv \tag{6–48}$$

for the force on the charge contained in the volume V_0.

*6–9 Thermodynamic interpretation of electrostatic energy. The electrostatic energy of a system of charged conductors and dielectrics has been obtained in a variety of forms, in particular we have

$$W = \tfrac{1}{2}\int_V \mathbf{D} \cdot \mathbf{E} \, dv, \tag{6–17}$$

where the integration extends over all dielectrics (including vacuum).

---

* Starred sections may be omitted without loss of continuity.

The question naturally arises whether W can be interpreted thermodynamically, i.e., does it form part of the internal energy of the system? To answer this question we must go back to the derivation of W, where we showed that W was the work done on the system in bringing it to its charged condition. Thus W is really a work term, and the problem at hand is to determine under what conditions a work increment may be identified with a thermodynamic property of the system.

From the first law of thermodynamics (which expresses conservation of energy), for a reversible process

$$dW_i = T \, dS + dW_m, \tag{6–49}$$

where dW_i represents the change in internal energy of the system, dS represents the change in entropy, dW_m is the mechanical work done on the system, and T is the absolute temperature. The quantity $T \, dS$, of course, is the heat added to the system during the process.

It is evident that the work increment dW_m may be identified with the change in internal energy dW_i only for an adiabatic process, that is, a process in which $dS = 0$. But the temperature of the system will change in general during an adiabatic process, and the dielectric coefficients, which are functions of the temperature, will change also. Recall that Eq. (6–17) was derived from Eq. (6–9), and the latter equation was obtained on the assumption that the various dielectric coefficients remained constant during the charging process. Hence we must restrict our interest to isothermal processes, and here it is not possible to identify dW_m with dW_i.

The thermodynamic quantity called the Helmholtz *free energy* of the system is defined by $F = W_i - TS$. Differentiating and combining the result with (6–49) yields

$$\begin{aligned} dF &= dW_i - T \, dS - S \, dT \\ &= -S \, dT + dW_m. \end{aligned} \tag{6–50}$$

This is just the equation we need. For an isothermal process, dF is equal to dW_m, and thus we may say that the electrostatic energy forms part of the *free energy* of the system. This energy represents the maximum work which can be extracted at a later time from the electrostatic field.

For a system kept at constant temperature, the free energy plays the same role as does the potential energy for a mechanical (i.e., a temperature-independent) system.

Problems

6-1. A fast electron (kinetic energy $= 3.0 \times 10^{-17}$ joule) enters a region of space containing a uniform electric field $E = 1000$ volts/m. The field is parallel to the electron's motion, and in a direction such as to decelerate it. How far does the electron travel before it is brought to rest? (Charge of electron $= 1.60 \times 10^{-19}$ coulomb.)

6-2. Given a spherical dielectric shell (inner radius a, outer radius b, dielectric constant K) and a point charge q, infinitely separated. Now let the point charge be placed at the center of the dielectric shell. Determine the change in energy of the system.

6-3. Given a spherical charge distribution of radius R, uniform charge density ρ_0. Determine the self-energy of the distribution in two ways: (a) by direct integration of Eq. (6–9); (b) by an integration over the field, $\frac{1}{2}\int \mathbf{E} \cdot \mathbf{D} \, dv$.

6-4. Let us assume that an electron is a uniformly charged, spherical particle of radius R. Assume further that the rest energy, mc^2 (where m is the mass of the electron, and c is the velocity of light), is electrostatic in origin and given by the result of Problem 6–3. By putting in appropriate numerical values for the charge and mass of the electron, determine its "classical radius" R.

6-5. Two spherical conductors are located in vacuum. Conductor 1, of radius R, is grounded (i.e., at zero potential). Conductor 2 is so small that it may be treated as a point charge. It bears the charge q and is located at distance d from the grounded sphere. What is the charge induced on the grounded sphere? (Use the concept of coefficient of potential.)

6-6. Given a system of two conducting objects in a linear dielectric medium. Conductor 1 is uncharged, and conductor 2 is grounded. Prove that conductor 1 is also at ground potential.

6-7. A parallel-plate capacitor is made with a composite dielectric. A sheet of dielectric of permittivity ϵ_1, thickness d_1, is placed on top of a second dielectric sheet (permittivity ϵ_2, thickness d_2). The combination is placed between parallel conducting plates which are separated by the distance $d_1 + d_2$. What is the capacitance per unit plate area of the capacitor?

6-8. A long, conducting cylinder of radius a is oriented parallel to and at distance h from an infinite conducting plane. Show that the capacitance of the system, per unit length of the cylinder, is given by

$$C = 2\pi\epsilon_0/\cosh^{-1}(h/a).$$

(See Section 3–11.)

6-9. Two identical air capacitors are connected in series, and the combination is maintained at the constant potential difference of 50 volts. If a dielectric sheet, of dielectric constant 10 and thickness equal to one-tenth of the air gap, is inserted into one of the capacitors, calculate the voltage across this capacitor.

6-10. The capacitance of a gold-leaf electroscope is not quite constant because the leaf moves closer to the case as ΔU increases. The expected form for the capacitance is

$$C = a + b(\Delta U)^2.$$

How would you determine the constants a and b for a particular instrument?

What is the energy of the electroscope when it is charged? Is the energy entirely electrical?

6–11. Two concentric, spherical, conducting shells of radii r_1 and r_2 are maintained at potentials U_1 and U_2, respectively. The region between the shells is filled with a dielectric medium. Show by direct calculation that the energy stored in the dielectric is equal to $C(U_1 - U_2)^2/2$, where C is the capacitance of the system.

6–12. Two coaxial, cylindrical conductors of approximately the same radius are separated in the radial dimension by the distance d. The cylinders are inserted normally into a liquid dielectric of susceptibility χ and mass density ζ. The cylinders are maintained at the potential difference ΔU. To what height h does the dielectric rise between the conductors? (Neglect surface tension.)

6–13. A parallel-plate capacitor has the region between its plates filled with a dielectric slab of dielectric constant K. The plate dimensions are width w and length l, and the plate separation is d. The capacitor is charged while it is connected to a potential difference $(\Delta U)_0$, after which it is disconnected. The dielectric slab is now partially withdrawn in the l dimension until only the length x remains between the plates. (a) What is the potential difference across the capacitor? (b) What is the force tending to pull the dielectric slab back to its original position?

6–14. The capacitance of a variable air capacitor changes linearly from 50 to 364 $\mu\mu f$ during a rotation from 0° to 180°. When set at 75°, a potential difference of 400 volts is maintained across the capacitor. What is the direction and magnitude of electrostatic torque experienced by the capacitor?

*6–15. An uncharged, conducting, spherical shell of mass m floats with one-fourth of its volume submerged in a liquid dielectric of dielectric constant K. To what potential must the sphere be charged to float half submerged? [*Hint:* Assume the electric field of the half-submerged, charged shell to be a purely radial field, and show later that the sum of $\sigma + \sigma_P$ over the spherical surface is such as to justify this assumption.]

6–16. A dielectric slab of thickness d and dielectric constant K fills the region between the plates of a parallel-plate capacitor. The plate area is A. Calculate the electrostatic force on one of the capacitor plates (a) on the assumption that the dielectric is in direct contact with the plate, (b) on the assumption that there is a narrow air space between dielectric and plate. The plates are maintained at the potential difference ΔU in both cases.

CHAPTER 7

ELECTRIC CURRENT

Up to this point we have been dealing with charges at rest; now we wish to consider charges in motion. This statement implies that we shall be dealing with conductors of electricity because, by definition, a conductor is a material in which the charge carriers are free to move (see Section 2–5). The preceding definition includes not only the conventional conductors such as metals and alloys, but also semiconductors, electrolytes, ionized gases, imperfect dielectrics, and even vacuum in the vicinity of a thermionic emitting cathode. In many conductors the charge carriers are electrons; in other cases the charge may be carried by positive or negative ions.

Moving charge constitutes a *current*, and the process whereby charge is transported is called *conduction*. To be precise: the current, I, is defined as the rate at which charge is transported past a given point in a conducting system. Thus

$$I = \frac{dQ}{dt},\qquad\qquad (7\text{--}1)$$

where $Q = Q(t)$ is the net charge transported in time t. The unit of current in the mks system is the ampere, named for the French physicist, André Marie Ampere. Evidently,

$$1 \text{ ampere} = 1\,\frac{\text{coulomb}}{\text{second}}.$$

7–1 Nature of the current. In a metal, current is carried entirely by electrons, while the heavy positive ions are fixed at regular positions in the crystal structure (Fig. 7–1). Only the valence (outermost) atomic

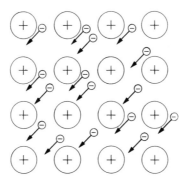

Fig. 7–1. Schematic diagram of the motion of conduction electrons in a metal.

123

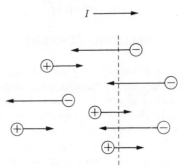

FIG. 7–2. Current produced by the motion of both positive and negative charge carriers.

electrons are free to participate in the conduction process; the other electrons are tightly bound to their ions. Under steady state conditions, electrons may be fed into the metal at one point and removed at another, producing a current, but the metal as a whole is electrostatically neutral. Strong electrostatic forces keep excess electrons from accumulating at any point in the metal. Similarly, a deficiency of electrons is remedied by electrostatic forces of the opposite sign. We shall see later that excess charge is dissipated extremely rapidly in a conductor. Thus we note that it is possible to study the subject of electric current without taking into account detailed electrostatic effects associated with the charge carriers.

In an electrolyte, the current is carried by both positive and negative ions, although, because some ions move faster than others, conduction by one type of ion usually predominates. It is important to note that positive and negative ions traveling in *opposite* directions (Fig. 7–2) contribute to the current in the *same* direction. The basis for this fact is evident from Eq. (7–1), since the net charge transported past a given point depends on both the sign of the charge carrier and the direction in which it is moving. Thus, in Fig. 7–2, both the positive and negative carrier groups produce currents to the right; by convention, the direction in which the positive carrier moves (or, equivalently, the direction opposite to that in which the negative carrier moves) is taken as the direction, or *sense*, of the current. In general, an electric current arises in response to an electric field. If an electric field is imposed on a conductor, it will cause positive charge carriers to move in the general direction of the field and negative carriers in a direction opposite to the field; hence all currents produced in the process have the same direction as the field.

In a gas discharge, the current is carried by both electrons and positive ions, but because the electrons are so much more mobile than the heavy ions, practically all of the current is carried by electrons. Gas conduction is somewhat complicated, because the electronic and ionic populations vary greatly with the experimental conditions (they are determined primarily by the gas pressure and the potential drop across the gas). Under certain conditions *cascading* occurs, in which process the few ions which are initially present accelerate and make inelastic collisions with neutral atoms, thereby producing additional ions and electrons. The additional ions can also give rise to ionizing collisions, with the result that the carrier density builds up enormously.

In Figs. 7–1 and 7–2 we have pictured the charge carriers as falling into groups, each of which has a common motion, called the *drift motion* of the group. The picture has been greatly oversimplified, however. Each group of charge carriers actually represents an assembly of particles in thermal equilibrium with its environment, and so each particle has thermal motion as well as drift motion. But the thermal motion, although it may be large, is also random, and hence gives rise to no organized transport of charge. The drift motion, on the other hand, is not random. In considering the conduction process, then, it is permissible to forget about the random motion, which in the end adds up to nothing, and to use the simple picture presented in Figs. 7–1 and 7–2. For certain other transport processes, however, such as conduction in a thermal gradient (which gives rise to the thermoelectric effect), it is necessary to take the thermal motion into account in a detailed way in order to understand the phenomena fully.

The currents we have described thus far in this section are known as *conduction currents*. These currents represent the drift motion of charge carriers through the medium; the medium itself may be, and usually is, at rest. Liquids and gases may also undergo hydrodynamic motion, and if the medium has a charge density, this hydrodynamic motion will produce currents. Such currents, arising from *mass transport*, are called *convection currents*. Convection currents are important to the subject of atmospheric electricity; in fact, the upward convection currents in thunderstorms are sufficient to maintain the normal potential gradient of the atmosphere above the earth. The motion of charged particles in vacuum (such as electrons in a vacuum diode) also constitutes a convection current. An important feature of the convection current is that it is not electrostatically neutral, and its electrostatic charge must usually be taken into account.

In the rest of this chapter we shall deal exclusively with conduction currents.

7–2 Current density. Equation of continuity.

We shall now consider a conducting medium which has only one type of charge carrier, of charge q. The number of these carriers per unit volume will be denoted by N. In accordance with the preceding section, we ignore their random thermal motion, and assign the same drift velocity $\mathbf{v}$ to each carrier. We are now in a position to calculate the current through an element of area da such

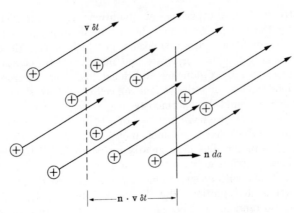

FIG. 7–3. The drift motion of charge carriers across the plane da in time δt.

as is shown in Fig. 7–3. During the time δt each carrier moves a distance $\mathbf{v}\,\delta t$; from the figure it is evident that the charge δQ which crosses da during time δt is q times the sum of all charge carriers in the volume $\mathbf{v} \cdot \mathbf{n}\,\delta t\,da$, where $\mathbf{n}$ is a unit vector normal to the area da. From Eq. (7–1), the current

$$dI = \frac{\delta Q}{\delta t} = \frac{qN\mathbf{v} \cdot \mathbf{n}\,\delta t\,da}{\delta t}$$

$$= Nq\mathbf{v} \cdot \mathbf{n}\,da. \tag{7–2}$$

If there is more than one kind of charge carrier present, there will be a contribution of the form (7–2) from each type of carrier. In general,

$$dI = \left[\sum_i N_i q_i \mathbf{v}_i\right] \cdot \mathbf{n}\,da \tag{7–3}$$

is the current through the area da. The summation is over the different carrier types. The quantity in brackets is a vector which has dimensions of current per unit area; this quantity is called the current density, and is given the symbol $\mathbf{J}$:

$$\mathbf{J} = \sum_i N_i q_i \mathbf{v}_i. \tag{7–4}$$

The current density may be defined at each point in a conducting medium and is, therefore, a vector point function. It is a useful quantity, one which enters directly into the differential equations of electromagnetic theory. The mks unit of $\mathbf{J}$ is amperes/meter^2

Equation (7–3) may be written as

$$dI = \mathbf{J} \cdot \mathbf{n}\,da,$$

and the current through the surface S, an arbitrarily shaped surface area of macroscopic size, is given by the integral

$$I = \int_S \mathbf{J} \cdot \mathbf{n}\, da. \qquad (7\text{-}5)$$

The current density $\mathbf{J}$ and the charge density ρ are not independent quantities, but are related at each point through a differential equation, the so-called *equation of continuity*. This relationship has its origin in the fact that charge can neither be created nor destroyed; the equation is most easily derived by applying (7–5) to an arbitrary *closed* surface S. The electric current entering V, the volume enclosed by S, is given by

$$I = - \oint_S \mathbf{J} \cdot \mathbf{n}\, da = - \int_V \operatorname{div} \mathbf{J}\, dv, \qquad (7\text{-}6)$$

the last integral being obtained through the use of the divergence theorem. The minus sign in (7–6) comes about because $\mathbf{n}$ is the outward normal and we wish to call I positive when the net flow of charge is from the outside of V to within. But from (7–1), I is equal to the rate at which charge is transported into V:

$$I = \frac{dQ}{dt} = \frac{d}{dt} \int_V \rho\, dv. \qquad (7\text{-}7\text{a})$$

Since we are dealing with a fixed volume V, the time derivative operates only on the function ρ. However, ρ is a function of position as well as of time, so that the time derivative becomes the partial derivative with respect to time when it is moved inside the integral. Hence

$$I = \int_V \frac{\partial \rho}{\partial t}\, dv. \qquad (7\text{-}7\text{b})$$

Equations (7–6) and (7–7b) may now be equated:

$$\int_V \left(\frac{\partial \rho}{\partial t} + \operatorname{div} \mathbf{J} \right) dv = 0. \qquad (7\text{-}8)$$

But V is completely arbitrary, and the only way that (7–8) can hold for an *arbitrary volume segment* of the medium is for the integrand to vanish at each point. Hence, the equation of continuity:

$$\frac{\partial \rho}{\partial t} + \operatorname{div} \mathbf{J} = 0. \qquad (7\text{-}9)$$

7–3 Ohm's law. Conductivity. It is found experimentally that in a metal at constant temperature the current density $\mathbf{J}$ is linearly proportional to the electric field (Ohm's law). Thus

$$\mathbf{J} = g\mathbf{E}. \qquad (7\text{-}10)$$

The constant of proportionality g is called the *conductivity*. Equation (7-10) has approximate validity for a large number of the common conducting materials; in the general case, however, Eq. (7-10) must be replaced by

$$\mathbf{J} = g(\mathbf{E})\,\mathbf{E},$$

where $g(\mathbf{E})$ is a function of the electric field. Materials for which Eq. (7-10) holds are called linear media or ohmic media. Here again, as with dielectrics, we shall be most concerned with the linear case.

The reciprocal of the conductivity is called the resistivity η; thus*

$$\eta = \frac{1}{g}. \qquad (7\text{-}11)$$

The unit of η in the mks system is volt·meters/ampere, or simply ohm·meters, where the ohm is defined by

$$1 \text{ ohm} = \frac{1 \text{ volt}}{1 \text{ ampere}}.$$

The unit of conductivity g is $\text{ohm}^{-1}\,\text{m}^{-1}$, or mho/meter.

Resistivities of a number of common materials are given in Table 7-1. Only the metals and metal alloys are true ohmic materials. It is apparent from this table that all materials conduct electricity to some extent, but that the materials we have called insulators (dielectrics) are much poorer conductors than the metals by a tremendous factor (10^{20} to 10^{26}). The distinction between a conductor and an insulator will be discussed in a more quantitative way in Section 7-7.

Consider a conducting specimen obeying Ohm's law, in the shape of a straight wire of uniform cross section whose ends are maintained at a constant potential difference ΔU. The wire is assumed to be homogeneous and characterized by the constant conductivity g. Under these conditions an electric field will exist in the wire, the field being related to ΔU by the relation

$$\Delta U = \int \mathbf{E} \cdot d\mathbf{l}. \qquad (7\text{-}12\text{a})$$

It is evident that there can be no component of electric field at right angles to the axis of the wire, since by (7-10) this would produce a charging of the wire's surface. As was mentioned earlier, excess charge is dis-

---

* The common symbols for resistivity and conductivity are ρ and σ, respectively, but to avoid the possibility of confusion with volume charge density ρ and surface charge density σ, we shall use the symbols η and g.

TABLE 7–1

RESISTIVITY η AND TEMPERATURE COEFFICIENT OF RESISTANCE α
OF SOME COMMON MATERIALS AT 20°C.

(Data from the *American Institute of Physics Handbook*, McGraw-Hill, 1957, and
the *Handbook of Chemistry and Physics*, Chem. Rubber Publishing Co., 1952.)

Material	η, ohm·m	$\alpha = \dfrac{1}{\eta}\dfrac{d\eta}{dT},\ (°C)^{-1}$
Aluminum	2.83×10^{-8}	0.0039
Copper	1.69×10^{-8}	0.00393
Gold	2.44×10^{-8}	0.0034
Iron (0°C)	8.85×10^{-8}	0.0050
Nickel	7.24×10^{-8}	0.006
Silver (0°C)	1.47×10^{-8}	0.0038
Mercury	95.8×10^{-8}	0.00089
Tungsten	5.51×10^{-8}	0.0045
Constantin (Cu 60, Ni 40)	44.0×10^{-8}	0.0000
Nichrome	100.0×10^{-8}	0.0004
Germanium (pure)	0.45	−0.048
Germanium ($5 \times 10^{-6}\%$ As)	0.011	*
Silicon (pure)	640.0	−0.075
Silicon ($10^{-4}\%$ As)	0.003	
NaCl Solution (saturated)	0.044	−0.005
Amber	5.0×10^{14}	
Glass	$10^{10} - 10^{14}$	
Hard rubber	$10^{13} - 10^{16}$	
Mica	$10^{11} - 10^{15}$	
Quartz (fused)	7.5×10^{17}	
Sulfur	10^{15}	
Wood	$10^{8} - 10^{11}$	

* α is not well defined for impurity-doped germanium since the resistivity is
a rather complicated function of the temperature (see C. Kittel, *Introduction
to Solid State Physics*, John Wiley and Sons, New York, 1956, p. 364). At higher
temperatures α approaches that of the pure material.

sipated extremely rapidly in a conductor, and because of the low potential
energy sink for charge carriers at one end of the wire, not even a surface
charge can be tolerated. Thus the electric field is purely longitudinal.
Furthermore, because of the geometry, the electric field must be the same

at all points along the wire. Therefore Eq. (7–12a) reduces to

$$\Delta U = El, \tag{7–12b}$$

where l is the length of the wire. But an electric field implies a current, of density $\mathbf{J} = g\mathbf{E}$. The current through any cross section of the wire is

$$I = \int_A \mathbf{J} \cdot \mathbf{n}\, da = JA, \tag{7–13}$$

where A is the cross-sectional area of the wire. Combining Eq. (7–13) with (7–10) and (7–12b), we obtain

$$I = \frac{gA}{l} \Delta U, \tag{7–14}$$

which provides a linear relationship between I and ΔU.

The quantity l/gA is called the *resistance* of the wire; resistance will be denoted by the symbol R. Using R, we may rewrite (7–14):

$$\Delta U = RI, \tag{7–15}$$

which is the familiar form of Ohm's law (R is evidently measured in units of ohms). In the next section it will be shown that Eq. (7–10) implies Eq. (7–15), independently of the shape of the conductor.

Equation (7–15) may be considered to be a definition of the resistance of an object or device that is passing a constant current. In the general case, R will depend upon the value of this current. However, as was mentioned earlier, we are primarily interested in linear materials, and here R is independent of the current.

7–4 Resistance networks. The resistance defined in the preceding section is a property of the material object under consideration, and it depends upon both the nature of the material from which the object is composed and its geometry. The resistivity, on the other hand, depends only upon the nature of the conducting material. A conducting object of convenient shape which is characterized primarily by its resistance is called a *resistor;* it is usually denoted by the symbol $-\!\wedge\!\wedge\!\wedge\!-$.

Resistors may be connected to form a resistance network; the ways in which two resistors may be combined are illustrated in Fig. 7–4. Part (a) shows a *series* connection; here the same current I passes through both resistors. Applying Eq. (7–15) to each resistor, and noting that the potential difference $\Delta U = \Delta U_1 + \Delta U_2$, we find that

$$\Delta U = R_1 I + R_2 I = (R_1 + R_2)I.$$

Thus the equivalent resistance of the combination is

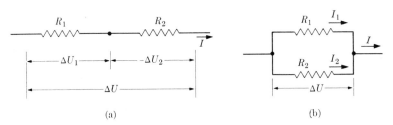

FIG. 7-4. (a) Series and (b) parallel connection of two resistors.

$$R = R_1 + R_2 \qquad \text{(series connection)}. \qquad (7\text{--}16)$$

In the *parallel* connection (Fig. 7–4b) the potential difference across each resistor is the same, and the total current through the combination is $I = I_1 + I_2$. Applying Eq. (7–15), we find

$$I = \frac{1}{R_1}\,\Delta U + \frac{1}{R_2}\,\Delta U = \left(\frac{1}{R_1} + \frac{1}{R_2}\right)\Delta U,$$

and the equivalent resistance R of the combination is obtained from

$$\frac{1}{R} = \frac{1}{R_1} + \frac{1}{R_2} \qquad \text{(parallel combination)}. \qquad (7\text{--}17)$$

The equivalent resistance of a more complicated network, like that in Fig. 7–5, may be determined by combining the resistors in pairs according to Eq. (7–16) or (7–17), and then repeating the process until only one equivalent resistance remains.

Let us now consider a conducting object composed of ohmic material, but which is not necessarily homogeneous, so that the conductivity g is independent of the local electric field but may vary from point to point in the medium; that is, $g = g(x, y, z)$. Suppose that two points on the boundary of the object are maintained at the potentials U_1 and U_2 respectively, as in Fig. 7–6(a). The current lines in the medium are the same

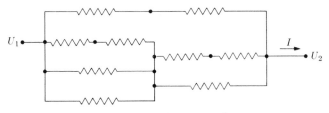

FIG. 7-5. A resistor network.

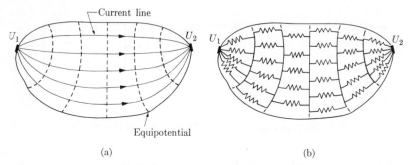

FIG. 7–6.   (a) A conducting object subjected to the potential difference
$U_1 - U_2$. (b) An equivalent resistor network of wire segments.

as those of the electric field, since $\mathbf{J} = g\mathbf{E}$, and the equipotential surfaces
intersect the current lines at right angles, as shown schematically in the
figure.   What we are dealing with is actually a large resistance network
(Fig. 7–6b) constructed from many elemental resistors R_i in the shape of
short wire segments.   According to the preceding section,

$$R_i = \frac{l_i}{g_i A_i}, \tag{7–18}$$

where $g_i = g(x, y, z)$ is the local conductivity, A_i is the cross-sectional
area of the segment, and l_i is the distance between equipotential surfaces.
In the limit where the number of equipotential surfaces between U_1 and
U_2 becomes very large and the number of elemental resistors becomes
correspondingly large, the resistors R_i fill the entire space occupied by
the conducting object.   From the discussion of the preceding paragraph,
this network has an equivalent resistance R, and the current through the
object is evidently given by

$$I = \frac{U_1 - U_2}{R}. \tag{7–19}$$

Since Ohm's law, Eq. (7–10), was assumed to hold for the medium,
each of the elemental resistors R_i is ohmic, and the equivalent resistance
of the network must therefore be ohmic.   In other words,

$$R = \frac{U_1 - U_2}{I}$$

is independent of the potential difference, $U_1 - U_2$.   Thus we have
shown that Eq. (7–10) implies Eq. (7–15), independently of the shape of
the conductor, and the two equations are equivalent expressions of Ohm's
law.

7–5 Electromotive force. In Chapter 2 it was shown that the integral of the tangential component of an *electrostatic* field around any closed path vanishes; i.e.,

$$\oint \mathbf{E} \cdot d\mathbf{l} = 0$$

for an electrostatic field. For an ohmic material, $\mathbf{J} = g\mathbf{E}$. In the general case this is modified to $\mathbf{J} = g(\mathbf{E})\,\mathbf{E}$, but $g(\mathbf{E})$ is always a positive quantity. Thus it follows that a purely electrostatic force cannot cause a current to circulate in the same sense around an entire circuit. Or, in other words, a steady current cannot be maintained by means of purely electrostatic forces.

A charged particle q may experience other forces (mechanical, "chemical," etc.) in addition to the electrostatic force. If the total force per unit charge on a charged particle is called the effective electric field $\mathbf{E}_{\mathrm{eff}}$, then the above line integral will not necessarily vanish:

$$\oint \mathbf{E}_{\mathrm{eff}} \cdot d\mathbf{l} = \mathcal{E}. \tag{7–20}$$

The quantity $\mathcal{E}$, the *electromotive force* or simply the emf, represents the "driving force" for the current in a closed circuit. The unit of emf in the mks system is joules/coulomb, or volt (the same as the unit for potential). In the previous sections we sidestepped the question concerning the cause of electric current by assuming that two points on a conducting object were maintained at the constant potential difference $U_1 - U_2$ by means of *external* energy sources; now we must consider these energy sources in some detail.

Let us examine all the forces which might act on a charge carrier q. First there is the electrostatic force $q\mathbf{E}_s$, where $\mathbf{E}_s$ denotes the electrostatic field:

$$\mathbf{E}_s(\mathbf{r}) = \frac{1}{4\pi\epsilon_0} \int_V \frac{(\rho + \rho_P)(\mathbf{r} - \mathbf{r}')}{|\mathbf{r} - \mathbf{r}'|^3}\, dv'$$

$+$ corresponding surface integral. (7–21)

If ρ or ρ_P is a function of the time, it is still possible to define a *quasi-electrostatic field* $\mathbf{E}_s$ by means of Eq. (7–21). Thus, $\mathbf{E}_s(\mathbf{r}, t)$, which is defined in terms of the instantaneous charge densities, has all the basic properties of the electrostatic field. In addition to $q\mathbf{E}_s$, we may have forces produced by a changing magnetic field (Faraday's law, Chapter 9) or forces arising from a concentration gradient of the charge carriers ("chemical" or "diffusion" forces). A magnetic force may be present, but this acts at right angles to the motion of q (Chapter 8), and hence performs no work on the particle. For this reason we specifically exclude magnetic forces unless they act in conjunction with some other force (see motional emf, Chapter 9). Finally, there may be mechanical forces which arise from the gross mechanical force exerted on the conductor containing our charged particle.* These forces are all basically electromagnetic in character; even the mechanical and so-called "chemical" forces are, in general, transmitted via interaction with atoms or other molecular particles, the fundamental interaction being electric or magnetic in origin.

If all the forces with the exception of $q\mathbf{E}_s$ are lumped together in the symbol $\mathbf{F}_w$, then by Newton's second law of motion

$$q\mathbf{E}_{\text{eff}} = q\mathbf{E}_s + \mathbf{F}_w = m\mathbf{f}, \tag{7–22}$$

where $\mathbf{f}$ is the acceleration of the charged particle and m is its mass.

If the charged particle q is in vacuum, it will continue to accelerate. This is not, however, the case of immediate interest. When the particle is inside a material conductor, it will accelerate for a short period, after which it makes a collision with one of the atoms of the material. As a result of this collision the charged particle q is thrown off in a random direction, so that the average effect of a collision is to reduce the velocity of the particle to zero. The particle will again accelerate until it makes a second collision, and so on. Taking the mean collision time to be τ, we find the average velocity, or drift velocity, of the particle in the direction of acceleration to be

$$\mathbf{v} = \tfrac{1}{2}\mathbf{f}\tau = \frac{1}{2m}\,(q\mathbf{E}_s + \mathbf{F}_w)\tau.$$

Suppose that we now introduce the effective field, $\mathbf{E}_{\text{eff}} = \mathbf{E}_s + (1/q)\mathbf{F}_w$, and note that the drift velocity $\mathbf{v}$ is related to the current density $\mathbf{J}$ by Eq. (7–4):

$$\mathbf{J} = \left[\sum_i \frac{N_i q_i^2 \tau_i}{2m_i} \right] \mathbf{E}_{\text{eff}}, \tag{7–23}$$

which is Ohm's law. Evidently the conductivity g is given by the expression

$$g = \sum_i \frac{N_i q_i^2 \tau_i}{2m_i}. \tag{7–24}$$

For our purposes, it is convenient to write Eq. (7–23) in the form

$$\mathbf{E}_s + \frac{1}{q}\,\mathbf{F}_w = \eta\mathbf{J}. \tag{7–23a}$$

---

* Gravitational forces need not be considered, since these are conservative forces which obviously contribute nothing to the line integral of Eq. (7–20).

If the scalar product of this expression with the line element $d\mathbf{l}$ is found, and the result is integrated from position a to position b, then

$$\int_a^b \mathbf{E}_s \cdot d\mathbf{l} + \frac{1}{q}\int_a^b \mathbf{F}_w \cdot d\mathbf{l} = \int_a^b \eta \mathbf{J} \cdot d\mathbf{l}.$$

The first integral is the potential difference $U_a - U_b$. The second will be called the emf of the segment $\overline{ab}$; it is given the symbol $\mathcal{E}_{ab}$. As was shown in Section 7–4, the last integral may be written $I R_{ab}$, where I is the total current from a to b, and R_{ab} is the equivalent resistance between a and b. Thus

$$U_b - U_a = \mathcal{E}_{ab} - I R_{ab}. \tag{7-25}$$

When $\mathcal{E}_{ab}$ is zero, the segment $\overline{ab}$ is called a *passive* circuit element; when $\mathcal{E}_{ab}$ is not zero, the element is called an *active* one or a *seat of emf*. Equation (7–25) is the fundamental equation of electric circuit analysis.

A steady current in the segment $\overline{ab}$ corresponds to the continuous transport of charge between points a and b. If in time dt the charge $dQ = I\,dt$ is transferred from a to b, the gain in electrical energy is

$$dQ\,(U_b - U_a) = (\mathcal{E}_{ab}I - I^2 R_{ab})\,dt. \tag{7-26}$$

The term $I^2 R_{ab}\,dt$ represents an irreversible conversion of electrical energy into heat. The charge carriers are continually making collisions, and it is this process which converts part of the organized drift motion of the carriers into random thermal motion. In an ideal seat of emf the term $\mathcal{E}_{ab}I\,dt$ represents a thermodynamically reversible conversion of some other form of energy into electrical energy. $\mathcal{E}_{ab}$ is positive if it has the same sense as the current; in this case the seat of emf supplies electrical energy to the circuit at the expense of some other form of energy. If $\mathcal{E}_{ab}$ is negative the seat absorbs electrical energy from the circuit and converts it to some other form. The chemical cell is an example of chemical-electrical conversion, the thermocouple of thermal-electrical conversion, and a dynamo (motor-generator) of mechanical-electrical conversion. (When a dynamo absorbs energy from the electric circuit it operates as a motor, when it supplies electrical energy it operates as a generator.)

Let the points a and b be joined so as to make a complete circuit from the segment $\overline{ab}$; then $U_a = U_b$, and

$$\mathcal{E} = IR; \tag{7-25a}$$

furthermore,

$$\mathcal{E}I = I^2 R. \tag{7-26a}$$

In this case $\mathcal{E}$ represents the entire emf in the circuit and R is the total resistance of the circuit.

7–6 Steady currents in media without sources of emf. There is a very close analogy between an electrostatic system of conductors and dielectrics, on the one hand, and a system that conducts a steady current, on the other. This analogy is the subject of the present section.

Let us consider a homogeneous, ohmic, conducting medium without internal sources of emf, under conditions of steady-state conduction. Since we are dealing specifically with the steady state, the local charge density $\rho(x, y, z)$ is at its equilibrium value, and $\partial\rho/\partial t = 0$ for each point in the medium. Hence, the equation of continuity (Eq. 7–9) reduces to

$$\operatorname{div} \mathbf{J} = 0, \quad \text{(steady currents)}. \tag{7–27}$$

Using Ohm's law in combination with (7–27), we obtain

$$\operatorname{div} g\mathbf{E} = 0,$$

which for a homogeneous medium reduces to

$$\operatorname{div} \mathbf{E} = 0.$$

But with no sources of emf, $\mathbf{E} = \mathbf{E}_s$ is derivable from a scalar potential:

$$\mathbf{E} = -\operatorname{grad} U.$$

Combination of the last two equations yields

$$\nabla^2 U = 0, \tag{7–28}$$

which is Laplace's equation.

We see, therefore, that a steady-state conduction problem may be solved in the same way as electrostatic problems. Laplace's equation is solved by one of the techniques discussed in Chapter 3, the appropriate solution being determined, as always, by the boundary conditions. Boundary conditions which are sufficient to solve the problem are those which specify either U or $\mathbf{J}$ at each point on the surface of the conducting medium. Specifying $\mathbf{J}$ at the surface is equivalent to specifying $\mathbf{E}$, since the two vectors are connected by Ohm's law. Once the appropriate solution to Laplace's equation has been found, $\mathbf{E}$ (and hence $\mathbf{J}$) may be determined at each point inside the medium from the gradient operation.

Under steady-state conduction the current which crosses an interfacial area between two conducting media may be computed in two ways: in terms of the current density in medium 1, or in terms of the current density in medium 2. Since the two procedures must yield the same result, the normal component of $\mathbf{J}$ must be continuous across the interface:

$$J_{1n} = J_{2n}, \tag{7–29a}$$

or

$$g_1 E_{1n} = g_2 E_{2n}. \tag{7–29b}$$

This equation replaces the analogous equation for the continuity of D_n across dielectric interfaces in electrostatic problems.

So long as there are no sources of emf in either medium,

$$\oint \mathbf{E} \cdot d\mathbf{l} = 0$$

for a closed path which links both media, and

$$E_{1t} = E_{2t} \tag{7–30}$$

by the derivation of Section 4–7. This equation is evidently the same for both types of problems (electrostatic and steady conduction).

An example of the ideas presented above is found in the "electrolytic tank" shown in Fig. 7–7. Here a number of metallic conductors which are connected to external sources of potential are placed in a liquid conducting medium of moderate conductivity (such as a salt solution). Since the conductivity of the salt solution is *much* smaller than that of a metal (see Table 7–1), the electric field in the metal (for the same current density) is *much* smaller than that in the solution. The ratio of fields is so small

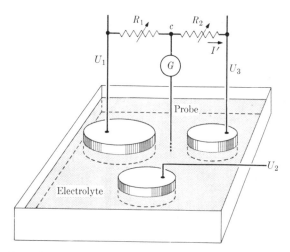

FIG. 7–7. Two-dimensional electrolytic tank. The three metallic conductors are maintained at potentials U_1, U_2, and U_3, where for convenience it is assumed that $U_1 > U_2 > U_3$. The symbol $\sim\!\!\wedge\!\!\wedge\!\!\wedge$ stands for a resistor whose resistance may be varied, and G is a galvanometer. The wires are taken to be of negligible resistance. If the resistors R_1 and R_2 are adjusted so that there is no current through G, then $U_{\mathrm{probe}} = U_c$, and the same current I' passes through both R_1 and R_2. In these circumstances $U_{\mathrm{probe}} = U_1 - I'R_1 = U_3 + I'R_2$, or $U_{\mathrm{probe}} = U_1 - (U_1 - U_3)R_1/(R_1 + R_2)$.

that $\mathbf{E}$ in the metal may be neglected, and each metallic conductor may be assumed to be an equipotential volume. A small conducting probe may be used, as shown in the figure, to explore the potential in the solution, and in this way a plot of the equipotential surfaces can be made. The advantage to this experimental approach is that it provides a solution to Laplace's equation which, in the case of complicated geometry, might be difficult or impossible to determine analytically. The solution found is not limited to the conduction problem but applies equally well to the equivalent electrostatic problem in which the same metallic conductors are surrounded by a dielectric medium (Fig. 7–8).

As a second example of the similarity between conduction and electrostatics, we consider two metallic conductors in a homogeneous, ohmic medium of moderate conductivity g. If the metallic conductors are maintained at the potentials U_1 and U_2, the current I between them is

$$I = \frac{U_1 - U_2}{R},$$

where R is the resistance of the medium. This current may be written in terms of the current density $\mathbf{J}$ in the medium:

$$I = \oint_S \mathbf{J} \cdot \mathbf{n} \, da,$$

where S is any closed surface which completely surrounds one of the conductors. But

$$\mathbf{J} = g\mathbf{E}.$$

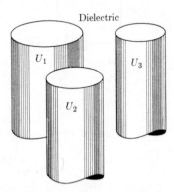

Dielectric

U_1 U_3

U_2

Fig. 7–8. The equivalent electrostatic problem to the conduction problem of the preceding figure. Since Fig. 7–7 depicted two-dimensional conduction, the electrostatic problem is also two-dimensional, and each conductor is an infinitely long cylinder.

Combining the last three equations, we obtain

$$\frac{U_1 - U_2}{R} = g \oint_S \mathbf{E} \cdot \mathbf{n}\, da. \tag{7-31}$$

If the identical electric field were produced by *electrostatic* charges on the two metallic conductors, then by Gauss' law

$$\oint_S \mathbf{E} \cdot \mathbf{n}\, da = \frac{1}{\epsilon} Q, \tag{7-32}$$

where Q is the charge on the metallic conductor surrounded by the surface S and ϵ is the permittivity of the medium. In these circumstances, the two conductors would form a capacitor:

$$Q = C(U_1 - U_2). \tag{7-33}$$

Insertion of (7–32) and (7–33) into (7–31) yields

$$RC = \frac{\epsilon}{g}, \tag{7-34}$$

which is a relation between the resistance of the medium and the capacitance of the equivalent electrostatic problem.

7–7 Approach to electrostatic equilibrium. In Chapter 2 it was shown that the excess charge on a conductor resides on its surface. This, of course, is the equilibrium situation. The approach to equilibrium was not studied, but it was stated that for good (metallic) conductors the attainment of equilibrium is extremely rapid. The poorer the conductor, the slower is the approach to electrostatic equilibrium; in fact, if the conductivity of the material is extremely low, it may take years or even longer for electrostatic equilibrium to obtain.

Consider a homogeneous, isotropic medium characterized by conductivity g and permittivity ϵ, which has a volume density of free charge $\rho_0(x, y, z)$. If this conducting system is suddenly isolated from sources of emf and time-dependent electric fields, it will tend toward the equilibrium situation where there is no excess charge in the interior of the system. According to the equation of continuity,

$$\frac{\partial \rho}{\partial t} + \operatorname{div} \mathbf{J} = 0 \tag{7-9}$$

which, with the aid of Ohm's law, becomes

$$\frac{\partial \rho}{\partial t} + g \operatorname{div} \mathbf{E} = 0. \tag{7-35}$$

But div $\mathbf{E}$ is related to the sources of the field; in fact, div $\mathbf{E} = \rho/\epsilon$, so that

$$\frac{\partial \rho}{\partial t} + \frac{g}{\epsilon} \rho = 0. \tag{7-36}$$

The solution to this partial differential equation is

$$\rho(x, y, z, t) = \rho_0(x, y, z)e^{-gt/\epsilon}, \tag{7-37}$$

and it is seen that the equilibrium state is approached exponentially.

From Eq. (7–37) it is evident that the quantity ϵ/g has the dimensions of time; it is called the time constant or relaxation time t_c of the medium:

$$t_c = \frac{\epsilon}{g} = \epsilon \eta. \tag{7-38}$$

The time constant is a measure of how fast the conducting medium approaches electrostatic equilibrium; precisely, it is the time required for the charge in a specified region to decrease to $1/e$ of its original value.

A material will reach its equilibrium charge distribution in a specific application when its time constant is much shorter than the characteristic time required to make the pertinent measurement. For some applications a time constant of less than 0.1 second is sufficient to ensure conductorlike behavior; since most permittivities fall into the range ϵ_0 to $10\epsilon_0$, this requires a material with resistivity less than 10^9 or 10^{10} ohm·m. For high-frequency applications a shorter time constant, and a correspondingly smaller resistivity, is required for true conductorlike behavior; in fact,

$$t_c \ll \frac{1}{f},$$

where f is the highest frequency involved in the experiment.

7–8 Kirchhoff's laws. Thus far we have discussed conduction primarily from the point of view of charge transport in a conducting medium, and have approached the problem in terms of the differential equations which must apply at each point. In these cases the important quantity to be determined is the current density, $\mathbf{J}$. But in many problems of practical interest the electric charge carriers are constrained to follow a high conduction path called a *circuit,* and then the quantities of interest are the *currents* in each part of the circuit. In this section we shall limit the discussion to circuits carrying steady currents, i.e., to *direct current circuits.*

A circuit may consist of several different branches, in fact, as a possible definition, a circuit is a network of conducting paths, each of which may contain seats of emf. The central problem of circuit analysis is: *given the resistance and emf of each circuit element, find the current in each of these*

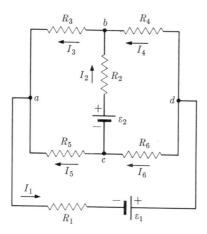

Fig. 7–9. A typical circuit requiring the application of Kirchhoff's laws. The symbol ——⊣⊢— is used to designate a seat of emf. In a typical circuit problem, the $\mathcal{E}$'s and R's are specified, the currents are to be found. Two of the six equations for the currents in the above circuit are $-I_1 + I_3 + I_5 = 0$ and $\mathcal{E}_1 = I_6R_6 + I_5R_5 + I_1R_1$.

elements. This problem can be solved in a systematic way by means of two rules known as Kirchhoff's laws.*

Before stating these laws, we define two terms. A *branch point* is a point of the circuit where three or more conductors are joined together, such as point a, b, c, or d in Fig. 7–9. A *loop* is any closed conducting path in the network. Kirchhoff's laws may now be stated:

I. *The algebraic sum of the currents flowing toward a branch point is zero;* i.e.,

$$\sum I_j = 0. \tag{I}$$

II. *The algebraic sum of the emf's in any loop of the network is equal to the algebraic sum of the IR products in the same loop,* i.e.,

$$\sum \mathcal{E}_j = \sum I_j R_j. \tag{II}$$

The first law is just a formal statement of the fact that charge does not accumulate at a branch point in the circuit as a result of the steady current. The second law follows directly from Eq. (7–25), as may readily be seen. If (7–25) is applied to each segment of the loop and the result summed, then the left side of the equation sums to zero and the right side to

$$\sum \mathcal{E}_j - \sum I_j R_j.$$

---

* Named for Gustav Robert Kirchhoff (1824–1887).

Before applying Kirchhoff's laws to a specific problem, it is necessary to assume directions for the currents in each of the branches. These directions should be indicated in the circuit diagram. The formulation of Eqs. (I) and (II) is then carried out on the basis of the assumed directions. If the numerical solution of these equations yields a negative value for a particular current, the correct direction of this current is opposite to that assumed. In the problem illustrated in Fig. 7–9, there are six unknown currents; these are designated by the symbols I_1, I_2, I_3, I_4, I_5, and I_6, each having been given an assumed direction.

Kirchhoff's Law I may be applied at each branch point of the circuit, but the equations so obtained are not all independent. The general rule is that if there are n branch points, only $n - 1$ of these will produce independent equations. In the problem shown in Fig. 7–9, there are six unknown currents; the solution requires three branch-point equations and three loop equations.

The summations in (I) and (II) are algebraic sums. In (I) the current is considered positive if its assumed direction points toward the branch point in question, or is taken with the negative sign if its assumed direction points away from the junction. In applying the loop equations, some direction (either clockwise or counterclockwise) must be taken as the traversal direction. An emf is taken with the positive sign if the emf (by itself) would produce a positive current in the traversal direction; an IR term is taken with the positive sign if the current through the resistor in question is in the direction of traversal of the loop.

7–9 Metallic conduction. It is evident from Table 7–1 that the group of materials with the highest electrical conductivity is that of the metals. These materials have high conductivity both because they contain a large density of charge carriers, of the order of one for each atom of the metal, and because the drift velocity per unit electric field is high.

In metals we deal with only one type of charge carrier, the electron. Hence the conduction equations are somewhat simpler in this case:

$$\mathbf{J} = -Ne\mathbf{v}, \tag{7–39}$$

$$g = Ne(v/E) = Ne^2\tau/2m, \tag{7–40}$$

where e is the absolute value of the electronic charge. The drift velocity of the electron per unit electric field (v/E) is called the *mobility* of the electron. A large mobility implies a long collision time τ or, equivalently, a long mean free path. In order to get some feeling for the mean free path of electrons in a metal, we have to appeal to the dynamics of electron collisions. We know that the conductor is electrostatically neutral only on the average, that there are large variations in potential over distances of the order of one angstrom unit, and that a charged particle, such as an electron, ought to collide or be scattered by variations in potential. But we know also that the wave nature of the electron plays an important role in its motion on an atomic scale.

A complete solution to the electron collision problem using wave-mechanical concepts is beyond the scope of this book; we merely state the result. *In a perfect crystal with a three-dimensional periodic potential, an electron wave makes no collision; its collision time τ is infinite.* Thus the finite conductivity of metals arises from imperfections in the perfectly periodic structure. These imperfections are of two types: (1) impurities and geometric imperfections (such as grain boundaries in polycrystalline material), and (2) thermally-induced imperfections arising from the thermal motion of the atoms in the structure. Both types contribute independently to the resistivity, so that

$$\eta = \eta_1 + \eta_2(T), \tag{7–41}$$

where T is the absolute temperature.

In very pure metals the dominant contribution to the resistivity at ordinary temperatures is the scattering of electron waves by thermally displaced atoms. Thus $\eta \approx \eta_2(T)$. The scattering cross section of a displaced atom is proportional to the square of its vibration amplitude (x^2), in other words, to its maximum potential energy. Assuming elastic restoring forces operating on the displaced atoms,

$$(\text{Potential energy})_{max} = (\text{Kinetic energy})_{max} \propto kT,$$

so that

$$\eta \approx \eta_2 \propto (\tau_2)^{-1} \propto x^2 \propto T, \tag{7–42}$$

or, in words, the resistivity of a pure metal is proportional to the absolute temperature. The temperature coefficient of resistance, $(1/\eta)\,d\eta/dT$, for a very pure metal is, therefore,

$$\alpha = \frac{1}{\eta}\frac{d\eta}{dT} \approx \frac{1}{T}, \tag{7–43}$$

in approximate agreement with the metal entries of Table 7–1. Strictly speaking, the preceding argument is valid only for temperatures above the Debye temperature of the metal (the temperature above which all the atomic vibration modes are excited). At temperatures somewhat below the Debye temperature, η drops below the linear relationship predicted by (7–42). At very low temperatures the contribution from η_1 cannot be neglected.

The addition of small amounts of a soluble impurity always increases resistivity. An alloy, which may be regarded as an impure metal, always

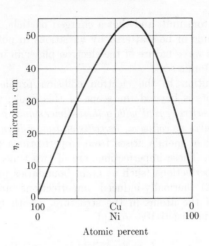

FIG. 7–10. Resistivity of copper-nickel alloys as a function of composition at 20°C.

has a higher resistivity than that of the lower resistivity parent metal (Fig. 7–10). The temperature coefficient α of an alloy is obviously lower than that of a pure metal just because its resistivity is higher, but certain alloys which have extremely small temperature coefficients have been developed.

PROBLEMS

7-1. (a) A copper specimen carries a current density of 1000 amp/m². On the assumption that each copper atom contributes one conduction electron, calculate the electronic drift velocity corresponding to this current density. (Avogadro's number: $N_0 = 6.02 \times 10^{23}$ atoms/mole; atomic weight of copper: 63.5; density of copper: 8.92 gm/cm³.) (b) Use the observed conductivity to calculate the average collision time for an electron in copper.

7-2. A system of charges and currents is completely contained *inside* the fixed volume V. The dipole moment of the charge-current distribution (see Section 2-9) is defined by

$$\mathbf{p} = \int_V \mathbf{r}\rho \, dv,$$

where $\mathbf{r}$ is the position vector from a fixed origin. Prove that

$$\int_V \mathbf{J} \, dv = \frac{d}{dt} \mathbf{p}.$$

[*Hint:* First prove the identity

$$\int_V \mathbf{J} \, dv = \oint_S \mathbf{r}\mathbf{J} \cdot \mathbf{n} \, da - \int_V \mathbf{r} \operatorname{div} \mathbf{J} \, dv,$$

and note that $\mathbf{J}$ vanishes on the surface S.]

7-3. Two infinite, plane, parallel plates of metal are separated by the distance d. The space between the plates is filled with two conducting media, the interface between the media being a plane which is parallel to the metal plates. The first medium (conductivity g_1, permittivity ϵ_1) is of thickness a, and the second (conductivity g_2, permittivity ϵ_2) is of thickness $d - a$. The metal plates are maintained at potentials U_1 and U_2, respectively. In the steady state, what is the potential of the interface separating the two media, and what is the surface density of free charge on this interface?

7-4. Given three resistors of 1 ohm, 2 ohms, and 3 ohms. Find eight different resistance combinations which can be made with these resistors.

7-5. A 0.4-watt lamp bulb is designed for operation with 2 volts across its terminals. A resistance R is placed in parallel with the bulb, and the combination is put in series with a 3-ohm resistor and a 3-volt battery (internal resistance, $\frac{1}{3}$ ohm). What should the value of R be if the lamp is to operate at design voltage?

*7-6. A resistance line, total resistance nR, is connected between the potential U_0 and ground (ground is reference potential). The line is supported by $n - 1$ poles at equal resistance intervals such that the line resistance between poles is R. The leakage resistance to ground at each pole is βR. If U_m is the line potential at the mth pole, show that

$$U_{m+1} - (2 + \beta^{-1})U_m + U_{m-1} = 0.$$

7-7. Two long cylindrical shells of metal (radii r_1 and r_2, with $r_2 > r_1$) are arranged coaxially. The plates are maintained at the potential difference

ΔU. (a) The region between the shells is filled with a medium of conductivity g. Use Ohm's law, $\mathbf{J} = g\mathbf{E}$, to calculate the electric current between unit lengths of the shells. (b) If the region between the shells is filled with a nonconducting medium of permittivity ϵ, the capacitance of the system may be computed from the definition $C = Q/\Delta U$. Show explicitly for this geometry that the product of resistance per unit length and capacitance per unit length = ϵ/g.

7–8. The leakage resistance of a rubber cable insulation is measured in the following way: a length l of the insulated cable is immersed in a salt-water solution, a potential difference is applied between the cable conductor and the solution, and the resulting cable current is measured. In a particular case 3 m of cable is immersed in the solution; with 200 volts between cable conductor and solution the current measured is 2×10^{-9} amp. The insulation thickness is equal to the radius of the central conductor. What is the electrical resistivity of the insulation?

7–9. A long copper wire of radius a is stretched parallel to and at distance h from an infinite copper plate. The region above the plate and surrounding the wire is filled with a medium of conductivity g. Show that the electrical resistance between the two copper electrodes, per unit length of the wire, is given by

$$R = \frac{1}{2\pi g} \cosh^{-1} \frac{h}{a}.$$

7–10. A homogeneous, isotropic sphere of conductivity g is subjected to a potential $U_0 \cos \theta$ at all points on its surface. Here θ is the usual polar angle measured with respect to an axis through the center of the sphere. Determine the current density $\mathbf{J}$ at all points inside the sphere.

7–11. Two cylindrical copper electrodes of radius a are oriented normal to a silicon disk of thickness s, and are separated axially by the distance b. The electrodes are embedded in the disk to the depth s; in other words, they go completely through the disk. The lateral dimensions of the disk are large compared with b, and may be considered infinite. Taking the conductivity of silicon to be g, find the current between the electrodes when their potential difference is ΔU.

*7–12. A square copper plate of length $20a$, thickness s, and conductivity g is subjected to a potential difference: two opposite edges of the plate are maintained at the potentials U_0 and $-U_0$, respectively. (a) What is the electrical resistance of the plate? (b) A small hole of radius a is drilled through the plate at its center. Determine the *approximate* fractional change in resistance. [*Hint:* Find the potential distribution in the plate with the aid of the cosine θ cylindrical harmonics. Unfortunately, this distribution is not quite correct, because the two opposite edges of the square are not exact equipotentials. An approximate solution is obtained by taking the average potential of the two edges equal to $\pm U_0$.]

7–13. Two seats of emf $\mathcal{E}_1$ and $\mathcal{E}_2$, with internal resistances R_1 and R_2 respectively, are connected in parallel with each other and with the load resistance R. (a) Find the current through the load. (b) If the load resistance is varied and other quantities kept fixed, what should R be in order that it dissipate maximum power?

7-14. A group of n identical cells of emf $\mathcal{E}$ and internal resistance R_i are used to supply current to a load resistor R. Show that if the n cells are connected in series with each other and with R, then $I = n\mathcal{E}/(R + nR_i)$, whereas if the cells are connected in parallel and the combination put in series with R, then $I = \mathcal{E}/(R + R_i/n)$.

7-15. Six identical resistors (R) are joined to form a hexagon. Six more resistors (all again of the same resistance R) are connected between the six vertices and the center of the hexagon. (a) What is the equivalent resistance between opposite vertices? (b) between adjacent vertices?

7-16. Six resistors form the sides of a tetrahedron. Five of the resistors are identical (R), the sixth is R_1. A potential difference is applied across one of the resistors adjoining R_1. Show that the Joule heat production in R_1 is maximum when $R_1 = (3/5)R$.

7-17. A Wheatstone-bridge circuit is obtained from the circuit of Fig. 7-9 by making $\mathcal{E}_2 = 0$, and substituting a galvanometer R_g for R_2. We shall also take $R_1 = 0$. The balance condition of the bridge (no current through the galvanometer) is obtained when $R_3 R_6 = R_4 R_5$. Thus an unknown resistance, for example R_6, may be determined in terms of known resistances: $R_6 = R_4 R_5/R_3$ at balance. (a) Find the current through the galvanometer when the bridge is off balance. (b) Assume that the bridge is to be balanced by varying R_4. The sensitivity of the bridge is defined by $S = CR_4(\partial I_2/\partial R_4)_0$, where C is the galvanometer deflection per unit current, and the subscript zero means that the derivative is to be evaluated at balance. Show that

$$S = \frac{C\mathcal{E}_1}{R_3 + R_4 + R_5 + R_6 + R_g(1 + R_5/R_6)(1 + R_4/R_3)}.$$

*7-18. The Wheatstone bridge of the preceding problem is nearly balanced. Let $R_5/R_3 = \alpha$, and $R_6/R_4 = \alpha(1 - \epsilon)$, where $\epsilon \ll 1$. If the resistance R_g is negligible, show that $I_2/I_1 = \alpha\epsilon/(\alpha + 1)^2$.

*7-19. A resistance of approximately 10 ohms is to be measured in the Wheatstone-bridge circuit of Problem 7-17. A large selection of standard resistances are available. The maximum power allowed in the bridge is 5 watts. If $R_g = 100$ ohms, and the galvanometer will just detect a signal of 4×10^{-9} amp, what is the highest precision one can obtain in measuring the unknown resistor? Assume that the standard resistors are exact, and do not limit the accuracy.

*7-20. A linear, conducting medium is connected at n points to electrodes with the fixed potentials: $U_1, U_2, \ldots, U_n$. Show that the Joule heat production in the medium is given by $\sum_{i=1}^{n} U_i I_i$, where I_i is the current *entering* the medium through electrode i.

CHAPTER 8

THE MAGNETIC FIELD OF STEADY CURRENTS

The second kind of field which enters into the study of electricity and magnetism is, of course, the magnetic field. Such fields or, more properly, the effects of such fields have been known since ancient times, when the effects of the naturally occurring permanent magnet magnetite (Fe_3O_4) were first observed. The discovery of the north- and south-seeking properties of this material had a profound influence on early navigation and exploration. Except for this application, however, magnetism was a little used and still less understood phenomenon until the early nineteenth century, when Oersted discovered that an electric current produced a magnetic field. This work, together with the later work of Gauss, Henry, Faraday and others, has brought the magnetic field into prominence as a partner to the electric field. The theoretical work of Maxwell and others (see Chapters 15, 16, and 17) has shown that this partnership is real, and that the electric and magnetic fields are inextricably intertwined. The efforts of practical men have resulted in the development of the motors, transformers, etc., which involve magnetic phenomena and play such an important role in our everyday life. In this chapter the basic definitions of magnetism will be given, the production of magnetic fields by steady currents will be studied, and some important groundwork for future work will be laid.

8–1 The definition of magnetic induction. In Chapter 2 an electric field was defined as the ratio of the force on a test charge to the value of the test charge, i.e.,

$$\mathbf{E} = \lim_{q \to 0} \left(\frac{\mathbf{F}}{q} \right).$$ (2–6)

Implicit in this definition is the absence of any nonelectrical force and the assumption that the charge is at rest. For the purpose of defining the magnetic induction it is convenient to define $\mathbf{F}_m$, the magnetic force (frequently called the Lorentz force), as that part of the force exerted on a moving charge which is neither electrostatic nor mechanical. The magnetic induction, $\mathbf{B}$, is then defined as the vector which satisfies

$$\mathbf{F}_m = q\mathbf{v} \times \mathbf{B}$$ (8–1)

for all velocities. It must be noted that some sort of limiting process should be included in Eq. (8–1) to ensure that the test charge does not affect the sources of $\mathbf{B}$. Also important is the fact that a single measurement is not sufficient to determine $\mathbf{B}$. Equation (1–13) provides the basis for properly inverting Eq. (8–1). If two measurements of $\mathbf{F}_m$ are made for two mutually perpendicular velocities $\mathbf{v}_1$ and $\mathbf{v}_2$, then Eq. (1–13) yields

$$\mathbf{B} = \frac{1}{q} \frac{\mathbf{F}_1 \times \mathbf{v}_1}{v_1^2} + k_1 \mathbf{v}_1, \tag{8-2}$$

$$\mathbf{B} = \frac{1}{q} \frac{\mathbf{F}_2 \times \mathbf{v}_2}{v_2^2} + k_2 \mathbf{v}_2 \tag{8-3}$$

Taking the scalar product of each of these with $\mathbf{v}_1$ and remembering that $\mathbf{v}_1$ and $\mathbf{v}_2$ are perpendicular, we obtain

$$k_1 v_1^2 = \frac{1}{q} \frac{\mathbf{F}_2 \times \mathbf{v}_2 \cdot \mathbf{v}_1}{v_2^2}. \tag{8-4}$$

Using this in Eq. (8–2) results in

$$\mathbf{B} = \frac{1}{q} \frac{\mathbf{F}_1 \times \mathbf{v}_1}{v_1^2} + \frac{1}{q} \left(\frac{\mathbf{F}_2 \times \mathbf{v}_2 \cdot \mathbf{v}_1}{v_1^2 v_2^2} \right) \mathbf{v}_1, \tag{8-5}$$

which explicitly demonstrates that two distinct measurements are sufficient.

Perfectly good definitions of the magnetic induction can be constructed by using the force on a current element or the torque on a current-carrying loop; however, Eq. (8–1) seems preferable, since it is so closely parallel to Eq. (2–6), which defines the electric field. The unit for magnetic induction in the mks system, according to Eq. (8–1), is the newton·second/coulomb·meter or newton/ampere·meter. It is customary to express this unit as the weber/meter^2; the weber is the mks unit of magnetic flux which will be defined in Section 8–9.

8-2 Forces on current-carrying conductors. From the definition of $\mathbf{B}$, an expression for the force on an element $d\mathbf{l}$ of a current-carrying conductor can be found. If $d\mathbf{l}$ is an element of conductor with its sense taken in the direction of the current I which it carries, then $d\mathbf{l}$ is parallel to the velocity $\mathbf{v}$ of the charge carriers in the conductor. If there are N charge carriers per unit volume in the conductor, the force on the element $d\mathbf{l}$ is

$$d\mathbf{F} = NA|d\mathbf{l}|q\mathbf{v} \times \mathbf{B}, \tag{8-6}$$

where A is the cross-sectional area of the conductor and q is the charge per charge carrier. If several kinds of charge carriers are involved, then a summation must be included in Eq. (8–6); however, the final result, Eq. (8–8), is unchanged. Since $\mathbf{v}$ and $d\mathbf{l}$ are parallel, an alternative form of Eq. (8–6) is

$$d\mathbf{F} = Nq|\mathbf{v}|A \, d\mathbf{l} \times \mathbf{B}; \tag{8-7}$$

however, $Nq|\mathbf{v}|A$ is just the current for a single species of carrier. Therefore the expression

$$d\mathbf{F} = I \, d\mathbf{l} \times \mathbf{B} \qquad (8\text{–}8)$$

is written for the force on an infinitesimal element of a charge-carrying conductor.

Equation (8–8) can be integrated to give the force on a complete (or closed) circuit. If the circuit in question is represented by the contour C, then

$$\mathbf{F} = \oint_C I \, d\mathbf{l} \times \mathbf{B}. \qquad (8\text{–}9)$$

So long as $\mathbf{B}$ depends on position, the only simplification that can be made in Eq. (8–9) is to factor I from under the integral sign. If, however, $\mathbf{B}$ is uniform, i.e., independent of position, then it too can be removed from under the integral, to give

$$\mathbf{F} = I\left\{\oint_C d\mathbf{l}\right\} \times \mathbf{B}.$$

The remaining integral is easy to evaluate. Since it is the sum of infinitesimal vectors forming a complete circuit, it must be zero. Thus

$$\mathbf{F} = \oint_C I \, d\mathbf{l} \times \mathbf{B} = 0 \qquad (\mathbf{B} \text{ uniform}). \qquad (8\text{–}10)$$

Another interesting quantity is the torque on a complete circuit. Since torque is moment of force, the infinitesimal torque $d\boldsymbol{\tau}$ is given by

$$d\boldsymbol{\tau} = \mathbf{r} \times d\mathbf{F} = I\mathbf{r} \times (d\mathbf{l} \times \mathbf{B}). \qquad (8\text{–}11)$$

The torque on a complete circuit is

$$\boldsymbol{\tau} = I \oint_C \mathbf{r} \times (d\mathbf{l} \times \mathbf{B}). \qquad (8\text{–}12)$$

Once again, unless $\mathbf{B}$ is uniform no further simplification can be made; however, if it is uniform a straightforward expansion is accomplished by writing

$$d\mathbf{l} \times \mathbf{B} = \mathbf{i}(dy B_z - dz B_y) + \mathbf{j}(dz B_x - dx B_z) + \mathbf{k}(dx B_y - dy B_x). \qquad (8\text{–}13)$$

From these components the components of $\mathbf{r} \times (d\mathbf{l} \times \mathbf{B})$ are readily found to be

$$[\mathbf{r} \times (d\mathbf{l} \times \mathbf{B})]_x = y \, dx B_y - y \, dy B_x - z \, dz B_x + z \, dx B_z,$$

$$[\mathbf{r} \times (d\mathbf{l} \times \mathbf{B})]_y = z \, dy B_z - z \, dz B_y - x \, dx B_y + x \, dy B_x, \qquad (8\text{–}14)$$

$$[\mathbf{r} \times (d\mathbf{l} \times \mathbf{B})]_z = x \, dz B_x - x \, dx B_z - y \, dy B_z + y \, dz B_y.$$

Since $\mathbf{B}$ is assumed to be independent of $\mathbf{r}$ (uniform field) the components of $\mathbf{B}$ may be factored out of the integrals appearing in the expansion of Eq. (8–12). The spatial integrations which must be performed are of two general forms:

$$\oint \xi \, d\xi \tag{8–15a}$$

and

$$\oint \xi \, d\eta, \tag{8–15b}$$

where ξ represents any coordinate and η represents any coordinate different from ξ. The first of these is trivial because it represents the integral from some lower limit ξ_1 to some upper limit ξ_2 of $\xi \, d\xi$, plus the integral from ξ_2 to ξ_1 of $\xi \, d\xi$. Since interchanging the limits introduces a minus sign, the result is zero, which eliminates six terms from Eq. (8–14). Integrals of the form (8–15b) involve only two variables, ξ, η, hence it makes no difference whether the integral is taken around the actual curve C or around its projection on the ξ, η-plane, as shown in Fig. 8–1. By using the projection on the ξ, η-plane it is easy to see what Eq. (8–15b) represents. In Fig. 8–2 the ξ, η-plane is shown along with the infinitesimal area $\xi \, d\eta$. The integral can be written

$$\oint \xi \, d\eta = \int_a^b \xi_1(\eta) \, d\eta + \int_b^a \xi_2(\eta) \, d\eta. \tag{8–16}$$

This, of course, gives just the area enclosed by the projected curve, and in the figure is positive. If ξ and η appear in cyclic order for a right-hand coordinate system, then the direction in which the contour is circled would give a normal in the positive ζ-direction. Thus we may write

$$\oint \xi \, d\eta = A_\zeta, \tag{8–17}$$

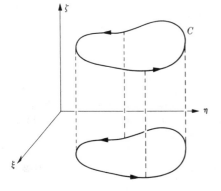

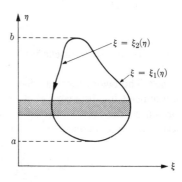

FIG. 8–1. Projection of the curve C on the ξ, η-plane.

FIG. 8–2. Evaluation of the integral $\int \xi \, d\eta$.

with ξ, η, ζ a cyclic permutation of x, y, z. Using this result to evaluate the integrals gives

$$\tau_x = I\oint_C [\mathbf{r} \times (d\mathbf{l} \times \mathbf{B})]_x = I(A_y B_z - A_z B_y), \qquad (8\text{-}18)$$

with similar expressions for the y and z components. The three expressions are neatly summarized in the expression

$$\boldsymbol{\tau} = I\mathbf{A} \times \mathbf{B}, \qquad (8\text{-}19)$$

where $\mathbf{A}$ is the vector whose components are the areas enclosed by projections of the curve C on the yz-, zx-, and xy-planes.* The quantity $I\mathbf{A}$ appears very frequently in magnetic theory, and is referred to as the *magnetic moment* of the circuit. The symbol $\mathbf{m}$ will be used for magnetic moment:

$$\mathbf{m} = I\mathbf{A}, \qquad (8\text{-}20)$$

with $\mathbf{A}$ defined as above.

It is easy to show, by the technique used above, that the integral of $\mathbf{r} \times d\mathbf{l}$ around a closed path gives twice the area enclosed by the curve. Thus

$$\tfrac{1}{2}\oint_C \mathbf{r} \times d\mathbf{l} = \mathbf{A}. \qquad (8\text{-}21)$$

This can be used to obtain

$$\mathbf{m} = \tfrac{1}{2}I\oint_C \mathbf{r} \times d\mathbf{l} \qquad (8\text{-}22)$$

as an alternative expression for the magnetic moment. If, instead of being confined to wires, the current exists in a medium, then the identification

$$I\,d\mathbf{l} \to \mathbf{J}\,dv \qquad (8\text{-}23)$$

is appropriate, as has been shown earlier. We then write

$$d\mathbf{m} = \tfrac{1}{2}\mathbf{r} \times \mathbf{J}\,dv, \qquad (8\text{-}24)$$

which is useful in discussing the magnetic properties of matter.

8–3 The law of Biot and Savart. In 1820, just a few weeks after Oersted announced his discovery that currents produce magnetic effects, Ampere presented the results of a series of experiments which may be generalized and expressed in modern mathematical language as

$$\mathbf{F}_2 = \frac{\mu_0}{4\pi} I_1 I_2 \oint_1 \oint_2 \frac{d\mathbf{l}_2 \times [d\mathbf{l}_1 \times (\mathbf{r}_2 - \mathbf{r}_1)]}{|\mathbf{r}_2 - \mathbf{r}_1|^3}. \qquad (8\text{-}25)$$

---

* Note that no restriction to plane curves has been imposed on C and that this definition of $\mathbf{A}$ makes any such restriction unnecessary.

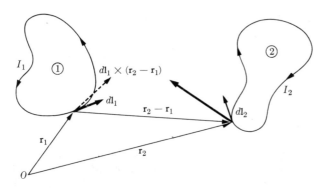

FIG. 8–3. Magnetic interaction of two current circuits.

This rather formidable expression can be understood with reference to Fig. 8–3. The force $\mathbf{F}_2$ is the force exerted on circuit 2 due to the influence of circuit 1, the dl's and $\mathbf{r}$'s are explained by the figure. The number $\mu_0/4\pi$ which appears in Eq. (8–25) plays the same role here as $1/4\pi\epsilon_0$ played in electrostatics, i.e., it is the constant which is required to make an experimental law compatible with a set of units. By definition,

$$\frac{\mu_0}{4\pi} = 10^{-7} \text{ n/amp}^2$$

exactly, and Eq. (8–25) serves as the primary definition of the ampere. Equation (8–25) appears, superficially, to violate Newton's third law because of the lack of symmetry; however, by using some of the theorems of vector analysis it can be shown that it is actually symmetric, that is, $\mathbf{F}_2 = -\mathbf{F}_1$.

From Eq. (8–9) it is apparent that Eq. (8–25) implies

$$\mathbf{B}(\mathbf{r}_2) = \frac{\mu_0}{4\pi} I_1 \oint_1 \frac{dl_1 \times (\mathbf{r}_2 - \mathbf{r}_1)}{|\mathbf{r}_2 - \mathbf{r}_1|^3}. \tag{8–26}$$

This equation is a generalization of the Biot and Savart law, which name will be used both for Eq. (8–26) and the differential form

$$d\mathbf{B}(\mathbf{r}_2) = \frac{\mu_0}{4\pi} \frac{I_1 \, dl_1 \times (\mathbf{r}_2 - \mathbf{r}_1)}{|\mathbf{r}_2 - \mathbf{r}_1|^3}. \tag{8–27}$$

(In passing, we mention that there has been some controversy over the naming of various laws. We do not wish to enter into this controversy, but refer the interested reader to Whittaker's excellent history.*) As

---

* E. T. Whittaker, *History of the Theories of Aether and Electricity*, Vol. I, Philosophical Library, New York, 1951.

a last point, Eqs. (8–26) and (8–27) take the forms

$$\mathbf{B}(\mathbf{r}_2) = \frac{\mu_0}{4\pi} \int_V \frac{\mathbf{J}(\mathbf{r}_1) \times (\mathbf{r}_2 - \mathbf{r}_1)}{|\mathbf{r}_2 - \mathbf{r}_1|^3} \, dv_1 \tag{8–28}$$

and

$$d\mathbf{B}(\mathbf{r}_2) = \frac{\mu_0}{4\pi} \frac{\mathbf{J}(\mathbf{r}_1) \times (\mathbf{r}_2 - \mathbf{r}_1)}{|\mathbf{r}_2 - \mathbf{r}_1|^3} \, dv_1 \tag{8–29}$$

for a continuous distribution of current described by the current density $\mathbf{J}(\mathbf{r})$.

It is an experimental observation that all magnetic induction fields can be described in terms of a current distribution. That is, $\mathbf{B}$ always has the form of Eq. (8–28), with some $\mathbf{J}(\mathbf{r}_1)$. This implies that there are no isolated magnetic poles and that

$$\operatorname{div} \mathbf{B} = 0. \tag{8–30}$$

Equation (8–30) is true for any $\mathbf{B}$ of the form (8–28) or (8–26), as can be verified mathematically; however, for the purpose of this text it is just as satisfactory to think of Eq. (8–30) as an experimental law. The mathematical derivation is given in Appendix III.

8–4 Elementary applications of the Biot and Savart law. The range of problems to which Eq. (8–28) (or Eq. 8–26) can be applied is limited primarily by the difficulty experienced in performing the integrations. Some of the tractable situations are considered in this section; in later sections other techniques for obtaining $\mathbf{B}$ will be considered.

As a first example, the magnetic field due to a long straight wire will be considered. The wire is imagined to lie along the x-axis from minus infinity to plus infinity and to carry a current I. The field will be computed at a typical point $\mathbf{r}_2$ on the y-axis. The geometry is best explained by Fig. 8–4. The magnetic induction is just

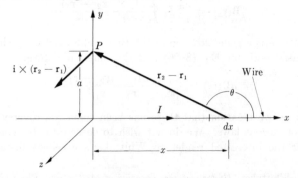

FIG. 8–4. Magnetic field at point P due to a long straight wire.

$$\mathbf{B}(\mathbf{r}_2) = \frac{\mu_0}{4\pi} I \int_{-\infty}^{\infty} \frac{dx\ \mathbf{i} \times (\mathbf{r}_2 - \mathbf{r}_1)}{|\mathbf{r}_2 - \mathbf{r}_1|^3}. \tag{8–31}$$

Since $\mathbf{r}_2 - \mathbf{r}_1$ lies in the xy-plane,

$$\mathbf{i} \times (\mathbf{r}_2 - \mathbf{r}_1) = |\mathbf{r}_2 - \mathbf{r}_1| \sin \theta\ \mathbf{k}. \tag{8–32}$$

Furthermore,

$$\frac{a}{x} = \tan (\pi - \theta) = -\tan \theta \tag{8–33}$$

and

$$|\mathbf{r}_2 - \mathbf{r}_1| = a \csc (\pi - \theta) = a \csc \theta. \tag{8–34}$$

Using these relationships to convert Eq. (8–31) to an integral on θ from 0 to π gives

$$\mathbf{B}(\mathbf{r}_2) = \frac{\mu_0}{4\pi} I\mathbf{k}\frac{1}{a} \int_0^{\pi} \sin \theta\ d\theta = \frac{\mu_0 I}{4\pi a} \mathbf{k}(-\cos \theta)\Big|_0^{\pi} = \frac{\mu_0 I}{2\pi a} \mathbf{k}. \tag{8–35}$$

To use this result more generally, it is only necessary to note that the problem exhibits an obvious symmetry about the x-axis. Thus we conclude that the lines of $\mathbf{B}$ are everywhere circles, with the conductor as center. This is in complete agreement with the elementary result which gives the direction of $\mathbf{B}$ by a right-hand rule.

As a second simple circuit, a circular turn will be considered. The magnetic field produced by such a circuit at an arbitrary point is very difficult to compute; however, if only points on the axis of symmetry are considered, the expression for $\mathbf{B}$ is relatively simple. In this example a complete vector treatment will be used to demonstrate the technique. Figure 8–5 illustrates the geometry and the coordinates to be used. The

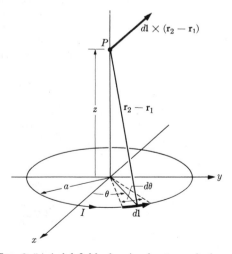

Fig. 8–5. Axial field of a circular turn of wire.

field is to be calculated at point $\mathbf{r}_2$ on the z-axis; the circular turn lies in the xy-plane. The magnetic induction is given by Eq. (8–26) in which, from Fig. 8–5, the following expressions are to be used:

$$d\mathbf{l} = a\,d\theta(-\mathbf{i}\sin\theta + \mathbf{j}\cos\theta),$$

$$\mathbf{r}_2 - \mathbf{r}_1 = -\mathbf{i}a\cos\theta - \mathbf{j}a\sin\theta + \mathbf{k}z, \qquad (8\text{–}36)$$

$$|\mathbf{r}_2 - \mathbf{r}_1| = (a^2 + z^2)^{1/2}.$$

Substituting these into Eq. (8–26) yields

$$\mathbf{B}(z) = \frac{\mu_0 I}{4\pi}\int_0^{2\pi}\frac{(\mathbf{i}za\cos\theta + \mathbf{j}za\sin\theta + \mathbf{k}a^2)}{(z^2 + a^2)^{3/2}}\,d\theta. \qquad (8\text{–}37)$$

The first two terms integrate to zero, leaving

$$\mathbf{B}(z) = \frac{\mu_0 I}{2}\frac{a^2}{(z^2 + a^2)^{3/2}}\mathbf{k}, \qquad (8\text{–}38)$$

which is, of course, entirely along the z-axis.

A frequently used current configuration is the Helmholtz coil, which consists of two circular coils of the same radius, with a common axis, separated by a distance chosen to make the second derivative of $\mathbf{B}$ vanish at a point on the axis halfway between the coils. Figure 8–6 shows such a configuration. The magnetic induction at point P is

$$B_z(z) = \frac{N\mu_0 Ia^2}{2}\left\{\frac{1}{(z^2 + a^2)^{3/2}} + \frac{1}{[(2b - z)^2 + a^2]^{3/2}}\right\}, \qquad (8\text{–}39)$$

which is obtained by applying Eq. (8–38) to each of the two coils. The factor N is included to handle the situation where each coil contains N turns. The first derivative of B_z with respect to z is

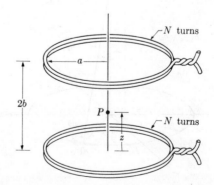

Fig. 8–6. Axial field of a Helmholtz coil.

$$\frac{dB_z}{dz} = \frac{\mu_0 N I a^2}{2} \left\{ -\frac{3}{2} \frac{2z}{(z^2 + a^2)^{5/2}} - \frac{3}{2} \frac{2(z - 2b)}{[(2b - z)^2 + a^2]^{5/2}} \right\}. \quad (8\text{-}40)$$

At $z = b$ this derivative vanishes. The second derivative with respect to z is

$$\frac{d^2 B_z}{dz^2} = -\frac{3\mu_0 N I a^2}{2} \left\{ \frac{1}{(z^2 + a^2)^{5/2}} - \frac{5}{2} \frac{2z^2}{(z^2 + a^2)^{7/2}} \right.$$

$$\left. + \frac{1}{[(2b - z)^2 + a^2]^{5/2}} - \frac{5}{2} \frac{2(z - 2b)^2}{[(2b - z)^2 + a^2]^{7/2}} \right\}.$$

At $z = b$ this reduces to

$$\frac{d^2 B_z}{dz^2}\bigg|_{z=b} = -\frac{3\mu_0 N I a^2}{2} \left\{ \frac{b^2 + a^2 - 5b^2 + b^2 + a^2 - 5b^2}{(b^2 + a^2)^{7/2}} \right\}, \quad (8\text{-}41)$$

which vanishes if $a^2 - 4b^2 = 0$. Thus the appropriate choice for b is

$$2b = a, \quad (8\text{-}42)$$

that is, the coil separation should equal the radius. With this separation, the magnetic induction at the midpoint is

$$B_z = \frac{\mu_0 N I}{a} \frac{8}{5^{3/2}}. \quad (8\text{-}43)$$

Helmholtz coils play an important role in scientific research, where they are frequently used to produce a relatively uniform magnetic field over a small region of space. Let us consider the magnetic field at a point on the axis near the midpoint between the coils. The field $B_z(z)$ can be developed in a Taylor's series about the point $z = \frac{1}{2}a$:

$$B_z(z) = B_z(\tfrac{1}{2}a) + (z - \tfrac{1}{2}a) \frac{\partial B_z}{\partial z}\bigg|_{z=\frac{1}{2}a} + \cdots$$

Since the first three derivatives vanish,

$$B_z(z) = B_z(\tfrac{1}{2}a) + \frac{1}{24}(z - \tfrac{1}{2}a)^4 \frac{\partial^4 B_z}{\partial z^4}\bigg|_{z=\frac{1}{2}a} + \cdots$$

If the fourth derivative is evaluated explicitly, $B_z(z)$ can be written as

$$B_z(z) = B_z(a/2) \left\{ 1 - \frac{144}{125} \left(\frac{z - a/2}{a} \right)^4 \right\}. \quad (8\text{-}44)$$

Thus for the region where $|z - a/2|$ is less than $a/10$, $B_z(z)$ deviates from $B_z(a/2)$ by less than one and a half parts in ten thousand.

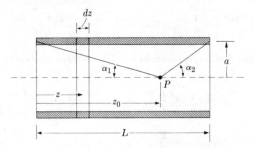

FIG. 8-7. Axial magnetic field of a solenoid.

The weber per square meter is a rather large unit for measuring laboratory fields; consequently the unit *gauss* for B has survived from an older system* of units: one gauss equals 10^{-4} weber/m^2. For reference purposes we give

$$B_z = \frac{32\pi N}{5^{3/2}a}\frac{I}{10}, \qquad I \text{ in } \textbf{amp}, \qquad a \text{ in } \textbf{cm}, \qquad B \text{ in } \textbf{gauss}, \qquad (8\text{-}43\text{a})$$

for the induction at the midpoint of the Helmholtz coil. Of course N is still the number of turns in each of the two coils.

Another device to which Eq. (8-38) can be applied is the solenoid. A solenoid may be described as N turns uniformly wound on a cylindrical form of radius a and length L. Such a configuration is shown in Fig. 8-7. The magnetic induction at point z_0 is found by dividing the length L into elements dz, such as the one shown, and applying Eq. (8-38) to each element and summing the results. Noting that the element dz contains Ndz/L turns, we find that

$$B_z(z_0) = \frac{\mu_0 NI}{L}\frac{a^2}{2}\int_0^L \frac{dz}{[(z_0 - z)^2 + a^2]^{3/2}}. \qquad (8\text{-}45)$$

The change of variable, $z - z_0 = a \tan\theta$, leads to

$$B_z(z_0) = \frac{\mu_0 NI}{2L}\int_{\theta_1}^{\theta_2} \cos\theta\, d\theta = \frac{\mu_0 NI}{L}\left[\frac{\sin\theta_2 - \sin\theta_1}{2}\right], \qquad (8\text{-}46)$$

where $\theta_1 = -\tan^{-1}(z_0/a)$ and $\theta_2 = \tan^{-1}(L - z_0)/a$. The fact that sines appear rather than just ones, as in the elementary formula, represents end corrections. To help understand the approximation which is usually made, namely, $B_z = \mu_0 NI/L$, it is convenient to introduce the angles α_1 and α_2 (both positive) shown in Fig. 8-7. In terms of these angles, Eq. (8-46) becomes

* Other systems of units are discussed in Appendix II.

$$B_z(z_0) = \frac{\mu_0 N I}{L} \left[\frac{\cos \alpha_1 + \cos \alpha_2}{2} \right]. \tag{8–47}$$

If the solenoid is long compared with its radius and z_0 is not too close to either zero or L, then α_1 and α_2 are both small angles and may be approximated by

$$\alpha_1 \cong \frac{a}{z_0} \; ; \qquad \alpha_2 \cong \frac{a}{L - z_0} \cdot \tag{8–48}$$

Maintaining quadratic terms in the expansions of $\cos \alpha_1$ and $\cos \alpha_2$, we obtain

$$B_z(z_0) \cong \frac{\mu_0 N I}{L} \left\{ 1 - \frac{a^2}{4z_0^2} - \frac{a^2}{4(L - z_0)^2} \right\}. \tag{8–49}$$

From this, we conclude that if $z_0 = L/2$ and $L/a = 10$, a 2% error results from neglecting the quadratic terms.

8–5 Ampere's circuital law. For magnetic induction fields given by Eq. (8–26) or (8–28) which are due to steady currents, i.e., to currents which satisfy

$$\text{div } \mathbf{J} = 0, \tag{8–50}$$

a very important equation for the curl of $\mathbf{B}$ can be derived. This is done* by simply calculating the curl of Eq. (8–28). The curl involves differentiation with respect to $\mathbf{r}_2$, and hence operates only on the factor $(\mathbf{r}_2 - \mathbf{r}_1)/|\mathbf{r}_2 - \mathbf{r}_1|^3$; however, once the derivative has been displayed so that it operates only on this factor it may be changed to differentiation with respect to $\mathbf{r}_1$ (with a minus sign) because of the symmetry between $\mathbf{r}_2$ and $\mathbf{r}_1$. Having changed the derivative in this way, an integration by parts can be used to move the derivative to the $\mathbf{J}(\mathbf{r}_1)$ factor in one term where it appears as div $\mathbf{J}(\mathbf{r}_1)$, which vanishes. The integral of the second term can be evaluated to give

$$\text{curl } \mathbf{B}(\mathbf{r}_2) = \mu_0 \mathbf{J}(\mathbf{r}_2), \tag{8–51}$$

which will be called the differential form of Ampere's law. In Chapter 10 this will be modified somewhat; however, Eq. (8–51) is still valid so long as there are no magnetic materials present and div $\mathbf{J} = 0$.

Stokes' theorem can be used to transform Eq. (8–51) into an integral form which is sometimes very useful. This application of Stokes' theorem is written

$$\int_S \text{curl } \mathbf{B} \cdot \mathbf{n} \, da = \oint_C \mathbf{B} \cdot d\mathbf{l}. \tag{1–45}$$

---

* The details of this calculation are rather involved; however, they are given explicitly in Appendix III.

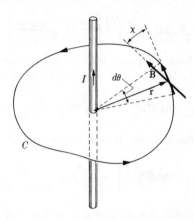

FIG. 8–8. Verification of Ampere's circuital law for long, straight-wire geometry.

Using Eq. (8–51) for **curl B** gives

$$\oint_C \mathbf{B} \cdot d\mathbf{l} = \mu_0 \int_S \mathbf{J} \cdot \mathbf{n} \, da, \qquad (8\text{–}52)$$

which simply says that the line integral of **B** around a closed path is equal to μ_0 times the total current through the closed path.

It is instructive to verify Eq. (8–52) for a simple case. The long straight wire provides a particularly good example. In this case **B** at a distance r from the conductor is given by $B(r) = \mu_0 I / 2\pi r$, and it is tangential to a circle of radius r with center at the conductor. Figure 8–8 illustrates the geometry. The current is directed upward, and C is described in the counterclockwise direction. From the figure,

$$\mathbf{B} \cdot d\mathbf{l} = |\mathbf{B}| \, |d\mathbf{l}| \cos \chi = |\mathbf{B}| r \, d\theta. \qquad (8\text{–}53)$$

With $|\mathbf{B}|$ as given above,

$$\oint_C \mathbf{B} \cdot d\mathbf{l} = \int_0^{2\pi} \frac{\mu_0 I}{2\pi r} r \, d\theta = \mu_0 I, \qquad (8\text{–}54)$$

which represents a special case of Eq. (8–52).

Ampere's circuital law, as Eq. (8–52) is called, is in many ways parallel to Gauss's law in electrostatics. By this is meant that it can be used to obtain the magnetic field due to a certain current distribution of high symmetry without having to evaluate the complicated integrals that appear in the Biot law. As an example, consider a coaxial cable consisting of a small center conductor of radius r_1 and a coaxial cylindrical outer cable conductor of radius r_2, as shown in Fig. 8–9. Assume that

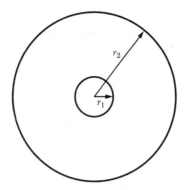

FIG. 8–9. Cross section through a coaxial cable.

the two conductors carry equal total currents of magnitude I in opposite directions, the center being directed out of the paper. From the symmetry of the problem it is clear that **B** must be everywhere tangent to a circle centered on the center conductor and drawn through the point at which **B** is being considered. Furthermore, **B** cannot depend on the azimuthal angle. The appropriate curves to use in the application of Eq. (8–52) are circles centered on the center conductor. For such a circle of radius r

$$\oint \mathbf{B} \cdot d\mathbf{l} = 2\pi r B, \qquad (8\text{–}55)$$

which must equal μ_0 times the total current through the loop. Thus

$$2\pi r B = \mu_0 I, \qquad r_1 < r < r_2,$$
$$2\pi r B = 0, \qquad r_2 < r. \qquad (8\text{–}56)$$

This apparently trivial result can be obtained by integration of the Biot law only with considerable difficulty.

8–6 The magnetic vector potential. The calculation of electric fields was much simplified by the introduction of the electrostatic potential. The possibility of making this simplification resulted from the vanishing of the curl of the electric field. The curl of the magnetic induction does not vanish; however, its divergence does. Since the divergence of any curl is zero, it is reasonable to assume that the magnetic induction may be written

$$\mathbf{B} = \operatorname{curl} \mathbf{A}. \qquad (8\text{–}57)$$

The only other requirement placed on **A** is that

$$\operatorname{curl} \mathbf{B} = \operatorname{curl} \operatorname{curl} \mathbf{A} = \mu_0 \mathbf{J}. \qquad (8\text{–}58)$$

Using the identity

$$\text{curl curl } \mathbf{A} = \text{grad div } \mathbf{A} - \nabla^2 \mathbf{A} \tag{8-59}$$

and specifying that div $\mathbf{A} = 0$, yields

$$\nabla^2 \mathbf{A} = -\mu_0 \mathbf{J}. \tag{8-60}$$

Integrating each rectangular component and using the solution for Poisson's equation as a guide leads to

$$\mathbf{A}(\mathbf{r}_2) = \frac{\mu_0}{4\pi} \int_V \frac{\mathbf{J}(\mathbf{r}_1)}{|\mathbf{r}_2 - \mathbf{r}_1|} \, dv_1. \tag{8-61}$$

The integrals involved in this expression are much easier to evaluate than those involved in the Biot law; however, they are also more complicated than those used to obtain the electrostatic potential.

An alternative way of obtaining Eq. (8–61) is by the direct transformation of Eq. (8–28) to the form of Eq. (8–57). This is done by noting that

$$\frac{\mathbf{r}_2 - \mathbf{r}_1}{|\mathbf{r}_2 - \mathbf{r}_1|^3} = -\text{grad}_2 \frac{1}{|\mathbf{r}_2 - \mathbf{r}_1|}, \tag{8-62}$$

where grad_2 indicates that the differentiation is with respect to $\mathbf{r}_2$. The vector identity

$$\text{curl } (\varphi \mathbf{A}) = \varphi \text{ curl } \mathbf{A} - \mathbf{A} \times \text{grad } \varphi, \tag{8-63}$$

which is valid for any vector $\mathbf{A}$ and any scalar φ, gives

$$\text{curl}_2 \left\{ \frac{1}{|\mathbf{r}_2 - \mathbf{r}_1|} \mathbf{J}(\mathbf{r}_1) \right\} = -\mathbf{J}(\mathbf{r}_1) \times \text{grad}_2 \frac{1}{|\mathbf{r}_2 - \mathbf{r}_1|}, \tag{8-64}$$

since $\mathbf{J}(\mathbf{r}_1)$ does not depend on $\mathbf{r}_2$. Combining these results in Eq. (8–28) leads to

$$\begin{aligned}
\mathbf{B}(\mathbf{r}_2) &= \frac{\mu_0}{4\pi} \int_V \mathbf{J}(\mathbf{r}_1) \times \frac{(\mathbf{r}_2 - \mathbf{r}_1)}{|\mathbf{r}_2 - \mathbf{r}_1|^3} \, dv_1 \\
&= -\frac{\mu_0}{4\pi} \int_V \mathbf{J}(\mathbf{r}_1) \times \text{grad}_2 \frac{1}{|\mathbf{r}_2 - \mathbf{r}_1|} \, dv_1 \\
&= \frac{\mu_0}{4\pi} \int_V \text{curl}_2 \frac{\mathbf{J}(\mathbf{r}_1)}{|\mathbf{r}_2 - \mathbf{r}_1|} \, dv_1.
\end{aligned} \tag{8-65}$$

The curl can be taken outside the integral, which puts Eq. (8–65) into exactly the form of Eq. (8–57). Thus

$$\mathbf{A}(\mathbf{r}_2) = \frac{\mu_0}{4\pi} \int_{V_1} \frac{\mathbf{J}(\mathbf{r}_1)}{|\mathbf{r}_2 - \mathbf{r}_1|} \, dv_1 \tag{8-61}$$

results also from this approach.

To avoid leaving a false impression, namely, that the vector potential is as useful as the electrostatic potential in computing simple fields, it must be noted that there are essentially no cases where $\mathbf{A}$ can be computed in simple closed form. The long straight wire gives an infinite result for $\mathbf{A}$ when Eq. (8–61) is used. The circular turn involves elliptic integrals, and so on. It should also be noted that evaluating the vector potential at a single point is not useful, because the magnetic induction is obtained by differentiation. The principal use of the vector potential is in approximations such as that discussed in the next section, and in problems involving electromagnetic radiation (see Chapters 15, 16, and 17).

8–7 The magnetic field of a distant circuit. The magnetic vector potential due to a small circuit at large distances can be evaluated relatively easily. The expression for the vector potential (8–61) may be applied to current circuits by making the substitution: $\mathbf{J}\, dv \to I\, d\mathbf{r}$. Thus

$$\mathbf{A}(\mathbf{r}_2) = \frac{\mu_0 I}{4\pi} \oint \frac{d\mathbf{r}_1}{|\mathbf{r}_2 - \mathbf{r}_1|}. \tag{8–66}$$

For circuits whose dimensions are small compared with $\mathbf{r}_2$ the denominator can be approximated. To do this, we write

$$|\mathbf{r}_2 - \mathbf{r}_1|^{-1} = (r_2^2 + r_1^2 - 2\mathbf{r}_1 \cdot \mathbf{r}_2)^{-1/2} \tag{8–67}$$

and expand in powers of r_1/r_2 to get

$$|\mathbf{r}_2 - \mathbf{r}_1|^{-1} = \frac{1}{r_2}\left[1 + \frac{\mathbf{r}_1 \cdot \mathbf{r}_2}{r_2^2} + \cdots\right] \tag{8–68}$$

to first order in r_1/r_2. Using this in Eq. (8–66) gives

$$\mathbf{A}(\mathbf{r}_2) = \frac{\mu_0 I}{4\pi}\left\{\frac{1}{r_2} \oint d\mathbf{r}_1 + \frac{1}{r_2^3} \oint d\mathbf{r}_1(\mathbf{r}_1 \cdot \mathbf{r}_2) + \cdots\right\}. \tag{8–69}$$

The first integral vanishes; the second integrand is one term in the expansion

$$(\mathbf{r}_1 \times d\mathbf{r}_1) \times \mathbf{r}_2 = -\mathbf{r}_1(\mathbf{r}_2 \cdot d\mathbf{r}_1) + d\mathbf{r}_1(\mathbf{r}_1 \cdot \mathbf{r}_2). \tag{8–70}$$

To eliminate the first term on the right in Eq. (8–70), the differential of $\mathbf{r}_1(\mathbf{r}_2 \cdot \mathbf{r}_1)$ for a small change in $\mathbf{r}_1$ is written as

$$d[\mathbf{r}_1(\mathbf{r}_2 \cdot \mathbf{r}_1)] = \mathbf{r}_1(\mathbf{r}_2 \cdot d\mathbf{r}_1) + d\mathbf{r}_1(\mathbf{r}_2 \cdot \mathbf{r}_1), \tag{8–71}$$

which is of course exact. Adding Eqs. (8–70) and (8–71) and dividing by two yields

$$d\mathbf{r}_1(\mathbf{r}_1 \cdot \mathbf{r}_2) = \tfrac{1}{2}(\mathbf{r}_1 \times d\mathbf{r}_1) \times \mathbf{r}_2 + \tfrac{1}{2}\,d[\mathbf{r}_1(\mathbf{r}_2 \cdot \mathbf{r}_1)]. \qquad (8\text{--}72)$$

Since the last term is an exact differential, it contributes nothing to the second integral in Eq. (8–69). Thus it follows that

$$\mathbf{A}(\mathbf{r}_2) = \frac{\mu_0}{4\pi}\left[\frac{I}{2}\oint \mathbf{r}_1 \times d\mathbf{r}_1\right] \times \frac{\mathbf{r}_2}{r_2^3}. \qquad (8\text{--}73)$$

Equation (8–22) defines the quantity in brackets as the magnetic moment, $\mathbf{m}$, of the circuit. Hence

$$\mathbf{A}(\mathbf{r}_2) = \frac{\mu_0}{4\pi}\frac{\mathbf{m} \times \mathbf{r}_2}{r_2^3}. \qquad (8\text{--}74)$$

In this derivation it has been assumed that all $r_1 \ll r_2$; hence Eq. (8–74) is not valid for an arbitrary origin, but only for an origin close to the circuit.

The magnetic induction can be determined by taking the curl of Eq. (8–74). This is readily accomplished by using vector identities. First,

$$\mathbf{B}(\mathbf{r}_2) = \operatorname{curl}\mathbf{A}(\mathbf{r}_2) = \frac{\mu_0}{4\pi}\operatorname{curl}\left(\mathbf{m} \times \frac{\mathbf{r}_2}{r_2^3}\right)$$

$$= \frac{\mu_0}{4\pi}\left[-(\mathbf{m} \cdot \mathbf{grad})\frac{\mathbf{r}_2}{r_2^3} + \mathbf{m}\operatorname{div}\frac{\mathbf{r}_2}{r_2^3}\right]. \qquad (8\text{--}75)$$

The first term in the brackets can be transformed by noting that

$$m_x\frac{\partial}{\partial x_2}\left(\frac{\mathbf{r}_2}{r_2^3}\right) = \frac{m_x\mathbf{i}}{r_2^3} - 3m_x x_2\frac{\mathbf{r}_2}{r_2^5}; \qquad (8\text{--}76)$$

hence

$$(\mathbf{m} \cdot \mathbf{grad})\frac{\mathbf{r}_2}{r_2^3} = \frac{\mathbf{m}}{r_2^3} - \frac{3(\mathbf{m} \cdot \mathbf{r}_2)\mathbf{r}_2}{r_2^5}. \qquad (8\text{--}77)$$

The second term involves only the calculation of

$$\operatorname{div}\frac{\mathbf{r}_2}{r_2^3} = \frac{3}{r_2^3} - \mathbf{r}_2 \cdot \frac{3\mathbf{r}_2}{r_2^5} = 0. \qquad (8\text{--}78)$$

Finally,

$$\mathbf{B}(\mathbf{r}_2) = \frac{\mu_0}{4\pi}\left[-\frac{\mathbf{m}}{r_2^3} + \frac{3(\mathbf{m} \cdot \mathbf{r}_2)\mathbf{r}_2}{r_2^5}\right] \quad \text{(magnetic dipole)}. \qquad (8\text{--}79)$$

Equation (8–79) shows that the magnetic field of a distant circuit does not depend on its detailed geometry, but only on its magnetic moment $\mathbf{m}$. Comparison with Eq. (2–36) shows that (8–79) is of the same form as the electric field due to an electric dipole, which explains the name *magnetic dipole* field. **m** is usually called the *magnetic dipole moment* of the circuit.

8-8 The magnetic scalar potential.

Equation (8-51) indicates that the curl of the magnetic induction is zero wherever the current density is zero. When this is the case, the magnetic induction in such regions can be written as the gradient of a scalar potential:

$$\mathbf{B} = -\mu_0 \operatorname{grad} U^*. \tag{8-80}$$

However, the divergence of **B** is also zero, which means that

$$\operatorname{div} \mathbf{B} = -\mu_0 \nabla^2 U^* = 0. \tag{8-81}$$

Thus U^*, which is called the magnetic scalar potential, satisfies Laplace's equation. Much of the work of electrostatics can be taken over directly and used to evaluate U^* for various situations; however, care must be taken in applying the boundary conditions.

The expression for the scalar potential of a magnetic dipole is particularly useful. If it is noted that Eq. (8-79) can be written

$$\mathbf{B}(\mathbf{r}_2) = -\mu_0 \operatorname{grad} \left(\frac{\mathbf{m} \cdot \mathbf{r}_2}{4\pi r_2^3} \right), \tag{8-82}$$

then it is clear that

$$U^*(\mathbf{r}_2) = \frac{\mathbf{m} \cdot \mathbf{r}_2}{4\pi r_2^3} \tag{8-83}$$

for a magnetic dipole **m**.

A large circuit C can be divided into many small circuits by means of a mesh, as shown in Fig. 8-10. If each small loop formed by the mesh carries the same current as originally was carried by the circuit C, then, because of the cancellation of currents in the common branch of adjacent loops, the net effect is the same as if the charge flowed only in the circuit C. For any one of the small loops, the magnetic moment may be written as

$$d\mathbf{m} = I n \, da, \tag{8-84}$$

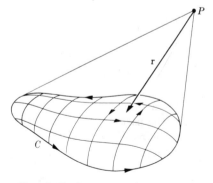

FIG. 8-10. A macroscopic current circuit constructed from elemental magnetic dipoles.

since each of the loops is sufficiently small to be regarded as planar. Using this expression in Eq. (8–83) and integrating over the surface bounded by C gives

$$U^*(P) = \frac{I}{4\pi} \int_S \frac{\mathbf{r}_2 \cdot \mathbf{n}\, da}{r_2^3}. \tag{8-85}$$

In this equation $\mathbf{r}_2$ must be interpreted as the vector from da to the point P, that is, $-\mathbf{r}$, as shown in Fig. 8–10. Making the change $\mathbf{r}_2 = -\mathbf{r}$ results in

$$U^*(P) = -\frac{I}{4\pi} \int_S \frac{\mathbf{r} \cdot \mathbf{n}\, da}{r^3}. \tag{8-86}$$

The quantity $\mathbf{r} \cdot \mathbf{n}\, da$ is just r times the projection of da on a plane perpendicular to $\mathbf{r}$. Thus $\mathbf{r} \cdot \mathbf{n}\, da/r^3$ is the solid angle subtended by da at P. Equation (8–86) may then be written as

$$U^*(P) = -\frac{I\Omega}{4\pi}, \tag{8-87}$$

where Ω is the solid angle subtended by the curve C at the point P.

The magnetic scalar potential can be used for the calculation of the magnetic field due either to current-carrying circuits or to magnetic double layers (layers of dipoles). This procedure is occasionally useful in dealing with circuit problems; however, its principal use is in dealing with magnetic materials.

8–9 Magnetic flux. The quantity

$$\Phi = \int_S \mathbf{B} \cdot \mathbf{n}\, da \tag{8-88}$$

is known as the *magnetic flux* and is measured in webers. It is analogous to the electric flux discussed earlier, but it is of much greater importance. The flux through a closed surface is zero, as can be seen by computing

$$\oint_S \mathbf{B} \cdot \mathbf{n}\, da = \int_V \operatorname{div} \mathbf{B}\, dv = 0. \tag{8-89}$$

From this it follows also that the flux through a circuit is independent of the particular surface used to compute the flux. Use will be made of these results in the next chapter, when electromagnetic induction is discussed.

Problems

8-1. A charged particle of mass m and charge q moves in a uniform magnetic induction field $\mathbf{B}_0$. Show that the most general motion of the particle traces out a helix, the cross section of which is a circle of radius $R = mv_\perp/qB$. (Here $v_\perp$ is the component of velocity of the particle which is perpendicular to $\mathbf{B}_0$.)

8-2. The Hamiltonian for a charged particle moving in a uniform magnetic induction field, $\mathbf{B}_0$, which is parallel to the z-axis, is given by

$$\mathcal{3C} = \frac{1}{2m} p^2 - \frac{qB_0}{2m} (xp_y - yp_x) + \frac{q^2 B_0^2}{8m} (x^2 + y^2).$$

Show that the equations of motion which may be derived from $\mathcal{3C}$ are consistent with the results of Problem 8-1.

8-3. A proton of velocity 10^7 m/sec is projected at right angles to a uniform magnetic induction field of 0.1 w/m². (a) How much is the particle path deflected from a straight line after it has traversed a distance of 1 cm? (b) How long does it take the proton to traverse a 90° arc?

8-4. Show that the force between parallel wires carrying currents I_1 and I_2, both in the same direction, is one of attraction. If the two parallel wires are very long and separated by distance a, find the magnetic force on segment dl_2 of wire 2.

8-5. Given a current circuit in the shape of a regular hexagon of side a. If the circuit carries the current I, find the magnetic induction at the center of the hexagon.

8-6. Given a thin strip of metal of width w and very long. The current in the strip is along its length; the total current is I. Find the magnetic induction in the plane of the strip at distance b from the nearer edge.

8-7. A large number N of closely spaced turns of fine wire are wound in a single layer upon the surface of a wooden sphere of radius a, with the planes of the turns perpendicular to the axis of the sphere and completely covering its surface. If the current in the winding is I, determine the magnetic field at the center of the sphere.

8-8. A solenoid 15 cm long is wound in two layers. Each layer contains 100 turns; the first layer is 2 cm in radius, the second 2.05 cm. If the winding carries a current of 3 amp, find the magnetic induction at various points along the axis of the solenoid. Make a plot of the axial magnetic induction as a function of distance, from the center to one end of the solenoid.

8-9. A solenoid of square cross section (i.e., a solenoid in which the individual turns are in the shape of a square) has N turns per unit length and carries current I. The cross-sectional dimension is a. If the solenoid is very long, find the axial magnetic induction at its center.

8-10. The magnetic induction at a point on the axis (z-axis) of a circular turn of wire carrying current I is given in Eq. (8–38). Use the fact that div $\mathbf{B} = 0$ to get an approximate expression for B_r (the radial component of the magnetic field) which is valid for points very near the axis.

8–11. The vertical component of the magnetic induction between the pole faces of a particle accelerator is given by $B_z = B_z(r, z)$, where $r = (x^2 + y^2)^{1/2}$ is the distance from the axis of the pole faces. (a) If $|B_z|$ is a decreasing function of r, show that the lines of magnetic intensity bow outward, as shown in Fig. 8–11, regardless of whether the upper pole is a north or south pole. [*Hint:* Use the fact that **curl B** $= 0$, and that $B_r = 0$ on the median plane.] (b) If the lines of **B** bow as shown in the figure, show that accelerated particles which drift away from the median plane experience a force tending to restore them to the median plane, regardless of whether they are positively or negatively charged.

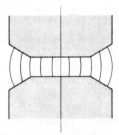

FIGURE 8–11

*8–12. It is evident from Eq. (8–30) that only a certain class of vector fields qualifies as a physically realizable magnetic induction field. Verify that

$$\mathbf{B} = (\mathbf{r}/r) \times \mathbf{grad}\, g(x, y, z),$$

with $g(x, y, z)$ a solution of Laplace's equation, is an appropriate magnetic field, and find the current density **J** producing it.

8–13. For a homogeneous, isotropic, nonmagnetic medium of conductivity g, in which there are steady currents, show that **B** satisfies the vector Laplace equation: $\nabla^2 \mathbf{B} = 0$.

8–14. By using Ampere's circuital law, find the magnetic induction at distance r from the center of a long wire carrying current I. Do this for both $r > R$ and $r < R$, where R is the radius of the wire. Show explicitly that the magnetic induction vanishes on the axis of the wire.

8–15. A toroid is wound uniformly, as shown in Fig. 9–2. It has N turns of wire which carry current I. The inner radius of the toroid is a, the outer b. Find the magnetic induction at various points inside the toroidal winding. Find the ratio b/a that will permit **B** in the ring to vary by no more than 25%.

8–16. Show that the magnetic vector potential for two long, straight, parallel wires carrying the same current, I, in opposite directions is given by

$$\mathbf{A} = \frac{\mu_0 I}{2\pi} \ln\left(\frac{r_2}{r_1}\right) \mathbf{n},$$

where r_2 and r_1 are the distances from the field point to the wires, and **n** is a unit vector parallel to the wires.

8-17. Given the following set of conductors: an infinitely long straight wire surrounded by a thin cylindrical shell of metal (at radius b) arranged coaxially with the wire. The two conductors carry equal but opposite currents, I. Find the magnetic vector potential for the system.

8-18. The magnetic dip angle is defined as the angle between the direction of the magnetic induction and the tangent plane at the earth's surface. Derive an expression for the dip angle as a function of geomagnetic latitude, on the assumption that the induction is a dipole field.

*8-19. (a) Show that the magnetic scalar potential for a point on the axis (z-axis) of a circular loop, of radius a, is given by

$$ U^* = \frac{1}{2} I \left\{ 1 - \frac{z}{\sqrt{a^2 + z^2}} \right\}. $$

(b) Expand this formula according to the binomial theorem to obtain a series expression valid for $z < a$.

(c) The magnetic, scalar potential U^* should satisfy Laplace's equation; furthermore, by symmetry, $U^* = U^*(r, \theta)$, where r is the distance from the center of the loop to the field point and θ is the angle between $\mathbf{r}$ and the z-axis. Show that by using the zonal harmonics, Eq. (3-18), a solution for U^* can be constructed which reduces to the potential obtained in (b) on the symmetry axis.

(d) Use the U^* obtained in (c) to find B_r and B_θ at points off the symmetry axis of the loop.

*8-20. A sphere of radius a carrying surface charge density σ (rigidly attached) is rotated about an axis through its center with constant angular velocity ω. Show that the magnetic field at an external point is a dipole field and find the equivalent dipole moment.

8-21. Two dipoles $\mathbf{m}_1$ and $\mathbf{m}_2$ are in the same plane; $\mathbf{m}_1$ is fixed but $\mathbf{m}_2$ is free to rotate about its center. Show that, for equilibrium, $\tan \theta_1 = -2 \tan \theta_2$, where θ_1, θ_2 are the angles between $\mathbf{r}$ and $\mathbf{m}_1$, $\mathbf{m}_2$ respectively ($\mathbf{r}$ is the vector displacement between $\mathbf{m}_2$ and $\mathbf{m}_1$).

CHAPTER 9

ELECTROMAGNETIC INDUCTION

The induction of electromotive force by changing magnetic flux was first observed by Faraday and by Henry in the early nineteenth century. From their pioneering experiments have developed modern generators, transformers, etc. This chapter is primarily concerned with the mathematical formulation of the law of electromagnetic induction and its exploitation in simple cases.

9–1 Electromagnetic induction. The results of a large number of experiments can be summarized by associating an emf

$$\mathcal{E} = -\frac{d\Phi}{dt} \tag{9–1}$$

with a change in magnetic flux through a circuit. This result, which is known as Faraday's law of electromagnetic induction, is found to be independent of the way in which the flux is changed—the circuit may be distorted or moved, or the value of **B** at various points inside the circuit may be changed. It is extremely important to realize that Eq. (9–1) represents an independent experimental law—it cannot be derived from other experimental laws and it certainly is not, as is sometimes stated, a consequence of conservation of energy applied to the energy balance of currents in magnetic fields.

Since by definition

$$\mathcal{E} = \oint \mathbf{E} \cdot d\mathbf{l} \tag{9–2}$$

and

$$\Phi = \int_S \mathbf{B} \cdot \mathbf{n} \, da, \tag{9–3}$$

Eq. (9–1) can be written

$$\oint \mathbf{E} \cdot d\mathbf{l} = -\frac{d}{dt} \int_S \mathbf{B} \cdot \mathbf{n} \, da. \tag{9–4}$$

If the circuit is a rigid stationary circuit, the time derivative can be taken inside the integral, where it becomes a partial time derivative. Furthermore, Stokes' theorem can be used to transform the line integral of **E** into the surface integral of **curl E**. The result of these transformations is

$$\int_S \mathbf{curl} \, \mathbf{E} \cdot \mathbf{n} \, da = -\int_S \frac{\partial \mathbf{B}}{\partial t} \cdot \mathbf{n} \, da. \tag{9–5}$$

Since this must be true for all surfaces S, it follows that

$$\operatorname{curl} \mathbf{E} = -\frac{\partial \mathbf{B}}{\partial t},\tag{9-6}$$

which is the differential form of Faraday's law.   Moving media and other subtleties require a more careful treatment, beyond the scope of this text.

The negative sign in Faraday's law indicates, as can be easily demonstrated, that the direction of the induced emf is such as to tend to oppose the change that produces it.   Thus if we attempt to increase the flux through a circuit, the induced emf tends to cause currents in such a direction as to decrease the flux.   If we attempt to thrust one pole of a magnet into a coil, the currents caused by the induced emf set up a magnetic field which tends to repel the pole.   All these phenomena are covered by Lenz's law, which may be stated as:

In case of a change in a magnetic system, that thing happens which tends to oppose the change.

It is clear that this accounts for the direction of the current and the direction of the force in the examples given above.   The utility of Lenz's law should not be underestimated.   In many cases it represents the quickest if not the only way of obtaining information about electromagnetic reactions.   Even if other methods are available, it affords a valuable check.

There is a special case of Faraday's law in which the emf can be derived from the Lorentz force and conservation of energy.   Suppose a straight conductor slides on a pair of horizontal rails separated by a distance l. Let there be a magnetic field $\mathbf{B}$ perpendicular to the plane of the rails and let a source of emf $\mathcal{E}_0$ be connected between the rails, as shown in Fig. 9–1.   Because of the current I, the conductor experiences a force of magnitude $F = BIl$ to the right.   Because of this force it accelerates to the right and is moving at a particular time with a velocity v; thus work is being done at the rate Fv.   Power is being supplied by the emf $\mathcal{E}_0$ at the rate $\mathcal{E}_0 I$.   Thus

$$\mathcal{E}_0 I = I^2 R + Fv.\tag{9-7}$$

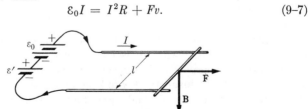

FIG. 9–1. Motional emf produced by a sliding wire in a magnetic field

As a result, I is less than the original value $\mathcal{E}_0/R$, and hence the magnetic force is different. To avoid this difficulty, an additional variable emf $\mathcal{E}'$ is added in series with $\mathcal{E}_0$, of such magnitude (variable) as to keep I constant. Then, instead of (9–7), we have

$$(\mathcal{E}_0 + \mathcal{E}')I = I^2R + Fv. \tag{9–8}$$

Because of the choice of $\mathcal{E}'$, $\mathcal{E}_0 I = I^2R$, leaving

$$\mathcal{E}'I = BIlv. \tag{9–9}$$

Cancelling the I's gives

$$\mathcal{E}' = Blv = \frac{d\Phi}{dt} ; \tag{9–10}$$

however, $\mathcal{E}'$ is not the induced emf; it is the negative of it, i.e., the emf which must be added to $\mathcal{E}_0$ to maintain the current constant. Therefore

$$\mathcal{E} = -\frac{d\Phi}{dt} , \tag{9–11}$$

in agreement with Eq. (9–1). The equation

$$\mathcal{E} = -Blv \tag{9–12}$$

can be generalized by writing it in vector notation. If $\mathbf{v}$ is arbitrarily oriented with respect to l, then only the component of $\mathbf{v}$ which is perpendicular to l contributes to $\mathcal{E}$. Thus $\mathcal{E}$ is proportional to $l \times \mathbf{v}$. For arbitrary $\mathbf{B}$, only the component perpendicular to the plane of l and $\mathbf{v}$ contributes to $\mathcal{E}$. Since $l \times \mathbf{v}$ is perpendicular to the $l,\mathbf{v}$-plane, $\mathcal{E}$ may be written as

$$\underline{\mathcal{E} = \mathbf{B} \cdot l \times \mathbf{v}} \tag{9–13}$$

except possibly for a minus sign. Comparison of Eq. (9–13) with Fig. 9–1 quickly shows that the correct sign already appears. Once again it must be noted that Eq. (9–13) is only a special case of Eq. (9–1). Deriving Eq. (9–13) does *not* prove Eq. (9–1), since the only kind of change which has been considered is a change in the area of the circuit. The emf in (9–13) is called a *motional emf.*

9–2 Self-inductance. In this section, the relationship between the flux and current associated with an isolated circuit will be considered and exploited for the purpose of introducing the practical circuit parameter: self-inductance. The magnetic flux linking an isolated circuit depends on the geometry of the circuit and, according to Eq. (8–26), is linearly dependent on the current in the circuit. Thus for a rigid stationary circuit the only changes in flux result from changes in the current. That is,

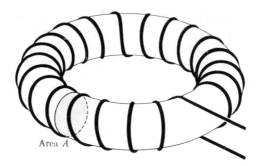

Area A

FIG. 9–2. A toroidal winding.

$$\frac{d\Phi}{dt} = \frac{d\Phi}{dI}\frac{dI}{dt}, \tag{9–14}$$

which is valid even when Eq. (8–26) is not; the only requirement is that Φ depend only on the current. If, however, Eq. (8–26) is valid or, more generally, if Φ is directly proportional to the current, then $d\Phi/dI$ is a constant, equal to Φ/I. In any case, the inductance, L, is defined as

$$L = \frac{d\Phi}{dI}. \tag{9–15}$$

When it is essential to distinguish between this and Φ/I, $d\Phi/dI$ is called the *incremental* inductance; unless otherwise specified it is safest to associate the word inductance with Eq. (9–15). From Eqs. (9–14), (9–15), and (9–1) it follows that the expression for the induced emf,

$$\mathcal{E} = -L\frac{dI}{dt}, \tag{9–16}$$

is an equation of considerable practical importance.

As an illustration of the use of Eq. (9–15) for the calculation of inductance, the self-inductance of a toroidal coil will be calculated. Such a coil is shown in Fig. 9–2. Equation (9–15) applies to an entire circuit, that is, not only to the toroidal coil of Fig. 9–2, but also to the external circuit connected to terminals 1 and 2. By using twisted leads or a coaxial cable, which produce essentially no external magnetic field, the field-producing portion of the external circuit can be removed to a sufficiently great distance that it does not contribute to the flux in the toroid. If this is done and if by emf we understand the emf between terminals 1 and 2, then Eq. (9–15) can be used to obtain the inductance of the toroidal coil. From Ampere's circuital law, the magnetic induction inside the toroidal coil is

$$B = \frac{\mu_0 N I}{l}, \tag{9–17}$$

where N is the number of turns, l the mean length, and I the current in the winding. [Equations (9–17) and (9–18) involve the approximation of neglecting the variation of the magnetic induction over the cross-sectional area. In Problem 9–8 the details of this approximation are considered.] The flux linking each turn is then

$$\Phi_1 = \frac{\mu_0 N I A}{l}, \tag{9–18}$$

and the total flux linking the N turns is

$$\Phi = \frac{\mu_0 N^2 A}{l} I. \tag{9–19}$$

The inductance is then simply

$$L = \frac{d\Phi}{dI} = \frac{\mu_0 N^2 A}{l}. \tag{9–20}$$

The practical unit of inductance is the henry which, from Eq. (9–15), is equal to one volt second/ampere. Equation (9–20) indicates that the dimensions of μ_0, which have been previously given as webers/ampere·meter, can alternatively be given as henries/meter.

9–3 Mutual inductance. In the preceding section only isolated circuits were considered, so that all of the flux linking the circuit was due to the current in the circuit itself. This restriction can be lifted by assuming that there are n circuits, labeled $1, 2, \ldots$ The flux linking one of these circuits, say the one labeled i, can be written as

$$\Phi_i = \Phi_{i1} + \Phi_{i2} + \cdots + \Phi_{ii} + \cdots + \Phi_{in} = \sum_{j=1}^{n} \Phi_{ij}. \tag{9–21}$$

That is, it may be written as a sum of fluxes due to each of the n circuits, Φ_{i1} being the flux through the ith circuit due to circuit 1, etc. The emf induced in the ith circuit, $\mathcal{E}_i$, can then be written as

$$\mathcal{E}_i = -\frac{d\Phi_i}{dt} = -\left\{ \frac{d\Phi_{i1}}{dt} + \cdots + \frac{d\Phi_{ii}}{dt} + \cdots + \frac{d\Phi_{in}}{dt} \right\} = -\sum_{j=1}^{n} \frac{d\Phi_{ij}}{dt}. \tag{9–22}$$

If each of the circuits is a rigid stationary circuit, the only changes in the Φ_{ij}'s are those which result from changes in the currents. Thus

$$\frac{d\Phi_{ij}}{dt} = \frac{d\Phi_{ij}}{dI_j} \frac{dI_j}{dt}. \tag{9–23}$$

The coefficients $d\Phi_{ij}/dI_j$ are constants, independent of the current, if

Eq. (8-26) is appropriate. If they are not constants, they may depend on the current because of the nonlinearity of magnetic media associated with the circuit configuration. In any case,

$$M_{ij} = \frac{d\Phi_{ij}}{dI_j}, \qquad i \neq j \tag{9-24}$$

is defined as the mutual inductance between circuit i and circuit j. It will be seen later that $M_{ij} = M_{ji}$ and hence there is no possibility of ambiguity in the subscripts. Of course $d\Phi_{ii}/dI_i$ is just the self-inductance of the ith circuit, for which L_i or M_{ii} is written. The units of mutual inductance are the same as those of self-inductance, namely, henries.

As an example of the calculation of mutual inductance, consider the configuration of Fig. 9-2 with a second toroidal winding of N_2 turns added. For this situation, a current I_1 in the first winding produces a magnetic induction

$$B = \frac{\mu_0 N_1 I_1}{l},$$

and consequently fluxes

$$\Phi_{11} = \frac{\mu_0 N_1^2 A I_1}{l}$$

and

$$\Phi_{21} = \frac{\mu_0 N_1 N_2 A I_1}{l}.$$

From these fluxes it follows that

$$L_1 = \frac{\mu_0 N_1^2 A}{l} \tag{9-25}$$

as before, and

$$M_{21} = \frac{\mu_0 N_1 N_2 A}{l}. \tag{9-26}$$

Reversing the procedure and considering a current I_2 gives

$$L_2 = \frac{\mu_0 N_2^2 A}{l}, \tag{9-27}$$

and

$$M_{12} = \frac{\mu_0 N_1 N_2 A}{l}, \tag{9-28}$$

thus demonstrating that for this case $M_{12} = M_{21}$. Furthermore, Eqs. (9-25), (9-26), and (9-27) may be combined to yield

$$M_{12} = \sqrt{L_1 L_2}. \tag{9-29}$$

Equation (9–29) represents a limit that is imposed on the mutual inductance between two circuits, namely, it is always less than or equal to the square root of the product of the self-inductances of the two circuits. In view of this limit, a coupling coefficient k is often introduced and defined by

$$M = k\sqrt{L_1 L_2}, \qquad |k| \leq 1. \tag{9–30}$$

9–4 The Neumann formula. For two rigid stationary circuits in a linear medium (vacuum for the present) the mutual inductance is just

$$M_{21} = \frac{\Phi_{21}}{I_1}. \tag{9–31}$$

This is valid simply because Φ_{21} is proportional to I_1, making Φ_{21}/I_1 and $d\Phi_{21}/dI_1$ equal. In this case, Eq. (8–26) can be used to calculate M_{21}. The flux is given by

$$\Phi_{21} = \frac{\mu_0}{4\pi} I_1 \int_{S_2} \left\{ \oint_{C_1} \frac{d\mathbf{l}_1 \times (\mathbf{r}_2 - \mathbf{r}_1)}{|\mathbf{r}_2 - \mathbf{r}_1|^3} \right\} \cdot \mathbf{n} \, da_2. \tag{9–32}$$

However,

$$\oint_{C_1} \frac{d\mathbf{l}_1 \times (\mathbf{r}_2 - \mathbf{r}_1)}{|\mathbf{r}_2 - \mathbf{r}_1|^3} = \mathbf{curl}_2 \oint_{C_1} \frac{d\mathbf{l}_1}{|\mathbf{r}_2 - \mathbf{r}_1|} ; \tag{9–33}$$

hence

$$M_{21} = \frac{\Phi_{21}}{I_1} = \frac{\mu_0}{4\pi} \int_{S_2} \mathbf{curl}_2 \left\{ \oint_{C_1} \frac{d\mathbf{l}_1}{|\mathbf{r}_2 - \mathbf{r}_1|} \right\} \cdot \mathbf{n} \, da_2. \tag{9–34}$$

Using Stokes' theorem to transform the surface integral gives

$$M_{21} = \frac{\mu_0}{4\pi} \oint_{C_2} \oint_{C_1} \frac{d\mathbf{l}_1 \cdot d\mathbf{l}_2}{|\mathbf{r}_2 - \mathbf{r}_1|} , \tag{9–35}$$

which is known as *Neumann's formula* for the mutual inductance. The symmetry alluded to earlier is apparent in Eq. (9–35).

Neumann's formula is equally applicable to self-inductance, in which case it is written as

$$L = \frac{\mu_0}{4\pi} \oint_{C_1} \oint_{C_1} \frac{d\mathbf{l}_1 \cdot d\mathbf{l}'_1}{|\mathbf{r}_1 - \mathbf{r}'_1|} . \tag{9–36}$$

Some care must be used in the application of Eq. (9–36) because of the singularity at $\mathbf{r}_1 = \mathbf{r}'_1$; however, if care is taken, Eq. (9–36) is sometimes useful.

Equations (9–35) and (9–36) are usually difficult to apply to the calculation of inductance except for circuits in which the geometry is simple.

But Eq. (9–35) in particular is very important in the study of forces and torques exerted by one circuit on another. This application will be exploited in Chapter 12.

9–5 Inductances in series and in parallel. Inductances are often connected in series and in parallel, and, as with resistors and capacitors, it is important to know the result of such connections. We could proceed with a derivation based simply on $\mathcal{E} = -L(dI/dt)$ and obtain formulas for the effective inductance of two inductances in series or in parallel; however, to do so would be to ignore the practical fact that an inductor always has a certain internal resistance. A perfect inductance is much more difficult to realize than a perfect capacitance or a perfect resistance. For this reason, the series and parallel combinations of this section will always involve resistances as well as inductances.

For two inductors in series, the circuit of Fig. 9–3 is appropriate. In adding the voltage drops along the circuit it is important to note that M can be either positive or negative [changing the direction in which either C_1 or C_2 is described reverses the sign of M in Eq. (9–35)]. Bearing this in mind, the sum of the voltage drops for the circuit of Fig. 9–3 is found to be

$$\Delta U + \mathcal{E}_1 + \mathcal{E}_2 = R_1 I + R_2 I,$$

or

$$\Delta U = R_1 I + L_1 \frac{dI}{dt} + M \frac{dI}{dt} + R_2 I + L_2 \frac{dI}{dt} + M \frac{dI}{dt}. \quad (9\text{–}37)$$

This is equivalent to

$$\Delta U = (R_1 + R_2)I + (L_1 + L_2 + 2M) \frac{dI}{dt}. \quad (9\text{–}38)$$

The circuit thus resembles a resistor of resistance $R_1 + R_2$ in series with an inductance $L_1 + L_2 + 2M$. The magnitude of the inductance is $L_1 + L_2 + 2|M|$ for positive coupling (i.e., for fluxes due to I_1 and I_2 in the same direction in each coil), and is $L_1 + L_2 - 2|M|$ for negative coupling. An alternative description of the mutual inductance is

$$M = k\sqrt{L_1 L_2}, \qquad -1 \le k \le 1. \quad (9\text{–}39)$$

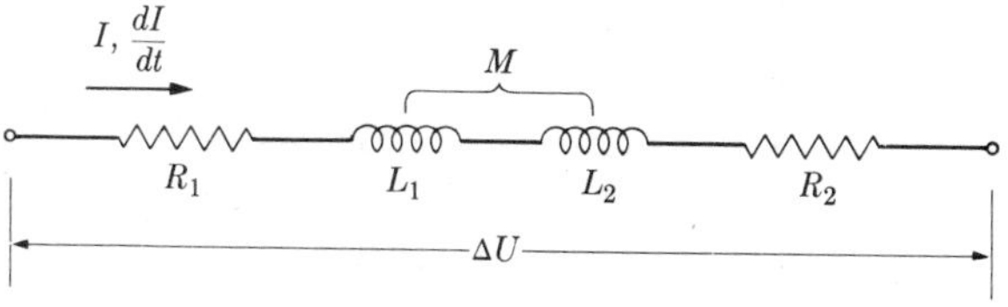

FIG. 9–3. Series connection of two inductors.

The effective inductance of the series circuit is then

$$L_{\text{eff}} = L_1 + 2k\sqrt{L_1 L_2} + L_2. \tag{9-40}$$

If k can be varied, then a variable inductance can be constructed. (In the early days of radio this was a popular way of tuning resonant circuits; see Chapter 13.)

The parallel connection shown in Fig. 9–4 is not as simple as the series circuit. In fact, the circuit shown does not behave like a simple series L-R circuit. Thus it is not possible to say that the effective inductance and effective resistance are certain functions of L_1, L_2, R_1, and R_2. If, however, R_1 and R_2 are negligible, then

$$\Delta U = L_1 \frac{dI_1}{dt} + M \frac{dI_2}{dt}$$
$$\Delta U = L_2 \frac{dI_2}{dt} + M \frac{dI_1}{dt}. \tag{9-41}$$

If first dI_1/dt and then dI_2/dt are eliminated from between Eqs. (9–41), there results

$$\Delta U(L_2 - M) = (L_1 L_2 - M^2) \frac{dI_1}{dt},$$
$$\Delta U(L_1 - M) = (L_1 L_2 - M^2) \frac{dI_2}{dt}. \tag{9-42}$$

Adding these gives

$$\Delta U = \frac{L_1 L_2 - M^2}{L_1 + L_2 - 2M} \frac{dI}{dt}. \tag{9-43}$$

Thus the effective inductance of two inductors in parallel is

$$L_{\text{eff}} = \frac{L_1 L_2 - M^2}{L_1 + L_2 - 2M}, \tag{9-44}$$

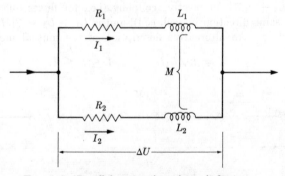

FIG. 9–4. Parallel connection of two inductors.

where again the sign of M depends on the way in which the inductors are connected.

The most important use of inductances is in alternating current circuits. For a circuit operating at a single frequency, an equivalent series circuit for Fig. 9–4 can be obtained; however, both the equivalent resistance and equivalent inductance are frequency dependent. This frequency dependency is the root of the difficulty encountered above.

PROBLEMS

9–1. A metallic conductor in the shape of a wire segment of length l is moved in a magnetic field $\mathbf{B}$ with velocity $\mathbf{v}$. From a detailed consideration of the Lorentz force on the electrons in the wire, show that the ends of the wire are at the potential difference: $\mathbf{B} \cdot \mathbf{1} \times \mathbf{v}$.

9–2. A metal rod one meter long rotates about an axis through one end and perpendicular to the rod, with an angular velocity of 12 rad/sec. The plane of rotation of the rod is perpendicular to a uniform magnetic field of 0.3 w/m². What is the emf induced between the ends of the rod?

9–3. Given a magnetic field of cylindrical symmetry, i.e., one with a z-component $B_z = B(r)$, where r is the distance from the symmetry axis. An ion of charge q and mass m revolves in a circular orbit at distance R from the symmetry axis with angular velocity $\omega = qB(R)/m$. If the magnetic field is slowly increased in magnitude, show that the emf induced around the ion's orbit is such as to accelerate the ion. Show that in order for the ion to stay in its same orbit, the *average* increase in $B(r)$ over the surface enclosed by the orbit must be twice as large as the increase in $B(R)$.

9–4. A dielectric cylinder of permittivity ϵ rotates about its axis with angular velocity ω. If a uniform magnetic field $\mathbf{B}$ exists parallel to the cylinder axis, find the induced polarization charge in the dielectric.

9–5. Two coupled circuits, A and B, are situated as shown in Fig. 9–5. Use Lenz's law to determine the direction of the induced current in resistor ab when (a) coil B is brought closer to coil A, (b) the resistance of R is decreased, (c) switch S is opened.

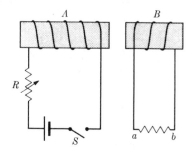

FIGURE 9–5

9-6. A 100-turn coil of circular cross section is wound compactly so that all loops lie in approximately the same plane. The average radius of the coil is 3 cm. The coil rotates about one of its diameters at 900 rev/min. When the rotation axis is vertical, the average induced emf in the coil is found to be 0.50 mv. What can be concluded about the earth's magnetic field at the location of the coil?

9-7. A circular disk rotates about its axis with angular velocity ω. The disk is made of metal with conductivity g, and its thickness is t. The rotating disk is placed between the pole faces of a magnet which produces a uniform magnetic field B over a small square area of size a^2 at the average distance r from the axis; B is perpendicular to the disk. Calculate the approximate torque on the disk. (Make a reasonable assumption about the resistance of the "eddy current circuit.")

9-8. A toroidal coil of N turns, such as is shown in Fig. 9-2, is wound on a nonmagnetic form. If the mean radius of the coil is b and the cross-sectional radius of the form is a, show that the self-inductance of the coil is given by $L = \mu_0 N^2 (b - \sqrt{b^2 - a^2})$.

9-9. A circuit consists of two coaxial cylindrical shells of radii R_1 and R_2 ($R_2 > R_1$) and common length L, connected by flat end plates. The charge flows down one shell and back up the other. What is the self-inductance of this circuit?

9-10. The toroidal coil of Problem 9-8 has 150 turns, $b = 4$ cm, and $a = 1.5$ cm. What is the self-inductance of the coil, in henries?

9-11. Two small circular loops of wire (of radii a and b) lie in the same plane at distance r apart. What is the mutual inductance between the loops if the distance r is sufficiently large that the dipole approximation may be used?

9-12. Two circular current loops with *parallel* axes are located at a distance r from each other that is sufficiently large so that the dipole approximation may be used. Show how one of the loops should be placed relative to the other so that their mutual inductance is zero.

9-13. Given two circuits: a very long straight wire, and a rectangle of dimensions h and d. The rectangle lies in a plane through the wire, the sides of length h being parallel to the wire and at distances r and $r + d$ from it. Calculate the mutual inductance between the two circuits.

9-14. Given two coaxial, circular loops of wire of radii a and b, separated by the axial distance x. Through the use of Neumann's formula, show that the mutual inductance of the loops is

$$M = \mu_0 (ab)^{1/2} \left[\left(\frac{2}{k} - k \right) K(k) - \frac{2}{k} E(k) \right],$$

where

$$k^2 = \frac{4ab}{(a + b)^2 + x^2},$$

and $K(k)$ and $E(k)$ are complete elliptic integrals defined by

$$K(k) = \int_0^{\pi/2} \frac{d\phi}{(1 - k^2 \sin^2 \phi)^{1/2}},$$

and

$$E(k) = \int_0^{\pi/2} (1 - k^2 \sin^2 \phi)^{1/2} \, d\phi.$$

9–15. Consider again the preceding problem. By expanding $1/|\mathbf{r}_2 - \mathbf{r}_1|$ in Neumann's formula according to the binomial theorem, integrate term by term to obtain

$$M = \frac{\mu_0 \pi a^2 b^2}{2h^3} \left(1 + 3 \frac{ab}{h^2} + \frac{75}{8} \frac{a^2 b^2}{h^4} + \cdots \right),$$

where $h^2 = x^2 + (a + b)^2$.

9–16. Two circuits with inductances L_1 and L_2 and resistances R_1 and R_2 are located near each other. If the mutual inductance between the circuits is M, show that a quantity of charge $Q = \mathcal{E}_0 M / R_1 R_2$ will circulate through one of them if a seat of emf $\mathcal{E}_0$ is suddenly connected in series with the other.

9–17. Given a nonmagnetic conducting medium of conductivity g which is subjected to a time-dependent magnetic field $\mathbf{B}(\mathbf{r}, t)$. Starting with the differential form of Faraday's law, Eq. (9–6), show that on the assumption of no accumulation of charge (i.e., div $\mathbf{J} = 0$) the induced eddy-current density in the medium satisfies the differential equation $\nabla^2 \mathbf{J} = g\mu_0(\partial \mathbf{J}/\partial t)$.

9–18. Show that the emf in a fixed circuit C is given by

$$\frac{d}{dt} \oint_C \mathbf{A} \cdot d\mathbf{l},$$

where $\mathbf{A}$ is the vector potential.

CHAPTER 10

MAGNETIC PROPERTIES OF MATTER

In Chapter 8 we discussed techniques for finding the magnetic induction field due to a *specified* distribution of currents. Thus, for example, if we are dealing with a current-carrying circuit consisting of a closed loop of wire, the magnetic field in the vacuum region surrounding the wire may be calculated with the aid of Biot's Law. Now let the region surrounding the wire be filled with a material medium; will the magnetic induction be altered by the presence of the matter? The answer is "yes."

All matter consists ultimately of atoms, and each atom consists of electrons in motion. These electron circuits, each of which is confined to a single atom, are what we shall call *atomic currents*. It thus appears that we have two kinds of current: (1) a true current which consists of charge transport, i.e., the motion of free electrons or charged ions, and (2) atomic currents, which are pure circulatory currents and give rise to no charge transport. However, both kinds of current may produce magnetic fields.

10–1 Magnetization. Each atomic current is a tiny closed circuit of atomic dimensions, and it may therefore be appropriately described as a magnetic dipole. In fact, the dipole moment is the quantity of interest here, since the distant magnetic induction field due to a single atom is completely determined by specifying its magnetic dipole moment, $\mathbf{m}$.

Let the magnetic moment of the ith atom be $\mathbf{m}_i$. We now define a macroscopic vector quantity, the *magnetization* $\mathbf{M}$, by the same method used to define polarization in Chapter 4. We sum up vectorially all of the dipole moments in a small volume element Δv, and then divide the result by Δv; the resulting quantity,

$$\mathbf{M} = \lim_{\Delta v \to 0} \frac{1}{\Delta v} \sum_i \mathbf{m}_i, \qquad (10\text{--}1)$$

is called the magnetic dipole moment per unit volume, or simply the magnetization. The limit process in Eq. (10–1) is our usual macroscopic limit process; Δv is made very small from the macroscopic point of view, but not so small that it does not contain a statistically large number of atoms. The quantity $\mathbf{M}$ then becomes a vector point function. In the unmagnetized state, the summation $\sum \mathbf{m}_i$ will sum to zero as a result of random orientation of the $\mathbf{m}_i$, but in the presence of an external exciting field $\mathbf{M}$ usually depends on this field. The specific dependence of $\mathbf{M}$ on $\mathbf{B}$ will be taken up in Section 10–6.

For the moment, we shall assume that $\mathbf{M}(x, y, z)$ is a known function, and shall compute the magnetized material's contribution to the magnetic field from the equations developed in Section 8–7.

The vector function $\mathbf{M}$ provides us with a macroscopic description of the atomic currents inside matter. Specifically, $\mathbf{M}$ measures the number of atomic current circuits per unit volume times the average or effective magnetic moment of each circuit. From the purely macroscopic point of view all magnetic effects due to matter can be described adequately in terms of $\mathbf{M}$, or by its derivatives. One of these derivatives, **curl M**, turns out to be the equivalent transport current density which would produce the same magnetic field as $\mathbf{M}$ itself; it is called the *magnetization current density* $\mathbf{J}_M$. Before we derive this important relationship linking $\mathbf{J}_M$ and $\mathbf{M}$, let us look at a simplified model of magnetized matter as though it consisted of atomic loop currents circulating in the same direction, side by side (Fig. 10–1). If the magnetization is uniform, the currents in the various loops tend to cancel each other out, and there is no net effective current in the interior of the material. If the magnetization is nonuniform, the cancellation will not be complete. As an example of nonuniform magnetization, consider the abrupt change in magnetization shown in Fig. 10–2; if we focus our attention on the region between the dotted lines, it is evident that there is more charge moving down than there is moving up. This we call the magnetization current. Thus, even though there is no charge transport, there is an effective motion of charge downward, and this "current" can produce a magnetic field.

It remains for us to derive the relationship between $\mathbf{J}_M$ and $\mathbf{M}$. Let us consider two small volume elements in a piece of magnetic material, each element of volume $\Delta x\,\Delta y\,\Delta z$, and located next to each other in the direction of the y-axis (Fig. 10–3). If the magnetization in the first volume element is $\mathbf{M}(x, y, z)$, then the magnetization in the second element is

$$\mathbf{M}(x, y, z) + \frac{\partial \mathbf{M}}{\partial y}\,\Delta y + \text{higher-order terms.}$$

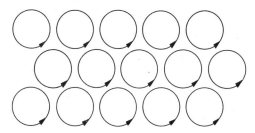

FIG. 10–1. Simplified picture of magnetic material consisting of atomic loop currents circulating in the same direction.

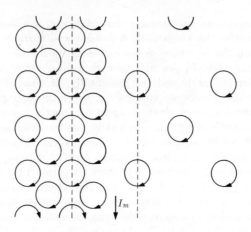

FIG. 10-2. Example of abrupt change in magnetization.

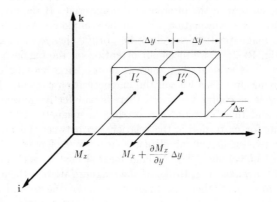

FIG. 10-3. Replacement of volume elements of magnetized material by circulating currents I_c' and I_c''.

The x-component of magnetic moment of the first element, $M_x \, \Delta x \, \Delta y \, \Delta z$, may be written in terms of a circulating current, I_c':

$$M_x \, \Delta x \, \Delta y \, \Delta z \,=\, I_c' \, \Delta y \, \Delta z. \qquad (10\text{-}2)$$

Similarly, the x-component of magnetic moment of the second element, neglecting higher-order terms which vanish in the limit where each volume element becomes very small, is

$$\left(M_x + \frac{\partial M_x}{\partial y} \Delta y\right) \Delta x \, \Delta y \, \Delta z \,=\, I_c'' \, \Delta y \, \Delta z. \qquad (10\text{-}3)$$

The net upward current in the middle region of the two volume elements is

$$I'_c - I''_c = -\frac{\partial M_x}{\partial y} \Delta x \, \Delta y. \tag{10-4}$$

We next consider two adjacent volume elements along the x-axis and focus our attention on the y-component of the magnetization in each cell. In the middle region of the two cells the net upward current due to the circulating currents which define the magnetic moments is

$$(I_c)_{up} = \frac{\partial M_y}{\partial x} \Delta x \, \Delta y. \tag{10-5}$$

These are the only circulating currents of a particular cell which give rise to a net current in the z-direction. This net current, which comes about from nonuniform magnetization, is called the magnetization current. This current is not a transport current but derives, as we have seen, from circulatory currents, i.e., from atomic currents in the material. The effective area for each of the currents in (10–4) and (10–5) is $\Delta x \, \Delta y$. Thus

$$(J_M)_z = \frac{\partial M_y}{\partial x} - \frac{\partial M_x}{\partial y} \tag{10-6a}$$

or

$$\mathbf{J}_M = \text{curl } \mathbf{M}. \tag{10-6b}$$

The magnetization current density is the curl of the magnetization.

10–2 The magnetic field produced by magnetized material. According to Eq. (10–1), each volume element $\Delta v'$ of magnetized matter is characterized by a magnetic moment

$$\Delta \mathbf{m} = \mathbf{M}(x', y', z') \, \Delta v'. \tag{10-7}$$

Using the results of Section 8–7, we may write the contribution to the magnetic field at point (x, y, z) from each $\Delta \mathbf{m}$ (or, equivalently, from each $\Delta v'$). The magnetic field is then obtained as an integral over the entire volume of material, V_0. This procedure is indicated schematically in Fig. 10–4.

Instead of calculating $\mathbf{B}$ directly, we find it expedient to work with the vector potential $\mathbf{A}$, and to obtain $\mathbf{B}$ subsequently by means of the curl operation. According to Section 8–7, the vector potential at (x, y, z) is given by

$$\mathbf{A}(x, y, z) = \frac{\mu_0}{4\pi} \int_{V_0} \frac{\mathbf{M}(x', y', z') \times (\mathbf{r} - \mathbf{r}')}{|\mathbf{r} - \mathbf{r}'|^3} \, dv'$$

$$= \frac{\mu_0}{4\pi} \int_{V_0} \mathbf{M}(x', y', z') \times \text{grad}' \frac{1}{|\mathbf{r} - \mathbf{r}'|} \, dv'. \tag{10-8}$$

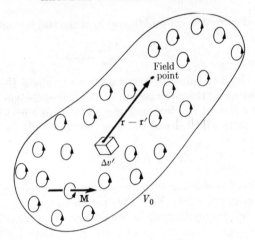

F<small>IG</small>. 10–4. Contribution to the magnetic induction from a distribution of magnetized material.

By means of the vector identities (I–9) and (I–17) in Table 1–1, this integral may be transformed to

$$\mathbf{A}(x, y, z) = \frac{\mu_0}{4\pi} \int_{V_0} \frac{\mathrm{curl'}\,\mathbf{M}}{|\mathbf{r} - \mathbf{r'}|}\,dv' + \frac{\mu_0}{4\pi} \int_{S_0} \frac{\mathbf{M} \times \mathbf{n}}{|\mathbf{r} - \mathbf{r'}|}\,da', \quad (10\text{–}9)$$

where S_0 is the surface of V_0. Using Eq. (10–6b) and defining a surface magnetization current density $\mathbf{j}_M$ (i.e., a magnetization current per unit length flowing in the surface layer) by the relation

$$\mathbf{j}_M = \mathbf{M} \times \mathbf{n}, \quad (10\text{–}10)$$

we may write Eq. (10–9) as

$$\mathbf{A}(\mathbf{r}) = \frac{\mu_0}{4\pi} \int_{V_0} \frac{\mathbf{J}_M(\mathbf{r'})\,dv'}{|\mathbf{r} - \mathbf{r'}|} + \frac{\mu_0}{4\pi} \int_{S_0} \frac{\mathbf{j}_M\,da'}{|\mathbf{r} - \mathbf{r'}|}. \quad (10\text{–}11)$$

We might have ventured to predict the final expression, Eq. (10–11). Nevertheless, it is gratifying to see that it has come out of the mathematics in a natural way. Thus the vector potential produced by a distribution of atomic currents inside matter has the same form as that produced by a distribution of true transport currents. We should point out that Eq. (10–10) is the proper expression for the surface current density which is consistent with $\mathbf{J}_M = \mathrm{curl'}\,\mathbf{M}$. The $\mathbf{j}_M$ must be introduced whenever $\mathbf{M}$ changes abruptly, as it might at the interface between two media, but if the region of discontinuity in $\mathbf{M}$ is imagined to be spread out over the distance $\Delta\xi$, then it can be shown that $\mathbf{j}_M$ is contained in the term $\mathbf{J}_M\,\Delta\xi$.

Although Eq. (10–11) is both correct and of such form that it integrates nicely with the results of Chapter 8, it presents some practical difficulties when it comes to the task of computing **B** from a specified distribution of magnetization.   First, there is the **curl M** operation to perform, and second, another curl operation is involved in obtaining **B** from the **A** field.   It certainly is preferable to work with scalar quantities if possible, and the gradient of a scalar field (such as we encountered in electrostatics) is easier to compute than the curl of a vector field.   For this reason we go back to Eq. (10–8) and try another approach.   We are interested, after all, in **B**, not **A**, so let us formally take the curl:

$$\mathbf{B}(\mathbf{r}) = \mathbf{curl\,A}$$

$$= \frac{\mu_0}{4\pi} \int_{V_0} \mathbf{curl} \left[\mathbf{M} \times \frac{(\mathbf{r} - \mathbf{r}')}{|\mathbf{r} - \mathbf{r}'|^3} \right] dv', \qquad (10\text{–}12)$$

where the differential operators in the curl act on the unprimed coordinates.

As the reader may have anticipated, our next job is to transform the integrand of Eq. (10–12).   To do so, we appeal to the vector identities of Table 1–1.

According to (I–10),

$$\mathbf{curl\,(a \times b)} = \mathbf{a}\,\mathrm{div}\,\mathbf{b} - \mathbf{b}\,\mathrm{div}\,\mathbf{a} + (\mathbf{b} \cdot \nabla)\mathbf{a} - (\mathbf{a} \cdot \nabla)\mathbf{b}.$$

Letting $\mathbf{a} = \mathbf{M}$ and $\mathbf{b} = (\mathbf{r} - \mathbf{r}')/|\mathbf{r} - \mathbf{r}'|^3$, and noting that the differentiations are with respect to the unprimed coordinates, we find that the identity reduces to

$$\mathbf{curl} \left[\mathbf{M} \times \frac{(\mathbf{r} - \mathbf{r}')}{|\mathbf{r} - \mathbf{r}'|^3} \right] = \mathbf{M}\,\mathrm{div} \left[\frac{(\mathbf{r} - \mathbf{r}')}{|\mathbf{r} - \mathbf{r}'|^3} \right]$$

$$- (\mathbf{M} \cdot \nabla) \frac{(\mathbf{r} - \mathbf{r}')}{|\mathbf{r} - \mathbf{r}'|^3}, \qquad (10\text{–}13)$$

since $\mathrm{div}\,\mathbf{M}(x', y', z') = 0$, etc.   Thus

$$\mathbf{B}(\mathbf{r}) = \mathbf{B}_\mathrm{I}(\mathbf{r}) + \mathbf{B}_\mathrm{II}(\mathbf{r}), \qquad (10\text{–}14)$$

where

$$\mathbf{B}_\mathrm{I}(\mathbf{r}) = \frac{\mu_0}{4\pi} \int_{V_0} \mathbf{M}\,\mathrm{div} \left[\frac{(\mathbf{r} - \mathbf{r}')}{|\mathbf{r} - \mathbf{r}'|^3} \right] dv', \qquad (10\text{–}14\mathrm{a})$$

$$\mathbf{B}_\mathrm{II}(\mathbf{r}) = - \frac{\mu_0}{4\pi} \int_{V_0} (\mathbf{M} \cdot \nabla) \frac{(\mathbf{r} - \mathbf{r}')}{|\mathbf{r} - \mathbf{r}'|^3}\, dv'. \qquad (10\text{–}14\mathrm{b})$$

We consider the $\mathbf{B}_\mathrm{I}$ integral first.   It is convenient to divide the volume of the magnet, V_0, into two regions: (1) a small *spherical* region V_1 surrounding the point (x, y, z) [Fig. 10–5], and (2) the remaining volume, $V_0 - V_1$. Then $\mathbf{B_I}$ is written as the sum of two integrals, one over V_1 and another over $V_0 - V_1$. Since the divergence term in the integrand vanishes everywhere except at the point $\mathbf{r'} = \mathbf{r}$, the integral over $V_0 - V_1$ is zero.   Hence

$$\mathbf{B_I}(\mathbf{r}) = \frac{\mu_0}{4\pi} \int_{V_1} \mathbf{M} \text{ div} \left[\frac{(\mathbf{r} - \mathbf{r'})}{|\mathbf{r} - \mathbf{r'}|^3} \right] dv'$$

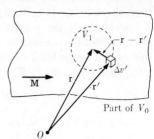

$$= -\frac{\mu_0}{4\pi} \int_{V_1} \mathbf{M} \text{ div}' \left[\frac{(\mathbf{r} - \mathbf{r'})}{|\mathbf{r} - \mathbf{r'}|^3} \right] dv'$$

$$= \frac{\mu_0}{4\pi} \int_{V_1} \mathbf{M} \text{ div}' \, (\mathbf{s}/s^3) \, dv',$$

FIG. 10–5.   Contribution from the vicinity of the field point.

where $\mathbf{s} \equiv \mathbf{r'} - \mathbf{r}$. The size of V_1 has not been specified, the only requirement is that it contain the point $\mathbf{s} = 0$. If V_1 is chosen small enough, $\mathbf{M}$ is essentially constant over the region V_1 and is equal to $\mathbf{M}(x, y, z)$.   Therefore

$$\mathbf{B_I}(\mathbf{r}) = \frac{\mu_0}{4\pi} \mathbf{M}(\mathbf{r}) \int_{V_1} \text{div}' \, (\mathbf{s}/s^3) \, dv'$$

$$= \frac{\mu_0}{4\pi} \mathbf{M}(\mathbf{r}) \int_{S_1} \frac{\mathbf{s} \cdot \mathbf{n}}{s^3} \, da'$$

$$= \mu_0 \mathbf{M}(\mathbf{r}). \tag{10–15}$$

We next consider the $\mathbf{B_{II}}$ integral.   The integrand may be transformed by means of a second identity (I–5) which becomes

$$\nabla \left[\mathbf{M} \cdot \frac{(\mathbf{r} - \mathbf{r'})}{|\mathbf{r} - \mathbf{r'}|^3} \right] = (\mathbf{M} \cdot \nabla) \frac{(\mathbf{r} - \mathbf{r'})}{|\mathbf{r} - \mathbf{r'}|^3}$$

$$+ \mathbf{M} \times \text{curl} \left[\frac{(\mathbf{r} - \mathbf{r'})}{|\mathbf{r} - \mathbf{r'}|^3} \right]. \tag{10–16}$$

The last term in (10–16) contains

$$\text{curl} \left[\frac{(\mathbf{r} - \mathbf{r'})}{|\mathbf{r} - \mathbf{r'}|^3} \right] = -\text{curl grad} \frac{1}{|\mathbf{r} - \mathbf{r'}|},$$

which vanishes identically.   Hence

$$\mathbf{B_{II}}(\mathbf{r}) = -\mu_0 \nabla \frac{1}{4\pi} \int_{V_0} \mathbf{M}(\mathbf{r'}) \cdot \frac{(\mathbf{r} - \mathbf{r'})}{|\mathbf{r} - \mathbf{r'}|^3} \, dv',$$

which may be written as

$$\mathbf{B}_{\mathrm{II}}(\mathbf{r}) = -\mu_0 \nabla U^*(\mathbf{r}). \tag{10–17}$$

The quantity $U^*(\mathbf{r})$ is a scalar field. We shall call it the magnetic scalar potential due to magnetic material:

$$U^*(\mathbf{r}) = \frac{1}{4\pi} \int_{V_0} \mathbf{M}(\mathbf{r}') \cdot \frac{(\mathbf{r} - \mathbf{r}')}{|\mathbf{r} - \mathbf{r}'|^3} \, dv'. \tag{10–18}$$

Adding the two contributions, (10–15) and (10–17), we find for the magnetic induction field:

$$\mathbf{B}(\mathbf{r}) = -\mu_0 \nabla U^*(\mathbf{r}) + \mu_0 \mathbf{M}(\mathbf{r}). \tag{10–19}$$

Thus the magnetic induction due to a magnetized distribution of matter may be expressed as the sum of two terms: the gradient of a scalar field plus a term proportional to the local magnetization. At an external point, i.e., in vacuum, $\mathbf{M}$ is zero, and the magnetic induction is then just the gradient of a scalar field.

10–3 Magnetic scalar potential and magnetic pole density. The expression for the magnetic scalar potential, Eq. (10–18), is similar in form to that for the electrostatic potential arising from polarized dielectric material. Here again mathematical transformation is suggested:

$$\begin{aligned} \frac{\mathbf{M} \cdot (\mathbf{r} - \mathbf{r}')}{|\mathbf{r} - \mathbf{r}'|^3} &= \mathbf{M} \cdot \mathbf{grad}' \frac{1}{|\mathbf{r} - \mathbf{r}'|} \\ &= \mathrm{div}' \frac{\mathbf{M}}{|\mathbf{r} - \mathbf{r}'|} - \frac{1}{|\mathbf{r} - \mathbf{r}'|} \mathrm{div}' \, \mathbf{M}, \end{aligned} \tag{10–20}$$

so that Eq. (10–18) becomes

$$U^*(\mathbf{r}) = \frac{1}{4\pi} \int_{S_0} \frac{\mathbf{M} \cdot \mathbf{n} \, da'}{|\mathbf{r} - \mathbf{r}'|} - \frac{1}{4\pi} \int_{V_0} \frac{\mathrm{div}' \, \mathbf{M}}{|\mathbf{r} - \mathbf{r}'|} \, dv', \tag{10–21}$$

where S_0 is the surface of the region V_0.

By analogy with Section 4–2, it is expedient to define two scalar quantities:

$$\rho_M(\mathbf{r}') \equiv -\mathrm{div}' \, \mathbf{M}(\mathbf{r}'), \tag{10–22}$$

called the *magnetic pole density*, and

$$\sigma_M(\mathbf{r}') \equiv \mathbf{M}(\mathbf{r}') \cdot \mathbf{n}, \tag{10–23}$$

the *surface density of magnetic pole strength*. These quantities are quite useful; they play the same role in the theory of magnetism that ρ_P and

σ_P play in dielectric theory. The units of ρ_M and σ_M are amp/m^2 and amp/m, respectively.

Consider, for example, a uniformly magnetized bar magnet. Since the magnetization is uniform, $\rho_M = 0$. The only surface densities which do not vanish are on those surfaces which have a normal component of the magnetization; these are called the *poles* of the magnet. This is a somewhat idealized example, yet not too different from the common laboratory bar magnet familiar to the reader. (In practice, the poles of a magnet exert a demagnetizing influence which destroys the uniformity of **M** and thus spreads each pole over a somewhat larger region than just the surface.)

The total pole strength of every magnet is zero. This statement follows directly from the divergence theorem:

$$\int_{V_0} (-\operatorname{div} \mathbf{M}) \, dv + \int_{S_0} \mathbf{M} \cdot \mathbf{n} \, da = 0.$$

We now complete the derivation which was started earlier. Equation (10–18) becomes

$$U^*(\mathbf{r}) = \frac{1}{4\pi} \int_{V_0} \frac{\rho_M \, dv'}{|\mathbf{r} - \mathbf{r}'|} + \frac{1}{4\pi} \int_{S_0} \frac{\sigma_M \, da'}{|\mathbf{r} - \mathbf{r}'|}, \qquad (10\text{–}18\text{a})$$

and $\mathbf{B}(x, y, z)$ is obtained as $-\mu_0$ times the gradient with respect to the unprimed coordinates, plus the term $\mu_0 \mathbf{M}$:

$$\mathbf{B}(\mathbf{r}) = \frac{\mu_0}{4\pi} \int_{V_0} \rho_M \frac{(\mathbf{r} - \mathbf{r}')}{|\mathbf{r} - \mathbf{r}'|^3} \, dv' + \frac{\mu_0}{4\pi} \int_{S_0} \sigma_M \frac{(\mathbf{r} - \mathbf{r}')}{|\mathbf{r} - \mathbf{r}'|^3} \, da' + \mu_0 \mathbf{M}(\mathbf{r}).$$
$$(10\text{–}19\text{a})$$

This equation represents the contribution from the magnetized material in V_0 to the magnetic induction at (x, y, z).

10–4 Sources of the magnetic field. Magnetic intensity. In the preceding sections we have seen how magnetized material produces a magnetic field. Furthermore, Chapter 8 dealt with the magnetic effects of conventional currents. In the general case, both types of magnetic sources are present: conventional or true currents which can be measured in the laboratory, and the atomic currents inside matter. It is important to realize that under certain conditions the same piece of matter may produce a magnetic field both because it is magnetized and because it is carrying a true current of charge carriers. Thus, for example, one of our best magnetic materials, iron, may carry a true current via its free electrons, but the fixed iron ions in the crystal contain atomic currents which can be oriented to produce a strong magnetization.

In general, the expression for the magnetic field may be written as

$$\mathbf{B}(\mathbf{r}) = \frac{\mu_0}{4\pi} \int_V \frac{\mathbf{J} \times (\mathbf{r} - \mathbf{r}')}{|\mathbf{r} - \mathbf{r}'|^3} \, dv' - \mu_0 \mathbf{\nabla} U^*(\mathbf{r}) + \mu_0 \mathbf{M}(\mathbf{r}), \quad (10\text{–}24)$$

where

$$U^*(\mathbf{r}) = \frac{1}{4\pi} \int_V \frac{\rho_M \, dv'}{|\mathbf{r} - \mathbf{r}'|} + \frac{1}{4\pi} \int_S \frac{\sigma_M \, da'}{|\mathbf{r} - \mathbf{r}'|}. \quad (10\text{–}25)$$

The volume V extends over all current-carrying regions and over all matter; the surface S includes all surfaces and interfaces between different media. The current density $\mathbf{J}$ includes all true currents of the charge transport variety, whereas the effect of atomic currents is found in the magnetization vector $\mathbf{M}$.

Equation (10–24) may be solved for $\mathbf{B}$ if $\mathbf{M}$ and $\mathbf{J}$ are specified at all points. In most problems, however, $\mathbf{J}$ is specified but $\mathbf{M}(x', y', z')$ depends on $\mathbf{B}(x', y', z')$, so that even if the functional form of $\mathbf{M}(\mathbf{B})$ is known, (10–24) provides at best an integral equation for $\mathbf{B}$. To help get around this difficulty we introduce an auxiliary magnetic vector, the *magnetic intensity* $\mathbf{H}$, defined by

$$\mathbf{H} = \frac{1}{\mu_0} \mathbf{B} - \mathbf{M}. \quad (10\text{–}26)$$

By combining (10–24) and (10–26) we obtain

$$\mathbf{H}(\mathbf{r}) = \frac{1}{4\pi} \int_V \frac{\mathbf{J} \times (\mathbf{r} - \mathbf{r}')}{|\mathbf{r} - \mathbf{r}'|^3} \, dv - \mathbf{\nabla} U^*(\mathbf{r}). \quad (10\text{–}27)$$

It appears that we have gained nothing by this maneuver, because $\mathbf{H}$ still depends on $\mathbf{M}$ through ρ_M and σ_M, but in the next section we shall show how $\mathbf{H}$ is related to the true current density $\mathbf{J}$ through a differential equation. The situation is similar to the electrostatic case, where the auxiliary vector $\mathbf{D}$ is related to the free charge density through its divergence.

The field vector $\mathbf{H}$ plays an important role in magnetic theory, particularly in problems involving permanent magnets. These will be discussed in later sections of the chapter. The units of $\mathbf{H}$ are the same as those of $\mathbf{M}$, namely, amp/m.

10–5 The field equations. In Chapter 8, the basic equations describing the magnetic effects of conventional currents were expressed in differential form:

$$\text{div } \mathbf{B} = 0, \qquad \text{curl } \mathbf{B} = \mu_0 \mathbf{J}.$$

We should now like to see how these equations are modified when the magnetic field $\mathbf{B}$ includes a contribution from magnetized material.

The reader will recall that the divergence equation (div $\mathbf{B} = 0$) came about because $\mathbf{B}$ could be written as the curl of a vector function $\mathbf{A}$. But this result is not limited to magnetic fields produced by conventional currents. The field produced by magnetized matter is also derivable from a vector potential; in fact, this approach was used in Section 10–2. Thus $\mathbf{B}$ may always be written as **curl A**, and the divergence equation follows of necessity:

$$\text{div } \mathbf{B} = 0. \tag{10–28}$$

The "curl equation" is the differential form of Ampere's circuital law. Here we must be careful to include all types of currents which can produce a magnetic field. Hence, in the general case, this equation is properly written as

$$\mathbf{curl\,B} = \mu_0(\mathbf{J} + \mathbf{J}_M), \tag{10–29}$$

where $\mathbf{J}$ is the true current density, and $\mathbf{J}_M$ is the magnetization current density. Equation (10–6b) may be combined with (10–29) to yield

$$\mathbf{curl}\left(\frac{1}{\mu_0}\mathbf{B} - \mathbf{M}\right) = \mathbf{J},$$

which, according to (10–26), is equivalent to

$$\mathbf{curl\,H} = \mathbf{J}. \tag{10–30}$$

Hence, the auxiliary magnetic vector $\mathbf{H}$ is related to the *true current density* through its curl.

Equations (10–28) and (10–30) are the fundamental magnetic field equations. These equations, together with appropriate boundary conditions and an experimental relationship between $\mathbf{B}$ and $\mathbf{H}$, are sufficient to solve magnetic problems. In some instances it is preferable to use an integral formulation of the theory. With the aid of Stokes' theorem, (10–30) may be converted to

$$\int_S \mathbf{curl\,H} \cdot \mathbf{n}\, da = \oint_C \mathbf{H} \cdot d\mathbf{l}$$

$$= \int_S \mathbf{J} \cdot \mathbf{n}\, da,$$

or

$$\oint_C \mathbf{H} \cdot d\mathbf{l} = I. \tag{10–31}$$

In other words, the line integral of the tangential component of the magnetic intensity around a closed path C is equal to the entire transport current through the area bounded by the curve C.

Because of the divergence theorem, Eq. (10–28) is equivalent to

$$\oint_S \mathbf{B} \cdot \mathbf{n} \, da = 0. \tag{10–32}$$

The magnetic flux through any closed surface is zero.

10–6 Magnetic susceptibility and permeability. Hysteresis. In order to solve problems in magnetic theory, it is essential to have a relationship between $\mathbf{B}$ and $\mathbf{H}$ or, equivalently, a relationship between $\mathbf{M}$ and one of the magnetic field vectors. These relationships depend on the nature of the magnetic material and are usually obtained from experiment.

In a large class of materials there exists an approximately linear relationship between $\mathbf{M}$ and $\mathbf{H}$. If the material is isotropic as well as linear,*

$$\mathbf{M} = \chi_m \mathbf{H}, \tag{10–33}$$

where the dimensionless scalar quantity χ_m is called the *magnetic susceptibility*. If χ_m is positive, the material is called *paramagnetic*, and the magnetic induction is strengthened by the presence of the material. If χ_m is negative, the material is *diamagnetic*, and the magnetic induction is weakened by the presence of the material. Although χ_m is a function of the temperature, and sometimes varies quite drastically with temperature, it is generally safe to say that χ_m for paramagnetic and diamagnetic materials is quite small; i.e.,

$$|\chi_m| \ll 1 \quad \text{(for paramagnetic, diamagnetic materials).} \tag{10–34}$$

The susceptibilities of some common materials are given in Table 10–1.

In most handbooks and tabulations of physical data χ_m is not listed directly, but instead is given as the *mass susceptibility*, $\chi_{m,\text{mass}}$, or the *molar susceptibility*, $\chi_{m,\text{molar}}$. These are defined by

$$\chi_m = \chi_{m,\text{mass}} \, d, \tag{10–35}$$

$$\chi_m = \chi_{m,\text{molar}} \frac{d}{A}, \tag{10–36}$$

where d is the mass density of the material and A is the molecular weight. Since $\mathbf{M}$ and $\mathbf{H}$ both have the dimensions of magnetic moment per unit volume, it is evident that $\chi_{m,\text{mass}} \mathbf{H}$ and $\chi_{m,\text{molar}} \mathbf{H}$ give magnetic moment per unit mass and magnetic moment per mole, respectively. For convenience, the mass susceptibility is also listed in Table 10–1.

---

* If the material is anisotropic but linear, Eq. (10–33) is replaced by the tensor relationships

$$M_x = \chi_{m,11} H_x + \chi_{m,12} H_y + \chi_{m,13} H_z,$$

etc. In these circumstances $\mathbf{M}$ does not necessarily have the same direction as $\mathbf{H}$. We shall restrict ourselves in this book to isotropic media.

TABLE 10–1

MAGNETIC SUSCEPTIBILITY OF SOME PARAMAGNETIC AND
DIAMAGNETIC MATERIALS AT ROOM TEMPERATURE.*

Material	χ_m	$\chi_{m,\text{mass}}$, m^3/kgm
Aluminum	2.3×10^{-5}	0.82×10^{-8}
Bismuth	-1.66×10^{-5}	-1.70×10^{-8}
Copper	-0.98×10^{-5}	-0.11×10^{-8}
Diamond	-2.2×10^{-5}	-0.62×10^{-8}
Gadolinium chloride (GdCl$_3$)	276.0×10^{-5}	114.0×10^{-8}
Gold	-3.6×10^{-5}	-0.19×10^{-8}
Magnesium	1.2×10^{-5}	0.69×10^{-8}
Mercury	-3.2×10^{-5}	-0.24×10^{-8}
Silver	-2.6×10^{-5}	-0.25×10^{-8}
Sodium	-0.24×10^{-5}	-0.25×10^{-8}
Titanium	7.06×10^{-5}	1.57×10^{-8}
Tungsten	6.8×10^{-5}	0.35×10^{-8}
Carbon dioxide (1 atm)	-0.99×10^{-8}	-0.53×10^{-8}
Hydrogen (1 atm)	-0.21×10^{-8}	-2.47×10^{-8}
Nitrogen (1 atm)	-0.50×10^{-8}	-0.43×10^{-8}
Oxygen (1 atm)	209.0×10^{-8}	155.0×10^{-8}

* Data obtained from the *Handbook of Chemistry and Physics*, 33rd edition, Chemical Rubber Publishing Co., Cleveland, Ohio. Practically all sources of data list magnetic susceptibilities in gaussian (cgs) units; if the superscript (1) is used to indicate the constant in the gaussian system, then $\chi_m = 4\pi\chi_m^{(1)}$ and $\chi_{m,\text{mass}} = 4\pi \times 10^{-3}\chi_{m,\text{mass}}^{(1)}$.

A linear relationship between **M** and **H** implies also a linear relationship between **B** and **H**:

$$\mathbf{B} = \mu\mathbf{H}, \tag{10–37}$$

where the *permeability* μ is obtained from the combination of Eqs. (10–26) and (10–33);

$$\mu = \mu_0(1 + \chi_m). \tag{10–38}$$

The dimensionless quantity

$$K_m = \frac{\mu}{\mu_0} = 1 + \chi_m \tag{10–39}$$

is sometimes tabulated instead of χ_m. This quantity, K_m is called the *relative permeability.* For the paramagnetic and diamagnetic materials of Table 10–1, it is evident that K_m is very close to unity.

The *ferromagnetics* form another class of magnetic material. Such a

TABLE 10–2

PROPERTIES OF FERROMAGNETIC MATERIALS AT ROOM
TEMPERATURE*

M_s = saturation magnetization, H_s = magnetic intensity
required for saturation, H_c = coercivity, B_r = remanence

Material	Composition, %	$\mu_0 M_s$, w/m^2	H_s, amp/m	K_m, maximum
Iron (annealed)		2.16	1.6×10^5	5,500
Cobalt		1.79	7.0×10^5	
Nickel		0.61	5.5×10^5	
ALLOYS			H_c amp/m	
Iron-silicon	96 Fe, 4 Si	1.95	24	7,000
Permalloy	55 Fe, 45 Ni	1.60	24	25,000
Mumetal	5 Cu, 2 Cr, 77 Ni, 16 Fe	0.65	4	100,000
Permendur	50 Co, 50 Fe	2.40	16	5,000
Mn-Zn ferrite	$Mn_xZn_{(1-x)}$ Fe_2O_4	0.34	16	2,500
Ni-Zn ferrite	$Ni_xZn_{(1-x)}$ Fe_2O_4	0.37	30	2,500
		B_r w/m^2		
Cobalt steel	52 Fe, 36 Co, 7W, 3.5 Cr, 0.7 C	0.95	18×10^3	
Alnico V	51 Fe, 8 Al, 14 Ni 24 Co, 3 Cu	1.25	44×10^3	

* Data from *American Institute of Physics Handbook*, McGraw-Hill, New
York, 1957.

material is characterized by a possible permanent magnetization and by
the fact that its presence usually has a profound effect on the magnetic
induction. Ferromagnetic materials are *not* linear, so that Eqs. (10–33)
and (10–37) with constant χ and μ *do not* apply. It has been expedient,
however, to use Eq. (10–37) as the defining equation for μ, i.e., with
$\mu = \mu(\mathbf{H})$, but the reader should be cautioned that this practice can
lead to difficulty in certain situations. If the μ of a ferromagnetic material
is defined by Eq. (10–37), then, depending on the value of $\mathbf{H}$, μ goes
through an entire range of values from infinity to zero and may be either
positive or negative. The best advice which can be given is to consider
each problem involving ferromagnetism separately, try to determine

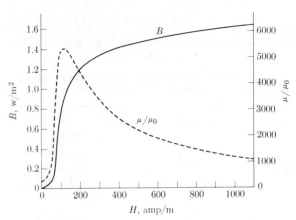

FIG. 10-6. Magnetization curve and relative permeability of commercial iron (annealed).

which region of the B-H diagram is important for the particular problem, and make approximations appropriate to this region.

First, let us consider an unmagnetized sample of ferromagnetic material. If the magnetic intensity, initially zero, is increased *monotonically*, then the **B-H** relationship will trace out a curve something like that shown in Fig. 10-6. This is called the *magnetization curve* of the material. It is evident that μ's taken from the magnetization curve, using the expression $\mu = B/H$, are always of the same sign (positive), but they show a rather large spectrum of values. The maximum permeability occurs at the "knee" of the curve; in some materials this maximum permeability is as large as $10^5 \mu_0$; in others it is much lower. The reason for the knee in the curve is that the magnetization **M** reaches a maximum value in the material, and

$$\mathbf{B} = \mu_0(\mathbf{H} + \mathbf{M})$$

continues to increase at large **H** only because of the $\mu_0\mathbf{H}$ term. The maximum value of **M** is called the *saturation magnetization* of the material.

Next consider a ferromagnetic specimen magnetized by the above procedure. If the magnetic intensity **H** is decreased, the **B-H** relationship does not follow back down the curve of Fig. 10-6, but instead moves along the new curve of Fig. 10-7 to point **r**. The magnetization, once established, does not disappear with the removal of **H**; in fact, it takes a reversed magnetic intensity to reduce the magnetization to zero. If **H** continues to build up in the reversed direction, then **M** (and hence **B**) will establish itself in the reversed direction, and Fig. 10-7 begins to show a certain symmetry. Finally, when **H** once again increases, the

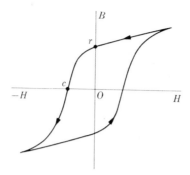

FIG. 10-7. Typical hysteresis loop of a ferromagnetic material.

operating point follows the lower curve of Fig. 10-7. Thus the **B-H** curve for increasing **H** is entirely different from that for decreasing **H**. This phenomenon is called *hysteresis*, from the Greek word meaning "to lag"; the magnetization literally lags the exciting field.

The curve of Fig. 10-7 is called the hysteresis loop of the material. The value of **B** at point r is known as the retentivity or *remanence;* the magnitude of **H** at point c is called the coercive force or *coercivity* of the material. From Fig. 10-7 it is evident that the value of μ, defined by Eq. (10-37), is negative in the second and fourth quadrants of the diagram. The shape of the hysteresis loop depends not only upon the nature of the ferromagnetic material (Fig. 10-8) but also on the maximum value of **H** to which the material is subjected (Fig. 10-9). However, once $\mathbf{H}_{max}$ is sufficient to produce saturation in the material, the hysteresis loop does not change shape with increasing $\mathbf{H}_{max}$.

For certain applications it is desirable to know the effective permeability of a material to a small alternating H-field superposed on a large constant field. Thus if ΔB is the change in magnetic field produced by a change ΔH in the magnetic intensity, the *incremental permeability* μ_{in} is defined by

$$\mu_{in} = \frac{\Delta B}{\Delta H},\qquad (10\text{-}40)$$

and is approximately equal to the slope of the hysteresis curve which goes through the point in question.

Ferromagnetic materials are used either (1) to increase the magnetic flux of a current circuit, or (2) as sources of the magnetic field (permanent magnets). For use as a permanent magnet, the material is first magnetized to saturation by placing it in a strong magnetic field (i.e., by placing it between the poles of an electromagnet or by placing it in a solenoid subjected to a momentary large current). However, when the

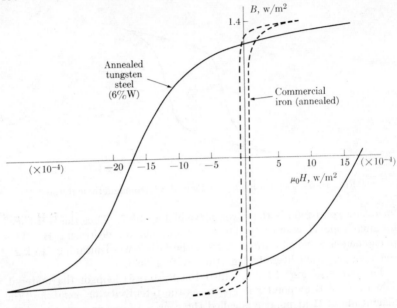

Fig. 10–8. Comparison of the hysteresis curves of several materials. (Note that $\mu_0 H$ is plotted along the abscissa instead of just H. $\mu_0 = 4\pi \times 10^{-7}$ w/amp·m.) Data from R. M. Bozorth, *Ferromagnetism*, Van Nostrand, N. Y. 1951.

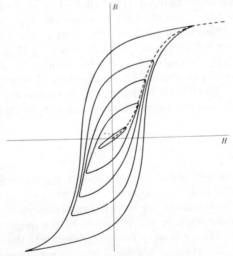

Fig. 10–9. Major hysteresis loop and several minor hysteresis loops for a typical material.

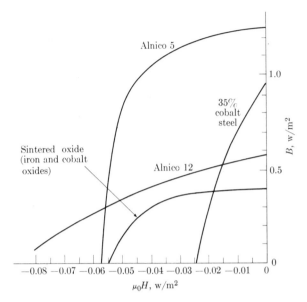

FIG. 10–10.   Hysteresis curves of permanent magnet materials. (Note that $\mu_0 H$ is plotted along the abscissa instead of just H.)

permanent magnet is removed from the external field, it will in general be subject to a demagnetizing field; this will be discussed in detail in Sections 10–10 and 10–11. Thus the second quadrant of the hysteresis loop diagram is the important part of the **B-H** relationship for a permanent magnet material (Fig. 10–10).

10–7 Boundary conditions on the field vectors. Before we can solve magnetic problems, even simple ones, we must know how the field vectors **B** and **H** change in passing an interface between two media. The interface to be considered may be between two media with different magnetic properties, or between a material medium and vacuum.

Consider two media, 1 and 2, in contact, as shown in Fig. 10–11. Let us construct the small pillbox-shaped surface S which intersects the interface, the height of the pillbox being negligibly small in comparison with the diameter of the bases. Applying the flux integral, Eq. (10–32), to the surface S, we find

$$\mathbf{B}_2 \cdot \mathbf{n}_2 \, \Delta S + \mathbf{B}_1 \cdot \mathbf{n}_1 \, \Delta S = 0,$$

where $\mathbf{n}_2$ and $\mathbf{n}_1$ are the outward-directed normals to the upper and lower surfaces of the pillbox. Since $\mathbf{n}_2 = -\mathbf{n}_1$, and since either of these

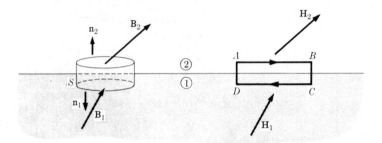

FIG. 10–11. Boundary conditions on the field vectors at the interface between two media may be obtained by applying Gauss' law to S, and integrating $\mathbf{H} \cdot d\mathbf{l}$ around the path $ABCDA$.

normals may serve as the normal to the interface,

$$(\mathbf{B}_2 - \mathbf{B}_1) \cdot \mathbf{n}_2 = 0, \tag{10–41a}$$

or

$$B_{2n} - B_{1n} = 0. \tag{10–41b}$$

Thus, the normal component of $\mathbf{B}$ is continuous across an interface.

A boundary condition on the $\mathbf{H}$-field may be obtained by applying Ampere's circuital law, Eq. (10–31), to the rectangular path $ABCD$ in Fig. 10–11. On this path the lengths AB and CD will be taken equal to Δl and the segments AD and BC will be assumed negligibly small. The current through the rectangle is negligible unless there is a true surface current. Therefore

$$\mathbf{H}_2 \cdot \Delta \mathbf{l} + \mathbf{H}_1 \cdot (-\Delta \mathbf{l}) = |\mathbf{j}_s \times \Delta \mathbf{l}|, \tag{10–42a}$$

or

$$H_{2t} - H_{1t} = |\mathbf{j}_s \times \mathbf{l}_0|, \tag{10–42b}$$

where $\mathbf{j}_s$ is the *surface* current density (transport current per unit length in the surface layer) and $\mathbf{l}_0$ is a unit vector in the direction of $\Delta \mathbf{l}$. Thus the tangential component of the magnetic intensity is continuous across an interface unless there is a true surface current. Finally, since Eq. (10–42) holds for any segment $\Delta \mathbf{l}$ which is parallel to the interface, the equation may be written as

$$\mathbf{n}_2 \times (\mathbf{H}_2 - \mathbf{H}_1) = \mathbf{j}_s. \tag{10–42c}$$

Before completing this section, we shall prove one other important property of the magnetic induction $\mathbf{B}$, namely, that its flux is everywhere continuous. Let us focus our attention on a region of space, and construct *magnetic field lines*, which are imaginary lines drawn in such

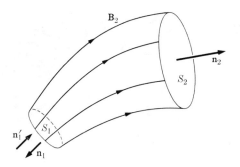

FIG. 10–12. A tube of magnetic induction.

a way that the direction of a line at any point is the direction of **B** at that point. Next we imagine a tube of flux, a volume bounded on the sides by lines of **B** but not cut by them (Fig. 10–12). The tube is terminated on the ends by the surfaces S_1 and S_2. Applying the divergence theorem, we obtain

$$\int_V \operatorname{div} \mathbf{B} \, dv = 0$$

$$= \int_{S_2} \mathbf{B} \cdot \mathbf{n} \, da - \int_{S_1} \mathbf{B} \cdot \mathbf{n}' \, da$$

$$= \Phi(S_2) - \Phi(S_1). \tag{10–43}$$

Thus the same magnetic flux enters the tube through S_1 as leaves through S_2. The flux lines can never terminate, but must eventually join back onto themselves, forming closed loops.

The previous statements apply, of course, to the **B**-field; it is perhaps worth while noting that they do not apply to the **H**-field, since div **H** = −div **M**, which is not everywhere zero. Thus, from the divergence theorem applied to a tube of magnetic intensity, we find

$$\int_{S_1} \mathbf{H} \cdot \mathbf{n} \, da - \int_{S_2} \mathbf{H} \cdot \mathbf{n}' \, da$$

$$= \int_V \rho_M \, dv. \tag{10–44}$$

The discontinuity in the magnetic intensity flux is determined by the total magnetic pole strength intercepted by the flux tube.

10–8 Current circuits containing magnetic media. In Chapter 8 we dealt with magnetic fields produced by current circuits *in vacuum*. One of the examples taken up in the problems (Problem 8–15) was that of a uniformly wound toroid of N turns carrying current I (Fig. 10–13).

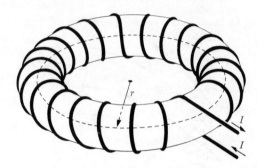

FIG. 10–13. A toroidal winding.

Let us solve the toroid problem again, but this time with the region inside the windings filled with a ferromagnetic material which we shall assume to be homogeneous, isotropic, and originally unmagnetized. The field vector obtained most easily is the magnetic intensity, since this is related to the current in the windings by means of Ampère's circuital law, Eq. (10–31). If we apply (10–31) to a circular path which is coaxial with the hole in the toroid, such as the dotted path shown in the figure, symmetry arguments tell us that $\mathbf{H}$ is the same at all points on the path:

$$H_t l = NI,$$

or

$$H_t = \frac{NI}{l}. \tag{10–45}$$

Here the subscript stands for the component tangent to the path, and $l = 2\pi r$ is the total path length. From Eq. (10–26),

$$B_t = \frac{\mu_0 NI}{l} + \mu_0 M_t. \tag{10–46}$$

Thus the magnetic field differs from that in the vacuum case by the additive term $\mu_0 M_t$.

Only the tangential component of $\mathbf{B}$ (and of $\mathbf{H}$) is obtained by the above procedure; nevertheless, this is the only component we expect to be present. According to Eq. (10–27) there are two kinds of sources for the magnetic intensity: true currents and magnetized material. It is easy to show that the current in the toroidal winding produces only a tangential field. The winding is equivalent to N circular loops of current; if we combine the loops in pairs (Fig. 10–14), it is evident that each pair of loops produces a tangential field at the point in question.

The second source of $\mathbf{H}$, the magnetized material itself, may possibly provide a contribution through the pole densities: $\rho_M = -\text{div } \mathbf{M}$ and

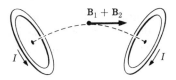

FIG. 10–14. Axial nature of the field in a toroidal winding is shown by combining the magnetic field of the current loops in pairs.

$\sigma_M = \mathbf{M} \cdot \mathbf{n}$. Since the ferromagnetic material in the toroid is isotropic, $\mathbf{M}$ will have the same direction as $\mathbf{H}$. But $\mathbf{M}$ arose in response to currents in the toroidal windings, and this field is a tangential one. Thus we expect an M_t only. On this basis, there are no surfaces in the toroidal specimen which are normal to $\mathbf{M}$, and hence no σ_M. Finally, ρ_M must equal zero; although M_t may be a function of r (the distance from the axis of the toroid), the term $\partial M_t/\partial r$ does not contribute to div $\mathbf{M}$. The interesting result is that the magnetized material provides no contribution to $\mathbf{H}$ in this case, and Eq. (10–46) gives the entire magnetic field.

Another problem, somewhat more complicated than the preceding one, is that of a toroidal winding of N turns surrounding a ferromagnetic specimen in which a narrow air gap of width d has been cut (Fig. 10–15). We shall not distinguish between an air gap and a vacuum gap, since it is evident from Table 10–1 that the permeability of air differs only slightly from μ_0. In this problem Ampere's circuital law does not suffice to determine $\mathbf{H}$, because symmetry arguments cannot be invoked to state that $\mathbf{H}$ is the same at all points on a circular path. Thus we first go to the source equation, (10–27).

Again we note that there are two contributions to the magnetic intensity, one from true currents and one from the magnetization. Since

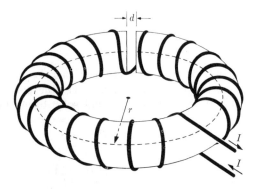

FIG. 10–15. A toroidal winding surrounding a ring of magnetic material with an air gap.

the toroidal winding is identical to that of the preceding problem, the contribution to **H** from the true currents must be the same as before. Denoting this contribution by the subscript 1, we may write

$$H_{1t} = \frac{NI}{l}. \tag{10-47}$$

Our problem then, is to evaluate H_2, or the ∇U^* term. To keep the problem simple, we make the plausible assumption of uniform tangential magnetization M_t throughout the ferromagnetic material; this will provide us with all the essential physics without complicating the algebra. Then ρ_M equals zero, but $\sigma_M = \pm M_t$ on the pole faces bordering the air gap. The situation here is strongly reminiscent of the electrostatic problem involving a charged parallel-plate capacitor. In fact, the mathematical formulation of the potential is identical in the two cases. If the air gap is exceedingly narrow, then, approximately,

$$\begin{align} H_{2t} &= M_t \quad \text{(in the gap)}, \\ H_{2t} &= 0 \quad \text{(elsewhere)}. \end{align} \tag{10-48}$$

However, this result is not consistent with Ampere's circuital law, since

$$\oint H_t \, dl = \oint (H_{1t} + H_{2t}) \, dl = NI + M_t d \neq NI \cdot$$

unless d is negligibly small. For a narrow, but not negligibly small, air gap, a better approximation is

$$H_{2t} = M_t \left(1 - \frac{d}{l}\right) \quad \text{(in the gap)},$$

$$H_{2t} = -M_t \frac{d}{l} \quad \text{(in the material)}, \tag{10-49}$$

which not only satisfies Ampere's circuital law, but also provides for the continuity of the normal component of **B** across the pole faces.

Combining Eqs. (10–47) and (10–49), and substituting the result in Eq. (10–26):

$$\mathbf{B} = \mu_0 (\mathbf{H} + \mathbf{M}),$$

we find

$$B_t = \frac{\mu_0 NI}{l} + \mu_0 M_t \left(1 - \frac{d}{l}\right) \tag{10-50}$$

both in the gap and in the magnetic material.

10–9 Magnetic circuits. The magnetic flux lines, as we have seen, form closed loops. If all the magnetic flux (or substantially all of it) associated with a particular distribution of currents is confined to a rather well-defined path, then we may speak of a *magnetic circuit*. Thus the examples discussed in Section 10–8 are magnetic circuits, since the magnetic flux is confined to the region inside the toroidal winding. In the first example, the circuit consisted of just one material, a ferromagnetic ring; in the second case, however, we encountered a series circuit of two materials: a ferromagnetic material and an air gap.

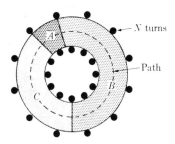

Fig. 10–16. A magnetic circuit.

Let us consider a more general series circuit of several materials surrounded by a toroidal winding of N turns carrying current I, such as that shown in Fig. 10–16. From the application of Ampere's circuital law to a path following the circuit (the dotted path in the figure),

$$\oint H\,dl = NI.$$

It is convenient to express H at each point along the path in terms of the magnetic flux Φ; using $B = \mu H$ and $\Phi = BA$, where A is the cross-sectional area of the circuit at the point under consideration, we find

$$\oint \frac{\Phi\,dl}{\mu A} = NI.$$

Since we are dealing with a magnetic circuit, we expect Φ to be essentially constant at all points in the circuit; hence we may take Φ outside the integral:

$$\Phi \oint \frac{dl}{\mu A} = NI. \tag{10–51}$$

This is the basic magnetic circuit equation which enables us to solve for the flux Φ in terms of the circuit parameters.

Equation (10–51) reminds us of the similar equation for a series current circuit: $IR = \mathcal{E}$. By analogy, we define the magnetomotive force (mmf):

$$\text{mmf} = NI, \tag{10–52}$$

and the reluctance $\mathcal{R}$,

$$\mathcal{R} = \oint \frac{dl}{\mu A}. \tag{10–53}$$

Using these definitions, we may rewrite (10–51), as

$$\Phi = \frac{\text{mmf}}{\mathcal{R}}. \tag{10–51a}$$

If the circuit is made from several homogeneous pieces, each of uniform cross section, the reluctance may be approximated:

$$\mathcal{R} = \sum_j \frac{l_j}{\mu_j A_j} = \sum_j \mathcal{R}_j. \tag{10–53a}$$

Hence the total reluctance of the series circuit is just the sum of the reluctances of the individual elements. The analogy between magnetic and current circuits is even closer than has been indicated, since the resistance of a current circuit is given by

$$R = \oint \frac{dl}{gA},$$

which differs from (10–53) only through the substitution of g for μ. Because of this analogy, it is apparent that series and parallel reluctance combinations may be combined in the same manner as series and parallel resistance combinations.

The magnetic circuit concept is of most use when applied to circuits containing ferromagnetic materials, but it is for just these materials that we experience a certain amount of difficulty. For a ferromagnetic material, $\mu = \mu(H)$, and we do not know H in the material until the circuit problem is completely solved and Φ determined. The situation is not hopeless, however; in fact, the problem can be solved rather easily by an iterative procedure: (1) As a first guess, we might take $H = NI/l_{\text{total}}$, where l_{total} is the total length of the circuit. (2) The permeability of each material in the circuit is obtained for this value of H from the appropriate magnetization curve. (3) The total reluctance of the circuit is computed, and (4) the flux Φ is calculated from Eq. (10–51a). (5) From Φ, the magnetic intensities in the various elements may be found and the permeabilities redetermined. (6) The procedure is repeated, starting again with item (3). One or two iterations are usually sufficient to determine Φ to within a few percent.

The reluctance $\mathfrak{R}_j$ is inversely proportional to the permeability μ_j. Since the permeability of ferromagnetic material may be 100 times μ_0, $10^3\mu_0$, or even $10^5\mu_0$ in certain circumstances, it is apparent that ferromagnetic material forms a low-reluctance path for the magnetic flux. If the magnetic flux encounters two parallel paths, one high reluctance $\mathfrak{R}_h$ and the other low reluctance $\mathfrak{R}_l$, then most of the flux will pass through the low reluctance path, and the equivalent reluctance of the combination is given by $\mathfrak{R} = \mathfrak{R}_h\mathfrak{R}_l/(\mathfrak{R}_h + \mathfrak{R}_l)$. Looking now at Fig. 10–17, we note that if materials A, B, and C are ferromagnetic, most of the flux will follow the ferromagnetic ring, because the air path between the ends of the solenoid is of relatively high reluctance. Thus the magnetic circuits of Figs. 10–16 and 10–17 are essentially equivalent.

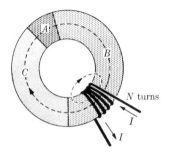

FIG. 10–17. This magnetic circuit is equivalent to the magnetic circuit of Fig. 10–16 if the permeabilities of A, B, and C are large.

If materials B and C are ferromagnetic, but A represents an air gap, the two circuits are no longer equivalent because there is some *leakage* of flux from the ends of the solenoid in Fig. 10–17. How much flux leaks out of the circuit depends on the reluctance ratio of magnetic circuit to leakage path. When the air gap A is small compared with the length of the solenoid, the leakage flux is small and in approximate calculations may be neglected. Reluctance of the leakage path has been worked out for many common geometries, and is given in a number of standard reference books.* The circuit concept is certainly a cruder approximation in the magnetic case than in the electrical one because (1) the ratio of circuit reluctance to leakage reluctance is not as small as the corresponding resistance ratio of the electrical case, and (2) the lateral dimensions of the magnetic circuit are usually not negligible in comparison with its length; nevertheless, the magnetic circuit concept has proved to be extremely useful.

---

* See, e.g., *Electromagnetic Devices* by Herbert C. Roters (John Wiley and Sons, Inc., New York, 1941) Chapters IV and V, and *Magnetic Circuits and Transformers*, by the M.I.T. Staff (John Wiley and Sons, Inc., New York, 1943).

10–10 Magnetic circuits containing permanent magnets. The magnetic circuit concept is useful also when applied to permanent-magnet circuits, i.e., to flux circuits in which Φ has its origin in permanently magnetized material. We shall find it convenient to use the abbreviation P-M for permanent magnet. Because of the complicated B-H relationship in P-M material, the procedure outlined in the preceding section is not well suited to the problem at hand. Instead, we start again with Ampere's circuital law, applied now to the flux path of the P-M circuit:

$$\oint H\,dl = 0,$$

or

$$\int_a^b H\,dl = -\int_{b(\mathrm{P\text{-}M})}^a H\,dl. \qquad (10\text{--}54)$$

In writing Eq. (10–54) we assume explicitly that the P-M material lies between the points b and a of the flux path, whereas from a to b the flux path encounters no P-M material. The use of $B = \mu H$ and $\Phi = BA$ in the left side of Eq. (10–54) yields

$$\Phi \int_a^b \frac{dl}{\mu A} = -\int_{b(\mathrm{P\text{-}M})}^a H\,dl. \qquad (10\text{--}55a)$$

The magnetic flux Φ is continuous throughout the entire circuit, so $\Phi = B_m A_m$, where B_m is the magnetic field in the permanent magnet and A_m is its cross-sectional area. The right side of Eq. (10–55) may be written $-H_m l_m$, where H_m is the average magnetic intensity in the magnet and l_m is the length of the magnet. Thus

$$B_m A_m \mathfrak{R}_{ab} = -H_m l_m \qquad (10\text{--}55b)$$

is the equation that links the unknown quantities B_m and H_m. This equation can be solved simultaneously with the hysteresis curve of the magnet to yield both B_m and H_m.

As an example of a P-M circuit, consider the circuit composed of a magnet, an air gap, and soft iron (Fig. 10–18). It is important to realize that soft iron is *not* a P-M material; its hysteresis is actually negligible

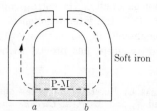

Fig. 10–18. A permanent-magnet circuit. For the circuit shown, the magnet has a rather large demagnetizing field acting upon it; the demagnetizing field can be reduced by increasing the length of P-M material, e.g. by placing additional magnets in the side arms of the circuit.

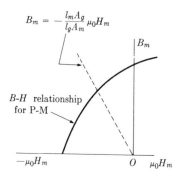

FIG. 10-19. Demagnetizing line for a magnetic circuit. (The subscript m stands for magnet.) Since $\mu_0 H_m$ is plotted instead of H_m, the slope of the demagnetizing line is just $-(l_m A_g / l_g A_m)$, in other words, a pure number.

compared with that of the magnet, and $\mu_i = B_i / H_i$ is a positive quantity. The reluctance $\mathcal{R}_{ab}$ is given by

$$\mathcal{R}_{ab} = \frac{l_i}{\mu_i A_i} + \frac{l_g}{\mu_0 A_g}, \tag{10-56}$$

where the subscripts i and g refer to the soft iron and air gap, respectively. If the air gap is not too narrow, Eq. (10-56) may usually be approximated by

$$\mathcal{R}_{ab} \approx \frac{l_g}{\mu_0 A_g},$$

which, when combined with (10-55b), yields

$$B_m = -\frac{l_m A_g}{l_g A_m} \mu_0 H_m, \tag{10-57}$$

a linear relationship between B_m and H_m. This equation is plotted along with the hysteresis curve of the magnet in Fig. 10-19. The intersection of the two curves gives the operating point of the magnet. The problem is now essentially solved: from a knowledge of B_m, the flux Φ and the flux density B_g are easily determined.

There are, however, two points which deserve to be mentioned. The first is: What does one use for the effective area A_g of the gap? As a first approximation, we might take A_g equal to the pole-face area of the soft iron, and if the air gap is not too large, this approximation is adequate. We shall not enter into a detailed discussion of this point, but instead refer the interested reader to the references cited in the previous section. Secondly, the problem of leakage flux is just as important in P-M circuits as it is in other types of magnetic circuits. For the problems presented in this book, however, we shall usually make the assumption that leakage flux may be neglected.

Finally, we note that H_m as determined from Fig. 10–19 is negative, i.e., the magnetic intensity in the magnet is a *demagnetizing* effect. This is a general result; when the magnetic flux has its origin in a permanent magnet, then the magnet itself is subjected to a demagnetizing field.

10–11 Boundary-value problems involving magnetic materials. In the preceding sections we saw how the magnetic circuit concept enabled us to obtain approximate solutions to certain types of magnetic problems. However, when the magnetic flux does not follow a well-defined path, then more powerful mathematical techniques must be brought to bear. In this section we shall be concerned with a particular class of problems, namely, calculation of magnetic fields inside magnetic material in which no transport current exists.

When $\mathbf{J} = 0$, the fundamental magnetic equations (10–28) and (10–30) reduce to
$$\operatorname{div} \mathbf{B} = 0, \tag{10–28}$$

$$\operatorname{curl} \mathbf{H} = 0. \tag{10–58}$$

Equation (10–58) implies that $\mathbf{H}$ can be derived as the gradient of a scalar field. This should not surprise us, because according to the source equation, (10–27), the contribution to $\mathbf{H}$ from magnetic material is already expressed in this form, and in Section 8–8 we showed that the field (actually the proof presented there must be generalized to the $\mathbf{H}$-field) produced by transport currents can be so derived when the local current density is zero. In accordance with Eq. (10–58), we write

$$\mathbf{H} = -\boldsymbol{\nabla} U^*, \tag{10–59}$$

where U^* is now the magnetic scalar potential due to all sources.

There are two types of magnetic material for which the magnetic field calculation reduces to a simple boundary-value problem: (1) linear or "approximately linear" magnetic material for which $\mathbf{B} = \mu\mathbf{H}$, and (2) a *uniformly* magnetized piece of material for which div $\mathbf{M} = 0$. In both cases Eq. (10–28) reduces to

$$\operatorname{div} \mathbf{H} = 0. \tag{10–60}$$

Combining this result with (10–59), we obtain

$$\nabla^2 U^* = 0, \tag{10–61}$$

which is Laplace's equation. Thus the magnetic problem reduces to finding a solution to Laplace's equation which satisfies the boundary conditions. $\mathbf{H}$ may then be calculated as minus the gradient of the magnetic potential, and $\mathbf{B}$ obtained from

$$\mathbf{B} = \mu \mathbf{H}$$

or

$$\mathbf{B} = \mu_0(\mathbf{H} + \mathbf{M}),$$

whichever is more appropriate.

Two magnetic problems serve to illustrate the usefulness of the method just described; additional exercises of this type will be found in the problems at the end of the chapter. Our first example deals with a sphere of linear magnetic material of radius a and permeability μ placed in a region of space containing an *initially* uniform magnetic field, $\mathbf{B}_0$. We should like to determine how the magnetic field is modified by the presence of the sphere and, in particular, to determine the magnetic field in the sphere itself. The problem is closely analogous to the case of a dielectric sphere in a uniform electric field, which was solved in Section 4–9. Thus, choosing the origin of our coordinate system at the center of the sphere and the direction of $\mathbf{B}_0$ as the polar direction (z-direction), we may express the potential as a sum of zonal harmonics. Again, all boundary conditions can be satisfied by means of the $\cos \theta$ harmonics:

$$U_1^*(r, \theta) = A_1 r \cos \theta + C_1 r^{-2} \cos \theta \qquad (10\text{–}62)$$

for the vacuum region (1) outside the sphere, and

$$U_2^*(r, \theta) = A_2 r \cos \theta + C_2 r^{-2} \cos \theta \qquad (10\text{–}63)$$

for the magnetic material region (2). The constants A_1, A_2, C_1, and C_2 must be determined from the boundary conditions.

At distances far away from the sphere, the magnetic field retains its uniform character: $\mathbf{B} = B_0 \mathbf{k}$, and $U_1^* \rightarrow -(B_0/\mu_0) r \cos \theta$. Hence $A_1 = -(B_0/\mu_0)$. Since U_2^* and its associated magnetic field cannot become infinite at any point, the coefficient C_2 must be set equal to zero. Having applied the boundary conditions at $r = \infty$ and at $r = 0$, we next turn our attention to the interface at $r = a$:

$$H_{1\theta} = H_{2\theta},$$

$$B_{1r} = B_{2r},$$

or

$$-\left(\frac{B_0}{\mu_0}\right) \sin \theta + \frac{C_1}{a^3} \sin \theta = A_2 \sin \theta, \qquad (10\text{–}64)$$

$$B_0 \cos \theta + 2\mu_0 \frac{C_1}{a^3} \cos \theta = -\mu A_2 \cos \theta. \qquad (10\text{–}65)$$

Solving these two equations simultaneously yields

$$A_2 = -\frac{3B_0}{(\mu + 2\mu_0)},$$

and

$$C_1 = [(\mu/\mu_0) - 1]\frac{B_0 a^3}{(\mu + 2\mu_0)},$$

whence the magnetic fields inside and outside the sphere are given by

$$\mathbf{B}_2 = \frac{3B_0\mathbf{k}}{1 + 2(\mu_0/\mu)} \qquad (10\text{-}66)$$

and

$$\mathbf{B}_1 = B_0\mathbf{k} + \left[\frac{(\mu/\mu_0) - 1}{(\mu/\mu_0) + 2}\right]\left(\frac{a}{r}\right)^3 B_0(2\mathbf{a}_r \cos\theta + \mathbf{a}_\theta \sin\theta). \quad (10\text{-}67)$$

The second problem we wish to solve deals with a permanent magnet. We should like to determine the magnetic field produced by a uniformly magnetized sphere of magnetization $\mathbf{M}$ and radius a when no other magnetic fields are present. Taking the magnetization along the z-axis and the origin of our coordinate system at the center of the sphere, we may expand the potential in zonal harmonics:

$$U_1^*(r,\,\theta) = \sum_{n=0}^{\infty} C_{1,n} r^{-(n+1)} P_n(\theta) \qquad (10\text{-}68)$$

for the vacuum region (1) outside the sphere, and

$$U_2^*(r,\,\theta) = \sum_{n=0}^{\infty} A_{2,n} r^n P_n(\theta) \qquad (10\text{-}69)$$

for the permanent magnet region (2). Here we have purposely left out the harmonics with positive powers of r from expansion (10–68) since these would become large at large distances, and we have left out the negative powers of r in (10–69) since these would become infinite at the origin. From the boundary conditions at $r = a$:

$$H_{1\theta} = H_{2\theta},$$

$$B_{1r} = B_{2r},$$

we obtain

$$\sum_{n=0}^{\infty} (C_{1,n}a^{-(n+1)} - A_{2,n}a^n)a^{-1}\frac{d}{d\theta}P_n(\theta) = 0 \qquad (10\text{-}70)$$

and

$$\mu_0 C_{1,0}a^{-2} + \mu_0 \sum_{n=1}^{\infty} P_n(\theta)\,[C_{1,n}\,(n+1)a^{-(n+2)} + A_{2,n}na^{n-1}]$$

$$-\mu_0 M \cos\theta = 0. \quad (10\text{-}71)$$

Since each $P_n(\theta)$ is a distinct function of θ, none of them can be constructed from a linear combination of other P_n's. Hence, in order for Eqs. (10–70) and (10–71) to hold, each of the terms involving a P_n or a $dP_n/d\theta$ must vanish individually. From the $n = 0$ terms,

$$\frac{dP_0}{d\theta} = 0,$$

and

$$\mu_0 C_{1,0} a^{-2} = 0.$$

Therefore $C_{1,0} = 0$, and $A_{2,0}$ is undetermined. But $A_{2,0}$ is just the constant term in the potential; this may be set equal to zero without affecting **H** or **B**.

From the $n = 1$ terms,

$$C_{1,1} a^{-3} - A_{2,1} = 0$$

and

$$2C_{1,1} a^{-3} + A_{2,1} - M = 0,$$

which may be solved simultaneously to yield

$$C_{1,1} = \tfrac{1}{3} M a^3$$

and

$$A_{2,1} = \tfrac{1}{3} M.$$

For all $n \geq 2$, the only $C_{1,n}$ and $A_{2,n}$ compatible with the two equations are $C_{1,n} = 0$ and $A_{2,n} = 0$.

Putting these results back into Eqs. (10–68) and (10–69), we obtain

$$U_1^*(r, \theta) = \tfrac{1}{3} M(a^3/r^2) \cos \theta \tag{10–72}$$

and

$$U_2^*(r, \theta) = \tfrac{1}{3} M r \cos \theta. \tag{10–73}$$

The magnetic intensity **H** may be calculated from the gradient operation, with the result:

$$\mathbf{H}_1 = \tfrac{1}{3} M(a^3/r^3)[2\mathbf{a}_r \cos \theta + \mathbf{a}_\theta \sin \theta], \tag{10–74}$$

$$\mathbf{H}_2 = -\tfrac{1}{3} M \mathbf{k}. \tag{10–75}$$

Thus the external field of the uniformly magnetized sphere is just a dipole field, arising from the dipole moment $\tfrac{4}{3}\pi a^3 \mathbf{M}$. The magnetic intensity *inside* the sphere is a demagnetizing field, a result which is in accord with remarks made earlier. We see, therefore, that the magnetized sphere is subjected to its own demagnetizing field. The factor $\tfrac{1}{3} = (1/4\pi)(4\pi/3)$ in Eq. (10–75) depends explicitly on the spherical geometry; the quantity $4\pi/3$ is known as the *demagnetization factor* of a sphere.

The demagnetization factors for other geometrical shapes have been calculated and are tabulated in many publications.*

The external magnetic field $\mathbf{B}_1$ is just μ_0 times Eq. (10–74). The magnetic induction in the sphere is

$$\mathbf{B}_2 = \tfrac{2}{3}\mu_0 M\mathbf{k} = \tfrac{2}{3}\mu_0\mathbf{M}. \tag{10–76}$$

Problems

10–1. A permanent magnet has the shape of a right circular cylinder of length L. If the magnetization $\mathbf{M}$ is uniform and has the direction of the cylinder axis, find the magnetization current densities, J_M and j_M. Compare the current distribution with that of a solenoid.

10–2. Find the distribution of magnetization currents corresponding to a uniformly magnetized sphere with magnetization $\mathbf{M}$. According to Eq. (10–76) the magnetic induction $\mathbf{B}$ is uniform inside such a sphere. Can you use this information to design a current winding which will produce a uniform magnetic field in a spherical region of space?

10–3. (a) The magnetic moment of a macroscopic body is defined as $\int_V \mathbf{M} \, dv$. Prove the relationship

$$\int_V \mathbf{M} \, dv = \int_V \mathbf{r}\rho_M \, dv + \oint_S \mathbf{r}\sigma_M \, da,$$

where S is the surface bounding V. [*Hint:* Refer to the similar problem involving $\mathbf{P}$ in Chapter 4.] (b) A permanent magnet in the shape of a sphere of radius R has uniform magnetization $\mathbf{M}_0$ in the direction of the polar axis. Determine the magnetic moment of the magnet from both the right and left sides of the equation in part (a).

10–4. (a) Given a magnet with magnetization specified: $\mathbf{M}(x, y, z)$. Each volume element dv may be treated as a small magnetic dipole, $\mathbf{M} \, dv$. If the magnet is placed in a uniform magnetic field $\mathbf{B}_0$, find the torque on the magnet in terms of its magnetic moment (defined in Problem 10–3). (b) A magnet in the shape of a right circular cylinder of length L, and cross section A is uniformly magnetized parallel to the cylinder axis with magnetization $\mathbf{M}_0$. The magnet is placed in a uniform magnetic field $\mathbf{B}_0$. Find the torque on the magnet in terms of its pole densities.

10–5. An ellipsoid with principal axes of lengths $2a$, $2a$, and $2b$ is magnetized uniformly in a direction parallel to the $2b$-axis. The magnetization of the ellipsoid is $\mathbf{M}_0$. Find the magnetic pole densities for this geometry.

---

* See, for example, E. C. Stoner, *Philosophical Magazine* **36**, p. 803 (1945), and R. M. Bozorth and D. M. Chapin, *Journal of Applied Physics* **13**, p. 320 (1942).

10–6. Given a spherical shell, inside radius R_1 and outside radius R_2, which is uniformly magnetized in the direction of the z-axis. The magnetization in the shell is $\mathbf{M}_0 = M_0\mathbf{k}$. Find the scalar potential U^* for points on the z-axis, both inside and outside the shell.

10–7. A permanent magnet in the shape of a right circular cylinder of length L and radius R is oriented so that its symmetry axis coincides with the z-axis. The origin of coordinates is at the center of the magnet. If the cylinder has uniform axial magnetization M, (a) determine $U^*(z)$ at points on the symmetry axis, both inside and outside the magnet, and (b) use the results of part (a) to find the magnetic induction B_z at points on the symmetry axis, both inside and outside the magnet.

10–8. A sphere of magnetic material of radius R is placed at the origin of coordinates. The magnetization is given by $\mathbf{M} = (ax^2 + b)\mathbf{i}$, where a and b are constants. Determine all pole densities and magnetization currents.

10–9. An annealed iron ring of mean length 15 cm is wound with a toroidal coil of 100 turns. Determine the magnetic induction in the ring when the current in the winding is (a) 0.1 amp, (b) 0.2 amp, and (c) 1.0 amp.

10–10. A soft-iron ring with a 1.0 cm air gap is wound with a toroidal winding such as is shown in Fig. 10–15. The mean length of the iron ring is 20 cm, its cross section is 4 cm^2, and its permeability is 3000 μ_0. The 200-turn winding carries a current of 10 amp. (a) Calculate the magnetic induction in the air gap. (b) Find B and H inside the iron ring.

10–11. Calculate the self-inductance of the current circuit described in Problem 10–10.

10–12. A magnetic circuit in the shape of

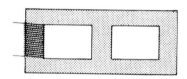

is wound with 100 turns of wire carrying a current of 1 amp. The winding is located on the extreme left-hand leg of the circuit. The height of the circuit is 10 cm, its length is 20 cm, the cross section of each leg is 6 cm^2, and its permeability is 5000 μ_0. Neglecting leakage, calculate the magnetic flux through the central leg and also through the extreme right-hand leg of the circuit.

10–13. A magnetic circuit in the form shown in Fig. 10–18 has a permanent magnet of length 8 cm, a soft-iron path length of 16 cm, and an air gap of 0.8 cm. The cross section of the iron and of the magnet is 4 cm^2 on the average, whereas the effective cross-sectional area of the air gap is 3 cm^2. The relative permeability of the iron is 5000. (a) Calculate the magnetic flux density in the gap for two different magnet materials: sintered oxide and 35% Co steel. Neglect leakage. (b) The dimensions of the magnetic circuit are altered in *one* respect: the air gap is decreased to 0.8 mm. Repeat the calculation called for in part (a).

10–14. Find the magnetic induction in a uniformly magnetized sphere for each of the materials shown in Fig. 10–10.

10-15. A magnetic circuit in the form shown in Fig. 10-18 has an Alnico V magnet of length 10 cm, a soft-iron path of 16 cm, and an air gap of 1 cm. It is also wound with 800 ampere-turns of wire (in a direction to aid the flux produced by the magnet). Find the magnetic flux density in the air gap. (Neglect leakage, take $K_m = 5000$ for the soft iron, and assume that the cross sections of the magnet, soft iron, and air gap are the same.)

*10-16. Calculate the demagnetizing factor of a long cylinder which is permanently magnetized at right angles to the cylinder axis. The magnetization is uniform.

10-17. A long cylinder of radius a and permeability μ is placed in a uniform magnetic field $\mathbf{B}_0$ such that the cylinder axis is at right angles to $\mathbf{B}_0$. Calculate the magnetic induction inside the cylinder. Make a semiquantitative sketch showing typical lines of induction through the cylinder. (Assume from the beginning that U^* can be completely specified in terms of the $\cos \theta$ cylindrical harmonics. This assumption is justified, since all boundary conditions can be satisfied in terms of the $\cos \theta$ harmonics.)

*10-18. A long cylindrical shell (outside radius b, inside radius a, relative permeability K_m) is oriented normal to a uniform magnetic induction field $\mathbf{B}_0$. (a) Show that the magnetic induction $\mathbf{B}_i$ in the vacuum region inside the shell is parallel to $\mathbf{B}_0$. (b) Show that the magnetic shielding factor h_m is given by

$$ h_m \equiv \frac{B_0}{B_i} = 1 + \frac{(K_m - 1)^2}{4K_m} \left(1 - \frac{a^2}{b^2} \right). $$

*CHAPTER 11

MICROSCOPIC THEORY OF THE MAGNETIC PROPERTIES OF MATTER

In the preceding chapter we were concerned with the macroscopic aspects of magnetization. The magnetic properties of matter were introduced explicitly through the function $\mathbf{M}$, and this was related to the magnetic induction by means of experimentally determined parameters. We now look at matter from the microscopic point of view (i.e., as an assembly of atoms or molecules) and see how the individual molecules respond to an imposed magnetic field. If this procedure were carried through completely, we should end up with theoretical expressions for susceptibility, and B-H relationships for all types of materials. Such a procedure is certainly beyond the scope of this book; nevertheless, we can show rather simply how the various kinds of magnetic behavior come about and, in addition, derive expressions which predict the correct order of magnitude for susceptibility in certain cases. A much more thorough discussion of the topics presented here is to be found in books on solid state physics.†

In the macroscopic formulation we dealt with two field vectors, $\mathbf{B}$ and $\mathbf{H}$, which we related through the equation $\mathbf{B} = \mu_0(\mathbf{H} + \mathbf{M})$. From the microscopic viewpoint the distinction between $\mathbf{B}$ and $\mathbf{H}$ largely disappears, because we deal with an assembly of molecules (i.e., with an assembly of magnetic dipoles or dipole groups) in vacuum. We are concerned with the magnetic field near a molecule in vacuum or at the position of a molecule when that molecule is removed from the system. Thus $\mathbf{B}_m = \mu_0\mathbf{H}_m$. Here the subscript m stands for "microscopic," but in the following sections of this chapter the symbol $\mathbf{B}_m$ (and $\mathbf{H}_m$) will denote a particular value of the microscopic field, namely, the field at the position of a molecule.

It is customary when discussing the microscopic field inside matter to relate $\mathbf{H}_m$ to the macroscopic $\mathbf{H}$ field, instead of $\mathbf{B}_m$ to the $\mathbf{B}$ field, because both $\mathbf{H}$ and $\mathbf{H}_m$ can be written simply in terms of integrals over the current and dipole distributions. It makes very little difference, however, whether we calculate $\mathbf{H}_m$ or $\mathbf{B}_m$, since they differ from each other only by the scale factor μ_0.

---

* This chapter may be omitted without loss of continuity.

† See, e.g., C. Kittel, *Introduction to Solid State Physics* (John Wiley & Sons, Inc., New York, 2nd ed., 1956), Chapters 9 and 15. Also, J. E. Goldman, *The Science of Engineering Materials* (John Wiley & Sons, Inc., New York, 1957).

11-1 Molecular field inside matter. The magnetic field which is effective in its interaction with atomic currents in an atom or molecule is called the molecular field $\mathbf{B}_m = \mu_0 \mathbf{H}_m$. In some textbooks it is called the *local field*. This is the magnetic field at a molecular (or atomic) position in the material; it is produced by all external sources and by all molecular dipoles in the material *with the exception* of the one molecule (or atom) at the point under consideration. It is evident that $\mathbf{B}_m$ need not be the same as the macroscopic magnetic induction field, since the latter quantity is related to the force on a current element whose dimensions are large compared with molecular dimensions.

The molecular field may be calculated by a procedure similar to that of Section 5-1 for the molecular electric field in a dielectric. We consider a material object of arbitrary shape, which for convenience we take to be uniformly magnetized with magnetization $\mathbf{M}$. Let us cut out a small piece of the object, leaving a spherical cavity surrounding the point at which the molecular field is to be computed. The material which is left is to be treated as a continuum, i.e., from the macroscopic point of view. Next we put the material back into the cavity, molecule by molecule, except for the molecule at the center of the cavity, where we wish to compute the molecular field. The molecules which have just been replaced are to be treated, not as a continuum, but as individual dipoles or dipole groups.

The *macroscopic* field $\mathbf{H}$, the magnetic intensity in the specimen, can be expressed, according to Eq. (10-27), as

$$\mathbf{H} = \frac{1}{4\pi} \int \frac{\mathbf{J} \times (\mathbf{r} - \mathbf{r}')}{|\mathbf{r} - \mathbf{r}'|^3}\, dv' + \frac{1}{4\pi} \int \frac{\rho_M (\mathbf{r} - \mathbf{r}')}{|\mathbf{r} - \mathbf{r}'|^3}\, dv'$$

$$+ \frac{1}{4\pi} \int_{\dot{S}} \frac{\sigma_M (\mathbf{r} - \mathbf{r}')}{|\mathbf{r} - \mathbf{r}'|^3}\, da',$$

where the integrals extend over all sources: $\mathbf{J}$, ρ_M, and σ_M. The molecular field $\mathbf{H}_m$ may be expressed in a similar way, except that now there are additional contributions from the surface of the cavity and from the individual dipoles in the cavity. The integral of $\rho_M (\mathbf{r} - \mathbf{r}')/|\mathbf{r} - \mathbf{r}'|^3$ over the cavity volume need not be excluded specifically, since $\rho_M = -\text{div}\,\mathbf{M} = 0$ in the uniformly magnetized specimen. Thus

$$\mathbf{H}_m = \mathbf{H} + \mathbf{H}_s + \mathbf{H}', \qquad (11\text{-}1)$$

where $\mathbf{H}$ is the macroscopic magnetic intensity in the specimen, $\mathbf{H}_s$ is the contribution from the surface pole density $\sigma_M = M_n$ on the cavity surface, and $\mathbf{H}'$ is the contribution of the various dipoles inside the cavity.

From the corresponding derivation in Section 5–1, $\mathbf{H}_s$ is seen to be

$$\mathbf{H}_s = \tfrac{1}{3}\mathbf{M}. \tag{11–2}$$

Furthermore, the dipole contribution,

$$\mathbf{H}' = \frac{1}{4\pi} \sum_i \left[\frac{3(\mathbf{m}_i \cdot \mathbf{r}_i)\mathbf{r}_i}{r_i^5} - \frac{\mathbf{m}_i}{r_i^3} \right], \tag{11–3}$$

where $\mathbf{r}_i$ is the distance from the ith dipole to the center of the cavity, is of the same form as the corresponding electric dipole term $\mathbf{E}'$ in Section 5–1. Thus if we restrict our interest to the rather large class of materials for which (11–3) vanishes, Eq. (11–1) reduces to

$$\mathbf{H}_m = \mathbf{H} + \tfrac{1}{3}\mathbf{M}, \tag{11–4}$$

and

$$\mathbf{B}_m = \mu_0 \mathbf{H}_m. \tag{11–5}$$

Equations (11–4) and (11–5) give the molecular field in terms of the macroscopic magnetic intensity and the magnetization in the sample. For most diamagnetic and paramagnetic materials the term $\tfrac{1}{3}\mathbf{M} = \tfrac{1}{3}\chi_m\mathbf{H}$ is negligibly small, but for ferromagnetic materials the correction is quite important.

11–2 Origin of diamagnetism. Diamagnetism is the result of Lenz's law operating on an atomic scale. Upon the application of a magnetic field, the electronic currents in each atom are modified in such a way that they tend to weaken the effect of this field. In order to calculate the diamagnetic susceptibility of an assembly of atoms we must know something about the electronic motion in the atom itself. We shall assume that each electron circulates around the atomic nucleus in some kind of orbit, and for simplicity we choose a circular orbit of radius R in a plane at right angles to the applied magnetic field. Quantum mechanics tells us that although this picture is approximately correct, the electrons do not circulate in well-defined orbits. To solve the problem properly we would have to solve the Schroedinger equation for an atomic electron in a magnetic field; nevertheless, our rather naive "classical" calculation will give the correct order of magnitude for the diamagnetic susceptibility.

Before the magnetic induction field is applied, the electron is in equilibrium in its orbit:

$$F_q = m_e \omega_0^2 R, \tag{11–6}$$

where F_q is the electric force holding the electron to its atom, ω_0 is the angular frequency of the electron in its orbit, and m_e is the electron mass. Application of a magnetic field exerts an additional force $-e\mathbf{v} \times \mathbf{B}_m$ on the electron; assuming that the electron stays in the same orbit, we find

$$F_q \pm e\omega R B_m = m_e \omega^2 R,$$

which, when combined with Eq. (11–6), yields

$$\pm e\omega B_m = m_e(\omega - \omega_0)(\omega + \omega_0). \tag{11–7}$$

The quantity $\Delta\omega = \omega - \omega_0$ is the change in angular frequency of the electron. Thus the electron either speeds up or slows down in its orbit, depending on the detailed geometry (i.e., on the direction of $\mathbf{v} \times \mathbf{B}_m$ relative to $\mathbf{F}_q$), but in either case in accordance with Lenz's law: the *change* in orbital magnetic moment is in a direction opposite to the applied field. This statement may be easily verified by the reader.

Even for the largest fields which can be obtained in the laboratory ($\sim$10 webers/m^2), $\Delta\omega$ is very small compared with ω_0, so that (11–7) may always be approximated by

$$\Delta\omega = \pm \frac{e}{2m_e} B_m. \tag{11–8}$$

The quantity $(e/2m_e)B_m$ is known as the Larmor frequency.

Up to this point we have merely *assumed* that the electron stays in the same orbit. We have used this assumption together with the equilibrium of forces to derive (11–8). For the electron to stay in its orbit, the change in its kinetic energy as determined from Faraday's law of induction must be consistent with Eq. (11–8). When the magnetic field is switched on, there is a change in flux through the orbit given by $\pi R^2 \Delta B_m$. This flux is linked by Δn electron loops, where Δn is the number of revolutions made by the electron during the time in which the field changes. The changing flux produces an emf

$$\mathcal{E} = \pi R^2 \frac{dB_m}{dt} \Delta n = \pi R^2 \frac{dn}{dt} \Delta B_m. \tag{11–9}$$

The energy given to the electron in this process is $\mathcal{E}e$, and this appears as a change in kinetic energy:

$$\tfrac{1}{2} m_e R^2(\omega^2 - \omega_0^2) = e\pi R^2 \frac{dn}{dt} \Delta B_m. \tag{11–10}$$

But ΔB_m is just the final value of the field B_m, and the average value of $dn/dt = (\omega + \omega_0)/4\pi$. Thus

$$\Delta\omega = \frac{e}{2m_e} B_m,$$

in agreement with Eq. (11–8). Thus the assumption of a constant orbit leads to no contradiction between (11–9) and the force equation.

The change in angular velocity predicted by Eq. (11–8) produces a change in magnetic moment given by

$$\Delta \mathbf{m} = - \frac{e}{2\pi} \pi R^2 \frac{e}{2m_e} \mathbf{B}_m$$

$$= - \frac{e^2}{4m_e} R^2 \mu_0 \mathbf{H}_m. \tag{11-11}$$

In order to find the magnetization, this result must be summed over all electrons in a unit volume. For a substance containing N molecules per unit volume, all of the same molecular species,

$$\mathbf{M} = - \frac{Ne^2 \mu_0}{4m_e} \mathbf{H}_m \sum_i R_i^2, \tag{11-12}$$

where the summation is over the electrons in one molecule. For diamagnetic materials, $\mathbf{H}_m$ differs very little from $\mathbf{H}$, so the diamagnetic susceptibility

$$\chi_m = - \frac{Ne^2 \mu_0}{4m_e} \sum_i R_i^2. \tag{11-13a}$$

This result has been obtained on the assumption that all electrons circulate in planes perpendicular to the field $\mathbf{H}_m$. When the orbit is inclined, so that a normal to the orbit makes an angle θ_i with the field, only the component of $\mathbf{H}_m$ along this normal ($H_m \cos \theta_i$) is effective in altering the angular velocity of the electron. Furthermore, the component of $\Delta \mathbf{m}$ parallel to the field is smaller by the factor $\cos \theta_i$. Hence a better approximation to the diamagnetic susceptibility is

$$\chi_m = - \frac{Ne^2 \mu_0}{4m_e} \sum_i R_i^2 \cos^2 \theta_i. \tag{11-13b}$$

Diamagnetism is presumably present in all types of matter, but its effect is frequently masked by stronger paramagnetic or ferromagnetic behavior that can occur in the material simultaneously. Diamagnetism is particularly prominent in materials which consist entirely of atoms or ions with "closed electron shells," since in these cases all paramagnetic contributions cancel out.

11–3 Origin of paramagnetism. The orbital motion of each electron in an atom or molecule can be described in terms of a magnetic moment; this follows directly from Eq. (8–22). In addition, it is known that the electron has an intrinsic property called *spin*, and an intrinsic magnetic moment associated with this spinning charge. Each molecule, then, has a magnetic moment $\mathbf{m}_i$ which is the vector sum of orbital and spin moments from the various electrons in the molecule. Briefly, paramagnetism results from the tendency of these molecular moments to align themselves with the applied field, just as the current circuit of Eq. (8–19) tends to align itself with the field.

The situation is not quite so straightforward as that for a current circuit, however. There are, in fact, two complications: (1) in the presence of a magnetic field the electronic motions are quantized such that each orbital and spin moment has only a discrete set of orientations relative to the field direction. Furthermore, no two electrons in the molecule can occupy the same quantum state, so that if there are just enough electrons per molecule to fill "electron shells," then all possible orientations must be used and $\mathbf{m}_i$ is zero. Of course, paramagnetism can occur only when $\mathbf{m}_i \neq 0$. (2) The electronic motion inside an atom which gives rise to $\mathbf{m}_i$ also produces an angular momentum about the atomic nucleus; in fact, $\mathbf{m}_i$ is linearly related to this angular momentum. Under these conditions the magnetic torque does not directly align the dipole moment $\mathbf{m}_i$ with the field, but causes it to precess around the field at constant inclination.* The atoms (or molecules) in our material system are in thermal contact with each other. In a gas or liquid the atoms are continually making collisions with one another; in a solid the atoms are undergoing thermal oscillation. Under these conditions the various $\mathbf{m}_i$ can interchange magnetic energy with the thermal energy of their environment and make transitions from one precessional state to another of a different inclination. The thermal energy of the system tries to act in such a way as to produce a completely random orientation of the $\mathbf{m}_i$, but orientations along or near the field direction have a lower magnetic energy and thus are favored. The situation is quite similar to that of polar molecules in an electric field, which was discussed in Section 5–3.

For a material composed entirely of one molecular species, each molecule having magnetic moment m_0, the fractional orientation is given approximately by the Langevin function, Eq. (5–21), with

$$y = \frac{m_0 \mu_0 H_m}{kT}. \tag{11–14}$$

The magnetization is given by

$$|\mathbf{M}| = N m_0 \left[\coth y - \frac{1}{y} \right], \tag{11–15a}$$

where N is the number of molecules per unit volume. Except for tem-

---

* A discussion of the precession of $\mathbf{m}_i$ in a uniform magnetic field is given in many textbooks. See, e.g., H. Goldstein, *Classical Mechanics* (Addison-Wesley Publishing Company, Inc., Reading, Mass., 1950), pp. 176–7.

peratures near absolute zero, the Langevin function can be approximated by the first term in its power series:

$$\mathbf{M} = \frac{N m_0^2}{3kT} \mu_0 \mathbf{H}_m,$$ (11–15b)

which yields the paramagnetic susceptibility

$$\chi_m = \frac{N m_0^2 \mu_0}{3kT}.$$ (11–16)

According to atomic theory, m_0 is in the range of a few Bohr magnetons (1 Bohr magneton $= eh/4\pi m_e$, where h is Planck's constant). Equations (11–16) and (11–13b) account for the order of magnitude of the χ_m's in Table 10–1.

We may summarize the results of this section briefly as follows: In order to exhibit paramagnetic behavior, the atoms (or molecules) of the system must have permanent magnetic moments, and these tend to orient in the applied field. The various molecular moments are decoupled, i.e., they precess around the magnetic field as individuals (not in unison), but they are able to exchange energy because of thermal contact with their environment. Except for temperatures near absolute zero and simultaneous large fields, the magnetization is far below the saturation value which would obtain when all the dipole moments are aligned.

11–4 Theory of ferromagnetism. In ferromagnetic materials the atomic (or molecular) magnetic moments are very nearly aligned even in the absence of an applied field. The cause of this alignment is the molecular field $\mathbf{H}_m$ which, according to Eq. (11–4), does not vanish when $\mathbf{H} = 0$ unless $\mathbf{M}$ vanishes simultaneously. A magnetization $\mathbf{M}$ does give rise to a molecular field, but unless this molecular field *produces* the same magnetization $\mathbf{M}$ which is presumed to exist in the material, the solution is inconsistent. Our problem is to determine in what set of circumstances the magnetization can maintain itself via the molecular field.

It will prove necessary to generalize Eq. (11–4) to a certain extent. For the molecular field, let us write $\mathbf{H}_m = \mathbf{H} + \gamma \mathbf{M}$, which, for $\mathbf{H} = 0$, reduces to

$$\mathbf{H}_m = \gamma \mathbf{M}.$$ (11–4a)

According to the simple theory of Section 11–1, $\gamma = \frac{1}{3}$. If the terms in Eq. (11–3) do not sum to zero, γ may be different from $\frac{1}{3}$; nevertheless, we expect γ to be of this order of magnitude.

Let us restrict our attention to a material composed entirely of one atomic species, each atom having magnetic moment m_0. There are N atoms per unit volume. If the atomic moments are to be very nearly aligned, M must be a substantial fraction of Nm_0; for the sake of definiteness however, let us say

$$M > 0.7Nm_0. \tag{11-17}$$

According to Eq. (11–15), this implies that $[\coth y - (1/y)] > 0.7$, or y [which is defined by Eq. (11–14)] > 3. Thus

$$y = \frac{m_0\mu_0 H_m}{kT} > 3,$$

which, when combined with (11–4a) and (11–17), yields

$$0.7 \frac{\gamma N\mu_0 m_0^2}{kT} > 3. \tag{11-18}$$

This, approximately, is the condition for the occurrence of ferromagnetism.

In the previous section it was stated that atomic theory predicts m_0 to be in the range of a few Bohr magnetons. On this basis, Eq. (11–18) requires a γ of about 10^3, which is orders of magnitude larger than can be accounted for in the derivation presented in Section 11–1. It would thus appear that the origin of ferromagnetism is considerably more complex than the corresponding situation in ferroelectrics (discussed in Section 5–4).

In 1907 Pierre Weiss* formulated his theory of ferromagnetism. Weiss appreciated the essential role played by the molecular field; he could not explain the large value of γ, but he accepted it as a fact and proceeded to develop his theory from this point. The predictions of his theory were found to be in close accord with experiment. For this reason the molecular field of Eq. (11–4a) is often called the Weiss molecular field.

It was left to Heisenberg,† some twenty years later, to explain the origin of the large value of γ. Heisenberg showed, first, that it is only the spin magnetic moments which contribute to the molecular field, and second, that the field is produced basically by electrostatic forces. On the basis of quantum mechanics he showed that when the spins on neighboring atoms change from parallel alignment to antiparallel alignment, there must be a simultaneous change in the electron charge distribution in the atoms. The change in charge distribution alters the electrostatic energy of the system and in certain cases favors parallel alignment (i.e., ferromagnetism). A spin-dependent energy, i.e., an energy which depends on the spin configuration of the system, can be viewed in terms of the force (or torque) which is produced on one of the atoms when the con-

---

* P. Weiss, *Journal de Physique* **6**, 667 (1907).

† W. Heisenberg, *Zeitschrift fur Physik* **49**, 619 (1928).

figuration is altered. The equivalent field turns out to be proportional to **M**, but with a coefficient which depends in detail upon the charge distribution in the atom under consideration.

The Weiss-Heisenberg theory can be used to predict the way in which the magnetization of a ferromagnet changes with temperature. It is evident that the theory depicts ferromagnetism as the limiting case of paramagnetism in an extremely large magnetic field, but with this field coming from the magnetization itself. Combining Eq. (11–4a) with (11–14) and (11–15) yields

$$M = Nm_0 \left[\coth y - \frac{1}{y} \right], \qquad (11\text{–}19)$$

and

$$M = \frac{kTy}{\gamma \mu_0 m_0}. \qquad (11\text{–}20)$$

The *spontaneous magnetization,* i.e., the magnetization at zero external field, for a given temperature is obtained from the simultaneous solution of Eqs. (11–19) and (11–20). This is easily done by a graphical procedure: We plot M versus y for *both* (11–19) and (11–20), as shown in Fig. 11–1.

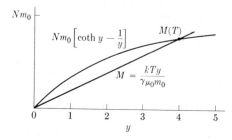

FIG. 11–1. Determination of the spontaneous magnetization $M(T)$ with the aid of the Langevin function.

The intersection of the two curves gives a magnetization $M(T)$ which is consistent with both equations. As the temperature is increased, the linear curve, Eq. (11–20), becomes steeper, but Eq. (11–19) is unchanged. Thus the intersection point moves to the left in the figure, and a lower value for the spontaneous magnetization obtains. Finally, a temperature is reached at which Eq. (11–20) is tangent to (11–19) at the origin; at this and higher temperatures the spontaneous magnetization is zero. This temperature is the *Curie temperature,* T_c, above which the spontaneous magnetization vanishes and ordinary paramagnetic behavior results.

A plot of $M(T)$ versus temperature, obtained according to the above

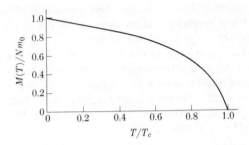

FIG. 11-2. The magnetization of a ferromagnetic material as a function of temperature. T_c is called the Curie temperature. (The curve shown has been calculated with the aid of the classical Langevin function; quantum-mechanical corrections change the shape of the curve somewhat, bringing it into agreement with experimental data.)

procedure, is displayed in Fig. 11-2. It is in approximate agreement[*] with experimentally determined values of the spontaneous magnetization for a ferromagnetic material.

11-5 Ferromagnetic domains. According to the preceding section, a ferromagnetic specimen should be magnetized very nearly to saturation (regardless of its previous history) at temperatures below the Curie temperature. This statement appears to be contrary to observation. We know, for example, that a piece of iron can exist in either a magnetized or unmagnetized condition. The answer to this apparent paradox is that a ferromagnetic material breaks up into *domains;* each domain is fully magnetized in accord with the results of the preceding section, but the various domains can be randomly oriented (Fig. 11-3) and thus present an unmagnetized appearance from the macroscopic point of view. The presence of domains was first postulated by Weiss in 1907.

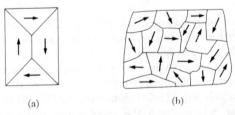

(a)   (b)

FIG. 11-3. Ferromagnetic domain structures: (a) single crystal, (b) polycrystalline specimen. Arrows represent the direction of magnetization.

---

[*] Detailed quantum corrections to the theory presented here bring the theoretical curve into good agreement with experiment.

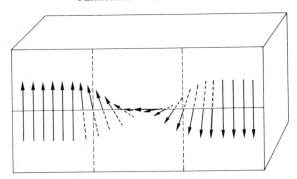

Fig. 11-4. Structure of transition region, or "Bloch wall," between domains in a ferromagnetic material.

In passing from one domain to an adjacent one, the atomic moment vector m_0 gradually rotates from its original to its new direction in the course of about 100 atoms (Fig. 11-4). This region between the two domains is called a *domain wall*. It would appear that an atomic spin moment in the wall region is subjected to a slightly lower molecular field than is an atomic spin moment inside the domain proper. This observation by itself would favor a single domain configuration. On the other hand, a specimen consisting of a single domain must maintain a large external magnetic field, whereas a multidomain specimen has a lower "magnetic energy" associated with its field structure. Thus the multidomain structure is usually energetically favored.

The macroscopic aspects of magnetization in ferromagnetic materials are concerned with changes in domain configuration. The increase in magnetization resulting from the action of an applied magnetic field takes place by two independent processes: by an increase in the volume of domains which are favorably oriented relative to the field at the expense of domains which are unfavorably oriented (domain wall motion), or by rotation of the domain magnetization toward the field direction. The two processes are illustrated schematically in Fig. 11-5.

In weak applied fields the magnetization usually changes by means of domain wall motion. In pure materials consisting of a single phase,

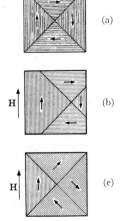

Fig. 11-5. Magnetization of a ferromagnetic material: (a) unmagnetized, (b) magnetization by domain wall motion, (c) magnetization by domain rotation.

the wall motion is to a large extent reversible in the weak-field region. In stronger fields the magnetization proceeds by irreversible wall motion, and finally by domain rotation; in these circumstances the substance remains magnetized when the external magnetic field is removed.

The experimental study of domains has been made possible by a technique first developed by F. H. Bitter.* A finely divided magnetic powder is spread over the surface of the specimen, and the powder particles, which collect along the domain boundaries, may be viewed under a microscope. By means of this technique, it has even proved possible to observe domain wall motion under the action of an applied magnetic field. The size of domains varies widely, depending on the type of material, its previous history, etc.; typical values are in the range from 10^{-6} to 10^{-2} cm^3.

11–6 Ferrites. According to the Heisenberg theory of ferromagnetism, there is a change in electrostatic energy associated with the change from parallel to antiparallel spin alignment of neighboring atoms. If this energy change favors parallel alignment, and is at the same time of sufficient magnitude, the material composed of these atoms is ferromagnetic. If the energy change favors antiparallel alignment, it is still possible to obtain an *ordered* spin structure, but with spins alternating from atom to atom as the crystal is traversed.

An ordered spin structure with zero net magnetic moment is called an *antiferromagnet* (Fig. 11–6b). The most general ordered spin structure contains both "spin-up" and "spin-down" components but has a net,

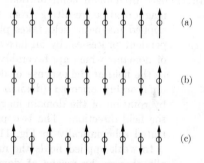

FIG. 11–6. Schematic representation of atomic spins in ordered spin structures: (a) ferromagnetic, (b) antiferromagnetic, (c) ferrimagnetic.

---

* F. H. Bitter, *Physical Review* **41**, 507 (1932). For a brief discussion of the technique, see L. F. Bates, *Modern Magnetism* (Cambridge University Press, 3rd ed., 1951), p. 457.

nonzero magnetic moment in one of these directions; such a material is called a *ferrimagnet* or simply a *ferrite*. The simplest ferrites of magnetic interest are oxides represented by the chemical formula $MOFe_2O_3$, where M is a divalent metal ion such as Co, Ni, Mn, Cu, Mg, Zn, Cd, or divalent iron. These ferrites crystallize in a rather complicated crystal structure known as the *spinel structure*. The classic example of a ferrite is the mineral magnetite (Fe_3O_4), which has been known since ancient times.

Ferrites are of considerable technical importance because, in addition to their relatively large saturation magnetization, they are poor conductors of electricity. Thus they can be used for high-frequency applications where the eddy-current losses in conducting materials pose serious problems. Typical resistivities of ferrites fall in the range from 1 to 10^4 ohm·m; for comparison, the electrical resistivity of iron is approximately 10^{-7} ohm·m.

PROBLEMS

11–1. A Bohr magneton is defined as the magnetic moment of an electron circulating in the classic "Bohr orbit" of the hydrogen atom. This orbit is a circular orbit of exactly one *de Broglie wavelength*, for which the coulomb attraction provides the centripetal acceleration (see, e.g., Sears and Zemansky, *University Physics*, Chapter 48, Addison-Wesley Publishing Co., Inc.). Show that 1 Bohr magneton = $eh/4\pi m_e$, where m_e is the mass of the electron and h is Planck's constant.

11–2. The Bohr magneton is a natural unit for measuring the magnetic moment of an atom. Calculate the magnetic moment per atom, in Bohr magneton units, for iron, nickel, and cobalt, under conditions of saturation magnetization. Use the data in Table 10–2.

11–3. Calculate the relative strength of the interaction between two typical magnetic dipoles, compared with the interaction between two typical electric dipoles. To be explicit: calculate the torque exerted on one dipole by the other when they are oriented perpendicularly to each other at a distance of one angstrom unit; take each magnetic dipole = 1 Bohr magneton, each electric dipole = $e \times 0.1$ angstrom. This calculation shows that the basic magnetic interaction is several orders of magnitude smaller than the electrical interaction in matter.

11–4. Calculate the diamagnetic susceptibility of neon at standard temperature and pressure (0°C, 1 atm) on the assumption that only the eight outer electrons in each atom contribute, and that their mean radius is $R = 4.0 \times 10^{-9}$ cm.

11–5. The magnetization of a ferromagnetic material drops essentially to zero at the Curie temperature. In Fig. 11–1 the Curie temperature is represented by the straight line which is tangent to the Langevin function at the origin. Use the experimental value of the Curie temperature of iron to determine γ for iron.

11–6. The gyromagnetic ratio of a current distribution is defined as the ratio of magnetic moment to angular momentum. Calculate the gyromagnetic ratio of a sphere of mass M and charge Q which is rotating with angular velocity ω about an axis through its center, on the assumption that the mass is distributed uniformly throughout and the charge is distributed uniformly on the surface of the sphere.

CHAPTER 12

MAGNETIC ENERGY

Establishing a magnetic field requires the expenditure of energy; this follows directly from Faraday's law of induction. If an external source of emf $\mathcal{E}_0$ is applied to a circuit, then, in general, the current through the circuit can be expressed by the equation

$$\mathcal{E}_0 + \mathcal{E} = IR, \tag{12–1}$$

where $\mathcal{E}$ is the induced emf and R is the resistance of the current circuit. The work done by $\mathcal{E}_0$ in moving the charge increment $dq = I\,dt$ through the circuit is

$$\mathcal{E}_0\,dq = \mathcal{E}_0 I\,dt = -\mathcal{E}I\,dt + I^2 R\,dt$$

$$= I\,d\Phi + I^2 R\,dt, \tag{12–2}$$

the last form of which is obtained with the aid of Faraday's law, Eq. (9–1). The term $I^2R\,dt$ represents the irreversible conversion of electrical energy into heat by the circuit, but this term absorbs the entire work input *only* in cases where the flux change is zero. The additional term, $I\,d\Phi$, is the work done against the induced emf in the circuit; it is that part of the work done by $\mathcal{E}_0$ which is effective in altering the magnetic field structure. Disregarding the $I^2R\,dt$ term, we write

$$dW_b = I\,d\Phi, \tag{12–3}$$

where the subscript b indicates that this is work performed by external electrical energy sources (e.g., by batteries). The work increment (12–3) may be either positive or negative. It is positive when the flux change $d\Phi$ through the circuit is in the same direction as the flux produced by the current I.

For a rigid stationary circuit showing no energy losses other than Joule heat loss (e.g., no hysteresis), the term dW_b is equal to the change in *magnetic energy* of the circuit. Hysteresis loss will be discussed in Section 12–4, but for the present we shall restrict our attention to reversible magnetic systems.

12–1 Magnetic energy of coupled circuits. In this section we shall derive an expression for the magnetic energy of a system of interacting current circuits. If there are n circuits, then, according to Eq. (12–3), the electrical work done against the induced emf's is given by

$$dW_b = \sum_{i=1}^{n} I_i\,d\Phi_i. \tag{12–4}$$

This expression is perfectly general; it is valid independently of how the flux increments $d\Phi_i$ are produced. We are particularly interested, however, in the case where the $d\Phi_i$ are produced by current changes in the n circuits themselves. In these circumstances the flux changes are directly correlated with changes in these currents:

$$d\Phi_i = \sum_{j=1}^{n} \frac{d\Phi_{ij}}{dI_j} dI_j = \sum_{j=1}^{n} M_{ij} dI_j. \qquad (12\text{--}5)$$

If the circuits are rigid and stationary, then no mechanical work is associated with the flux changes $d\Phi_i$, and dW_b is just equal to the change in magnetic energy, dW, of the system. Note that here we restrict our attention to stationary circuits, so that the magnetic energy can be calculated as a work term. Later we shall let the various circuits move relative to one another, but then we will not be able to identify dW with dW_b.

The magnetic energy W of a system of n rigid stationary circuits is obtained by integrating Eq. (12–4) from the zero flux situation (corresponding to all $I_i = 0$) to the final set of flux values. For a group of *rigid circuits* containing, or located in, *linear magnetic media*, the Φ_i are linearly related to the currents in the circuits, and the magnetic energy is independent of the way in which these currents are brought to their final set of values. Since this situation is of considerable importance, let us restrict our attention to the rigid-circuit, linear case.

Because the final energy is independent of the order in which the currents are varied, we may choose a particular scheme for which W is easily calculated. This scheme is one in which all currents (and hence all fluxes) are brought to their final values in concert, i.e., at any instant of time all currents (and all fluxes) will be at the same fraction of their final values. Let us call this fraction α. If the final values of the current are given the symbols

$$I_1^{(f)}, \qquad I_2^{(f)}, \qquad \ldots, \qquad I_n^{(f)},$$

then $I_i = \alpha I_i^{(f)}$; furthermore, $d\Phi_i = \Phi_i^{(f)} d\alpha$. Integration of Eq. (12–4) yields

$$W = \sum_{i=1}^{n} I_i^{(f)} \Phi_i^{(f)} \int_0^1 \alpha \, d\alpha$$

$$= \tfrac{1}{2} \sum_{i=1}^{n} I_i^{(f)} \Phi_i^{(f)}.$$

Having used the superscript (f) merely to designate a quantity which remains constant while α varies, we now find it convenient to drop the superscripts and write

$$W = \tfrac{1}{2} \sum_{i=1}^{n} I_i \Phi_i \qquad \text{(rigid circuits, linear media).} \qquad (12\text{-}6)$$

With the aid of Eq. (12–5), which for a rigid-circuit, linear system may be integrated directly, the magnetic energy may be expressed in the following form:

$$W = \tfrac{1}{2} \sum_{i=1}^{n} \sum_{j=1}^{n} M_{ij} I_i I_j$$

$$= \tfrac{1}{2}L_1 I_1^2 + \tfrac{1}{2}L_2 I_2^2 + \cdots + \tfrac{1}{2}L_n I_n^2$$

$$+ M_{12} I_1 I_2 + M_{13} I_1 I_3 + \cdots + M_{1n} I_1 I_n$$

$$+ M_{23} I_2 I_3 + \cdots + M_{n-1,n} I_{n-1} I_n \qquad (12\text{-}7)$$

$$\text{(rigid circuits, linear media).}$$

Here we have used the results and notation of Sections 9–3 and 9–4: $M_{ij} = M_{ji}$; $M_{ii} \equiv L_i$.

For *two* coupled circuits, the last equation reduces to

$$W = \tfrac{1}{2}L_1 I_1^2 + M I_1 I_2 + \tfrac{1}{2}L_2 I_2^2, \qquad (12\text{-}8)$$

where, for simplicity, we have written M for M_{12}. The term $M I_1 I_2$ may be either positive or negative, but the total magnetic energy W must be positive (or zero) for any pair of current values: I_1 and I_2. Denoting the current ratio I_1/I_2 by x, we obtain

$$W = \tfrac{1}{2}I_2^2(L_1 x^2 + 2Mx + L_2) \geq 0. \qquad (12\text{-}9)$$

The value of x which makes W a minimum (or maximum) is found by differentiating W with respect to x and setting the result equal to zero:

$$x = -\frac{M}{L_1}. \qquad (12\text{-}10)$$

The second derivative of W with respect to x is positive, which shows that (12–10) is the condition for a minimum. The magnetic energy $W \geq 0$ for any x; in particular, the minimum value of W (defined by $x = -M/L_1$) is greater than or equal to zero. Thus

$$\frac{M^2}{L_1} - \frac{2M^2}{L_1} + L_2 \geq 0$$

or

$$L_1 L_2 \geq M^2, \qquad (12\text{-}11)$$

a result which was stated, but not proved, in Section 9–3.

12–2 Energy density in the magnetic field. Equation (12–7) gives the magnetic energy of a current system in terms of circuit parameters: currents and inductances. Such a formulation is particularly useful because these parameters are capable of direct experimental measurement. On the other hand, an alternative formulation of the magnetic energy in terms of the field vectors **B** and **H** is of considerable interest because it provides a picture in which energy is stored in the magnetic field itself. This picture can be extended, as is done in Chapter 15, to show how energy moves through the electromagnetic field in nonstationary processes.

Consider a group of rigid current-carrying circuits, none of which extends to infinity, immersed in a medium with linear magnetic properties. The energy of this system is given by Eq. (12–6). For the present discussion it is convenient to assume that each circuit consists of only a single loop; then the flux Φ_i may be expressed as

$$\Phi_i = \int_{S_i} \mathbf{B} \cdot \mathbf{n} \, da = \oint_{C_i} \mathbf{A} \cdot d\mathbf{l}_i, \qquad (12\text{--}12)$$

where **A** is the local vector potential. Substitution of this result into (12–6) yields

$$W = \tfrac{1}{2} \sum_i \oint_{C_i} I_i \mathbf{A} \cdot d\mathbf{l}_i. \qquad (12\text{--}13a)$$

We should like to make Eq. (12–13a) somewhat more general. Suppose that we do not have well-defined current circuits, but instead each "circuit" is a closed path in the medium (which we take to be conducting). Equation (12–13a) may be made to approximate this situation very closely by choosing a large number of contiguous circuits (C_i), replacing $I_i \, d\mathbf{l}_i \rightarrow \mathbf{J} \, dv$, and, finally, by the substitution of

$$\int_V \qquad \text{for} \qquad \sum_i \oint_{C_i}.$$

Hence

$$W = \tfrac{1}{2} \int_V \mathbf{J} \cdot \mathbf{A} \, dv. \qquad (12\text{--}13b)$$

The last equation may be further transformed by using the field equation $\mathbf{curl}\,\mathbf{H} = \mathbf{J}$, and the vector identity (I–7):

$$\mathrm{div}\,(\mathbf{A} \times \mathbf{H}) = \mathbf{H} \cdot \mathbf{curl}\,\mathbf{A} - \mathbf{A} \cdot \mathbf{curl}\,\mathbf{H},$$

whence

$$W = \tfrac{1}{2} \int_V \mathbf{H} \cdot \mathbf{curl}\,\mathbf{A} \, dv - \tfrac{1}{2} \int_S \mathbf{A} \times \mathbf{H} \cdot \mathbf{n} \, da, \qquad (12\text{--}14)$$

where S is the surface which bounds the volume V. Since, by assumption, none of the current "circuits" extends to infinity, it is convenient to move the surface S out to a very large distance so that all parts of this surface are far from the currents. Of course, the volume of the system must be increased accordingly. Now $\mathbf{H}$ falls off at least as fast as $1/r^2$, where r is the distance from an origin near the middle of the current distribution to a characteristic point on the surface S; $\mathbf{A}$ falls off at least as fast as $1/r$; and the surface area is proportional to r^2. Thus the contribution from the surface integral in (12–14) falls off as $1/r$ or faster, and if S is moved out to infinity, this contribution vanishes.

By dropping the surface integral in (12–14) and extending the volume term to include all space, we obtain

$$W = \tfrac{1}{2} \int_V \mathbf{H} \cdot \mathbf{B} \, dv, \tag{12–15}$$

since $\mathbf{B} = \operatorname{curl} \mathbf{A}$. This result is completely analogous to the expression for electrostatic energy, Eq. (6–17). Equation (12–15) is restricted to systems containing linear magnetic media, since it was derived from Eq. (12–6).

By reasoning similar to that of Section 6–3, we are led to the concept of energy density in a magnetic field:

$$w = \tfrac{1}{2}\mathbf{H} \cdot \mathbf{B}, \tag{12–16a}$$

which, for the case of isotropic, linear, magnetic materials reduces to

$$w = \tfrac{1}{2}\mu H^2. \tag{12–16b}$$

12–3 Forces and torques on rigid circuits. Up to this point we have developed a number of alternative expressions for the magnetic energy of a system of current circuits. These are given by Eqs. (12–6) and (12–7), and (12–15). We shall now show how the force, or torque, on one of these circuits may be calculated from a knowledge of the magnetic energy.

Suppose we allow one of the circuits to make a rigid displacement $d\mathbf{r}$ under the influence of the magnetic forces acting upon it, all currents remaining constant. The mechanical work performed *by* the system in these circumstances is

$$dW_m = \mathbf{F} \cdot d\mathbf{r}. \tag{12–17}$$

But conservation of energy requires that

$$dW + dW_m = dW_b, \tag{12–18}$$

where dW is the change in magnetic energy of the system and dW_b is the work performed by external energy sources against the induced emf's.

Before we can proceed to an expression linking W and the force on a circuit, it will be necessary to eliminate dW_b from Eq. (12–18). This is easily done for a system of rigid circuits in *linear* magnetic media. If the geometry of the system is changed but all currents remain unaltered, then, according to Eq. (12–6),

$$dW = \tfrac{1}{2} \sum_i I_i \, d\Phi_i. \tag{12–19}$$

But, from Eq. (12–4),

$$dW_b = \sum_i I_i \, d\Phi_i.$$

Thus

$$dW_b = 2 \, dW. \tag{12–20}$$

Using this equation to eliminate dW_b from (12–18) and combining the result with (12–17), we obtain

$$dW = \mathbf{F} \cdot d\mathbf{r},$$

or

$$\mathbf{F} = \text{grad } W. \tag{12–21}$$

The force on the circuit is the gradient of the magnetic energy.

If the circuit under consideration is constrained to move in such a way that it rotates about an axis, then Eq. (12–17) may be replaced by

$$dW_m = \boldsymbol{\tau} \cdot d\boldsymbol{\theta} = \tau_1 \, d\theta_1 + \tau_2 \, d\theta_2 + \tau_3 \, d\theta_3,$$

where $\boldsymbol{\tau}$ is the magnetic torque on the circuit and $d\boldsymbol{\theta}$ is an angular displacement. Under these conditions,

$$\tau_1 = \frac{\partial W}{\partial \theta_1}, \tag{12–22}$$

and so on.

Just as in the electrostatic case (discussed in Section 6–7), in order to make use of the energy method it is necessary to express W in analytic form, i.e., the specific dependence of W on the variable coordinates $(x, y, z, \theta_1, \theta_2, \text{ or } \theta_3)$ must be given. When this is done, however, the energy method becomes a powerful technique for calculating forces and torques.

We shall illustrate the method by considering two examples. Additional exercises of this type will be found in the problems at the end of the chapter. For our first example let us calculate the force between two rigid current circuits. The magnetic energy is given by Eq. (12–8), and the force on circuit 2 is

$$\mathbf{F}_2 = \text{grad}_2 \, W = I_1 I_2 \, \text{grad}_2 \, M, \tag{12–23}$$

where the mutual inductance M must be written so that it displays its dependence on $\mathbf{r}_2$. Neumann's formula, Eq. (9–35), shows this dependence explicitly, so we may write

$$\mathbf{F}_2 = \frac{\mu_0}{4\pi} I_1 I_2 \oint_{C_1} \oint_{C_2} (d\mathbf{l}_1 \cdot d\mathbf{l}_2) \, \mathbf{grad}_2 \frac{1}{|\mathbf{r}_2 - \mathbf{r}_1|}$$

$$= -\frac{\mu_0}{4\pi} I_1 I_2 \oint_{C_1} \oint_{C_2} (d\mathbf{l}_1 \cdot d\mathbf{l}_2) \frac{(\mathbf{r}_2 - \mathbf{r}_1)}{|\mathbf{r}_2 - \mathbf{r}_1|^3}, \qquad (12\text{–}24)$$

an expression which evidently shows the proper symmetry, i.e., $\mathbf{F}_2 = -\mathbf{F}_1$. However, we already have an expression for the force between two circuits, Eq. (8–25), and this appears to be at variance with the formula just derived. Actually, the two expressions are equivalent, as may be easily verified. Let us expand the triple product in the integrand of Eq. (8–25):

$$d\mathbf{l}_2 \times [d\mathbf{l}_1 \times (\mathbf{r}_2 - \mathbf{r}_1)] = d\mathbf{l}_1[d\mathbf{l}_2 \cdot (\mathbf{r}_2 - \mathbf{r}_1)] - (\mathbf{r}_2 - \mathbf{r}_1)(d\mathbf{l}_1 \cdot d\mathbf{l}_2).$$

The integral containing the last term on the right is identical with (12–24); that containing the first term may be written

$$\frac{\mu_0}{4\pi} I_1 I_2 \oint_{C_1} d\mathbf{l}_1 \oint_{C_2} \frac{d\mathbf{l}_2 \cdot (\mathbf{r}_2 - \mathbf{r}_1)}{|\mathbf{r}_2 - \mathbf{r}_1|^3}. \qquad (12\text{–}25)$$

Now $d\mathbf{l}_2 \cdot (\mathbf{r}_2 - \mathbf{r}_1)$ is $|\mathbf{r}_2 - \mathbf{r}_1|$ times the projection of $d\mathbf{l}_2$ on the vector $\mathbf{r}_2 - \mathbf{r}_1$. Let us denote $|\mathbf{r}_2 - \mathbf{r}_1|$ by r_{21}; then the projection of $d\mathbf{l}_2$ is just dr_{21}. The integral over C_2 may be carried out at fixed $d\mathbf{l}_1$:

$$\oint_{C_2} \frac{dr_{21}}{r_{21}^2} = -\frac{1}{r_{21}}\Big|_a^a,$$

the upper and lower limit being identical because of the complete circuit. Thus (12–25) vanishes, and Eq. (12–24) is equivalent to Eq. (8–25).

As a second example, consider a long solenoid of N turns, and length l carrying current I. A thin iron rod of permeability μ and cross-sectional area A is inserted along the solenoid axis. If the rod is withdrawn (Fig. 12–1a) until only one-half of its length remains in the solenoid, calculate approximately the force tending to pull it back into place.

Solution. The magnetic field structure associated with this problem is quite complicated; fortunately, however, we do not have to calculate the entire magnetic energy of the system but merely the difference in energy between the two configurations shown in Fig. 12–1(a) and (b). The primary field structure (produced by the currents) is relatively uniform in the solenoid. The field structure associated with the magnetized iron rod is complicated, but it moves along with rod. The essen-

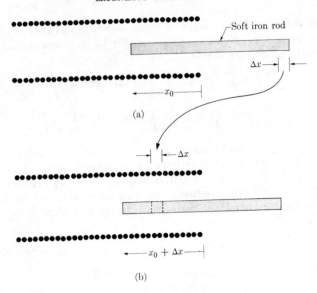

Fig. 12-1. Force on soft-iron rod inserted into a solenoid (by the energy method).

tial difference between configurations (a) and (b) is that a length Δx from the extreme right-hand end of the rod (outside the field region) is effectively transferred to the uniform field region inside the solenoid, at a place beyond the demagnetizing influence of the magnet pole. Thus

$$W(x_0 + \Delta x) \approx W(x_0) + \frac{1}{2} \int_{A\,\Delta x} (\mu - \mu_0) H^2 \, dv$$

$$= W(x_0) + \frac{1}{2}(\mu - \mu_0) \frac{N^2 I^2}{l^2} A \, \Delta x,$$

and

$$F_x \approx \frac{1}{2}(\mu - \mu_0) \frac{N^2 I^2 A}{l^2}. \tag{12-26}$$

12-4 Hysteresis loss. In the preceding sections we have limited our discussion to reversible magnetic systems, and in most instances to linear systems. We shall now say something about energy changes in systems containing permanent magnet material, that is, systems in which hysteresis plays a prominent role. Let us consider an electrical circuit, in the form of a closely wound coil of N turns, which surrounds a piece of ferromagnetic material (Fig. 12-2). If the coil is connected to an external source of electrical energy, the work done against the induced emf in the coil is given by Eq. (12-3). In (12-3), however, the flux change $d\Phi$

is the total flux change through the circuit; for the present purpose it is convenient to let the symbol $d\Phi$ stand for the flux change through a single turn of the coil. Thus, on the assumption that the same flux links every turn,

$$\delta W_b = NI \, \delta\Phi. \tag{12–3a}$$

Let us treat the ferromagnetic specimen as forming part of a magnetic circuit. Then NI may be replaced by $\oint \mathbf{H} \cdot d\mathbf{l}$ around a typical flux path, and Eq. (12–3a) becomes*

$$\delta W_b = \oint \delta\Phi \mathbf{H} \cdot d\mathbf{l} = \oint A \, \delta B H \cdot d\mathbf{l},$$

where A is the cross section of the magnetic circuit appropriate to the length interval $d\mathbf{l}$. Since $d\mathbf{l}$ is always tangent to the flux path, the preceding equation may be written as

$$\delta W_b = \oint A \, \delta\mathbf{B} \cdot \mathbf{H} \, dl = \int_V \delta\mathbf{B} \cdot \mathbf{H} \, dv, \tag{12–27}$$

where V is the volume of the magnetic circuit, i.e., the region of space in which the magnetic field is different from zero.

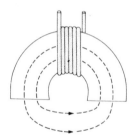

Fig. 12–2. A ferromagnetic specimen forming part of a magnetic circuit.

If the ferromagnetic material in the system shows reversible magnetic behavior, Eq. (12–27) may be integrated from $\mathbf{B} = 0$ to its final value, to yield the magnetic energy of the system. For "linear" material, the

---

* The analysis presented here may be put on a somewhat more rigorous basis by replacing the magnetic circuit with a large number of magnetic flux paths of various lengths (magnetic circuits in parallel). Equation (12–3a) then becomes

$$\delta W_b = NI \sum_i \delta\Phi_j = \sum_i \oint_j \delta\Phi_j \mathbf{H} \cdot d\mathbf{l}_j,$$

where $\delta\Phi_j$ is the flux change associated with one of these paths. The final result, Eq. (12–27), is unchanged.

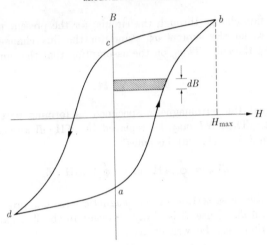

FIG. 12–3. Work done per unit volume in cycling a ferromagnetic material.

energy so obtained is identical with that expressed by Eq. (12–15). But Eq. (12–27) is much more general than this; it correctly predicts the work done on the magnetic system even for cases in which there is hysteresis.

According to Eq. (12–27), a change in the magnetic field structure implies a work input

$$dw_b = \mathbf{H} \cdot d\mathbf{B} \qquad (12\text{–}28)$$

associated with each unit volume of magnetic material (or vacuum) in the system. Of particular interest is the case where the material is cycled, as it would be when the coil surrounding the specimen is subjected to alternating current operation. In one cycle the magnetic intensity H (for a typical point in the specimen) starts at zero, increases to a maximum, $H_{\max}$, decreases to $-H_{\max}$, and then returns to zero. The magnetic induction B shows a similar variation, but for a typical ferromagnetic will lag behind H, thus tracing out a hysteresis curve (Fig. 12–3). The work input (per unit volume) required to change the magnetic induction from point a to b on the hysteresis curve,

$$(w_b)_{ab} = \int_a^b H \, dB,$$

is just the area between the hysteresis segment ab and the B-axis; it is positive because both H and dB are positive. The contribution $(w_b)_{bc}$ is also the area between the appropriate hysteresis segment (bc) and the B-axis, but it must be taken negative, since H and dB are of opposite sign. Similar arguments can be made about $(w_b)_{cd}$ and $(w_b)_{da}$. Thus, in cycling the material once around the hysteresis loop, the work required per unit volume is

$$w_b = \oint H \, dB, \tag{12–29}$$

which is the area enclosed by the hysteresis loop.

At the end of one complete cycle, the magnetic state of the material is the same as it was at the start of the cycle; hence the "magnetic energy" of the material is the same. It is evident, then, that Eq. (12–29) represents an energy loss. This loss appears as heat; it comes about through the irreversible changes in domain structure of the material. Hysteresis loss is an important factor in circuits subjected to alternating current operation. Equation (12–29) represents the energy loss per unit volume *per cycle;* thus the energy loss per unit time is directly proportional to the frequency of the alternating current.

According to Eq. (12–28), the work required to change the magnetic induction in a unit volume of material is

$$dw_b = \mathbf{H} \cdot d\mathbf{B} = \mu_0 H \, dH + \mu_0 \mathbf{H} \cdot d\mathbf{M}. \tag{12–28a}$$

It is sometimes convenient to regard the $\mu_0 H \, dH$ term (the work done on the vacuum) as taking place whether the material is present or not. From this point of view, then, the term $\mu_0 \mathbf{H} \cdot d\mathbf{M}$ is the specific work done on the material. This is the approach usually taken in thermodynamics textbooks; it forms the basis for discussion of such processes as "magnetic cooling."

Since the integral of $H \, dH$ vanishes for a complete cycle, Eq. (12–29) is equivalent to

$$w_b = \mu_0 \oint H \, dM. \tag{12–29a}$$

PROBLEMS

12-1. Given a current circuit in a prescribed magnetic field. The magnetic force on each circuit element $d\mathbf{l}$ is given by $I\,d\mathbf{l} \times \mathbf{B}$. If the circuit is allowed to move under the influences of the magnetic forces, such that a typical element is displaced $\delta\mathbf{r}$ and at the same time the current I is held constant, show by direct calculation that the mechanical work done by the circuit is $dW_m = I\,d\Phi$, where $d\Phi$ is the additional flux through the circuit.

12-2. Given a set of interacting current circuits in a linear magnetic medium. All circuits with the exception of circuit 1 are held stationary, but circuit 1 is allowed to move rigidly. The currents are all held constant by means of batteries. Show from the combination of Eqs. (12-4), (12-6), and (12-18), that the mechanical work done by the moving circuit is $dW_m = I_1\,d\Phi_1$, where $d\Phi_1$ is the change in flux through circuit 1.

12-3. Consider two interacting current circuits characterized by the inductances $L_1 = \beta I_1^s$, $M_{12} = M_{21} = \beta I_1^{s/2} I_2^{s/2}$, and $L_2 = \beta I_2^s$, where β and s are constants. This is a reversible magnetic system but not a linear one. Calculate the magnetic energy of the system in terms of the final currents $I_1^{(f)}$ and $I_2^{(f)}$. Do this in two ways: first, by bringing the currents to their final values in concert; second, by keeping $I_2 = 0$ while I_1 is brought to its final value, then changing I_2.

12-4. A circuit in the form of a circular turn of wire of radius b is placed at the center of a larger turn of radius a, $b \ll a$. The small circuit is fixed so that it is free to rotate about one of its diameters, this diameter being located in the plane of the larger circuit. The circuits carry the steady currents I_b and I_a, respectively. If the angle between the normals to the two circuits is θ, calculate the torque on the movable circuit. In what direction is this torque when I_b and I_a circulate in the same sense?

*12-5. A U-shaped electromagnet of length l, pole separation d, and permeability μ has a square cross section of area A. It is wound with N turns of wire carrying a current I. Calculate the force with which the magnet holds a bar of the same material, of same cross section, against its poles.

12-6. A permanent magnet with constant magnetization, and a circuit which is connected to a battery, form an isolated system. The circuit is allowed to move relative to the magnet, the current I in the circuit being maintained constant. The mechanical work done by the circuit is given in Problem 12-1. What conclusion can you draw about the change in magnetic energy of this system?

12-7. The magnetic induction field between the poles of an electromagnet is relatively uniform and is held at the constant value $\mathbf{B}_0$. A paramagnetic rod which is constrained to move vertically is placed in the field as shown in Fig. 12-4. The susceptibility of the rod is χ_m and its cross-sectional area is A. (a) Calculate the force on the rod. (b) Obtain a numerical value for the force if the rod material is titanium, $A = 1$ cm^2 and $B_0 = 0.25$ w/m^2.

*12-8. From the result of Problem 12-1, the force on a current circuit in a prescribed magnetic field is given by $\mathbf{F} = I\,\boldsymbol{\nabla}\Phi$. If the circuit is very small, the magnetic field $\mathbf{B}$ may be treated as constant over the surface bounded by

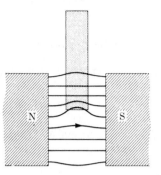

FIG. 12-4. A paramagnetic rod inserted between the pole faces of a magnet.

the circuit; furthermore, the circuit itself may be characterized by its magnetic dipole moment **m**. Show that when the prescribed magnetic field has no sources (i.e., **J**, $\mathbf{J}_M = 0$) at the position of the dipole, the force on the dipole is

$$\mathbf{F} = (\mathbf{m} \cdot \boldsymbol{\nabla})\mathbf{B}.$$

12-9. A rigid circuit consisting of a single loop of wire is located in a radial, inverse-square, magnetic induction field, $\mathbf{B} = K\mathbf{r}/r^3$. Show that the force on the circuit is $\mathbf{F} = KI\boldsymbol{\nabla}\Omega$, where Ω is the solid angle the circuit subtends at the field center, and I is the current in the circuit.

12-10. The center of a plane circular circuit of radius R and consisting of one turn lies on the x-axis at distance x from the origin. The circuit carries the current I, and its positive normal points in the $-x$ direction. Find the force exerted on the circuit by a radial induction field diverging from the origin, $\mathbf{B} = K\mathbf{r}/r^3$.

12-11. Estimate the areas enclosed by the two hysteresis curves shown in Fig. 10-8, and calculate the power loss per unit volume due to hysteresis in these materials at 60 cycles/sec operation.

12-12. The core of a generator armature is made of iron whose average hysteresis loop under operating conditions has an area of 2000 joules/m³. The core is cylindrical in shape, with a length of 0.4 m and a diameter of 0.15 m. If it rotates at 1800 rpm, calculate the rate at which heat is produced in the core.

12-13. A current circuit in a prescribed magnetic field moves under the influence of magnetic forces. The mechanical work done by the circuit is given in Problem 12-1. Suppose now that the circuit is an *atomic circuit*, and that the atomic current is held constant because of general quantum principles (note that we are neglecting a small change in current due to diamagnetism). What is the change in magnetic energy of the circuit? The result of this problem is the basis for the magnetic dipole energy in the calculation in Section 11-3.

CHAPTER 13

SLOWLY VARYING CURRENTS

13-1 Introduction. In Chapter 7 the idea of an electrical circuit was introduced, and an analysis was made of the currents in such circuits when they are excited by constant emf's. These ideas will now be expanded to include slowly varying emf's and the resulting slowly varying currents. To understand properly what is meant by "slowly varying," Maxwell's equations* must be used; however, the general ideas can be understood without recourse to the details of these equations.

For sinusoidal variations of emf in circuits containing linear elements, the basis for elementary circuit theory, the behavior of a circuit is characterized by a frequency ω.† An electromagnetic wave of this frequency in free space has a wavelength $\lambda = 2\pi c/\omega$, where c is the velocity of light. The principal restriction to be imposed in order that the current in the circuit may be called slowly varying is that the circuit should not radiate an appreciable amount of power. This restriction can be met by requiring that the maximum linear dimension of the system, L, be much smaller than the free space wavelength associated with the driving frequency, that is,

$$L \ll \frac{2\pi c}{\omega} \quad \text{or} \quad \omega \ll \frac{2\pi c}{L}. \qquad (13\text{-}1)$$

If this condition is satisfied, then for every element $d\mathbf{l}$ of the circuit carrying a current I there is, much less than one wavelength away, a corresponding element $-d\mathbf{l}$ carrying the same current. This clearly ensures cancellation of the fields produced by these elements at distances of the order of a few wavelengths in all directions, and thus shows that the fields associated with the circuit are confined to the vicinity of the circuit. To see what practical restrictions are imposed by Eq. (13-1), $L \sim \lambda/10$ has been used as the maximum circuit dimension in constructing Table 13-1. The frequencies chosen are a power line frequency, a low radiofrequency (broadcast band), a high radiofrequency, and a microwave

---

* Maxwell's equations are treated in some detail in Chapter 15. For those who are particularily interested, it is worth correlating the material presented in Chapter 15 with that presented here.

† The quantity ω is 2π times the frequency and is sometimes called the angular frequency. The use of ω instead of $2\pi f$ is of considerable advantage in many branches of physics. In particular, for the present discussion it eliminates a multitude of 2π's from the circuit equations.

TABLE 13–1

f, cycles/sec	ω, rad/sec	λ, m	L, m
60	376	5×10^6	5×10^5 (250 mi)
10^6	6.28×10^6	300	30
30×10^6	1.88×10^8	10	1
10^{10}	6.28×10^{10}	0.03	0.003

frequency. It is clear that for the first three frequencies it is feasible to construct circuits confined to the distances indicated; however, for the last one the circuit must be built in a cube about 0.1 inch on a side, which is a jeweler's job at best. It should also be noted that at 30 megacycles/sec (30 Mc) the wavelength and circuit dimensions are of laboratory size, and hence that care must be used in applying ordinary circuit theory at this and higher frequencies. In the balance of this chapter it will be assumed that the slowly varying criterion is satisfied, without further explicit comment.

13–2 Transient and steady-state behavior. If a network of passive elements is suddenly connected to a source or sources of emf, currents arise. Regardless of the nature of the applied emf's, the initial variation of the currents with time is nonperiodic. If, however, the emf's vary periodically with the time, then a long time after the application of the emf's the currents will also be found to vary periodically with the time. (Actually, of course, they become strictly periodic only after infinite time; however, any desired approximation to periodicity can be attained by waiting a sufficiently long time.) It is convenient to discuss the behavior of circuits in two phases, according to whether the periodic or nonperiodic behavior is important. The periodic behavior is referred to as the *steady-state* behavior while the nonperiodic behavior is known as the *transient* behavior. Both aspects are governed by the same basic integro-differential equations; however, the elementary techniques used in solving them are radically different in the two cases. The analysis presented here will be restricted to elementary transient analysis (primarily excitation by constant emf's) and steady-state analysis for sinusoidal excitations. For further details the reader is referred to the books of Guillemin and of Bode,* and to others too numerous to mention.

---

* E. A. Guillemin, *Communication Networks*, 2 vols., John Wiley & Sons, New York, (1931 and 1935), and H. W. Bode, *Network Analysis and Feedback Amplifier Design*, D. Van Nostrand Co., Princeton, N.J. (1945).

13–3 Kirchhoff's laws. In Chapter 7, Kirchhoff's laws were introduced for direct current (d-c) circuits; these must now be generalized to include slowly varying currents. The first generalization is to note that not only resistors but also capacitors and inductors must be included as circuit elements. Each such element has a potential difference between its terminals which must be included in Kirchhoff's loop law. The name "IR-drop" is no longer appropriate for all of these, therefore the name *counter voltage* will be adopted to specify the difference in potential between the terminals of a passive element. The other generalization is to observe that both of Kirchhoff's laws must apply at each instant of time, that is, they must apply to the instantaneous values of the currents, emf's, and counter voltages. The laws may now be stated:

I. *The algebraic sum of the instantaneous emf's in a closed loop equals the algebraic sum of the instantaneous counter voltages in the loop.*

II. *The algebraic sum of the instantaneous currents flowing toward a junction is zero.*

The meaning of the second of these laws is clear: if currents directed toward a junction are called positive then those oppositely directed should be called negative, and the law says that as much current enters the junction as leaves it. Basically, the first law represents conservation of energy; however, it is beset with difficulties in sign convention. The sign convention to which we will adhere is best explained in terms of a single simple mesh, as shown in Fig. 13–1. In this figure a source of emf $\mathcal{E}(t)$ is shown connected in series with a resistance R, an inductance L, and a capacitance C. An arrow labeled $I(t)$ has been drawn to indicate the assumed (arbitrary) positive direction for the current. All signs are ultimately referred to this direction. The emf $\mathcal{E}(t)$ is positive if it tends to cause the current to move in the assumed direction, i.e., if the top terminal in Fig. 13–1 is positive with respect to the bottom terminal. The resistive counter voltage is just IR, as in d-c circuits. If dI/dt is positive,

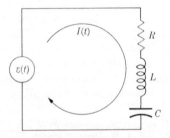

Fig. 13–1. A series circuit of circuit elements.

an emf will be induced in the inductance which tends to cause a current in the opposite direction to that assumed for I, i.e., the upper terminal of L must be positive with respect to the lower teminal. Since this is the same sense as IR with respect to the direction of I, the counter voltage is just $L(dI/dt)$.* The capacitative counter voltage depends on the charge on the capacitor, which may be either positive or negative, depending on whether we consider the upper or the lower conductor. This difficulty is resolved by writing

$$Q = \int_{t_0}^{t} I(t)\, dt, \qquad (13\text{--}2)$$

where t_0 is chosen so that $Q(t_0)$ is zero. With this choice of Q a positive Q makes the upper terminal of the capacitor positive, and thus produces the capacitative counter voltage $+Q/C$. Kirchhoff's emf law for the circuit of Fig. 13–1, and indeed for any single loop, is

$$\mathcal{E}(t) = RI + L\frac{dI}{dt} + \frac{1}{C}\int_{t_0}^{t} I\, dt, \qquad (13\text{--}3)$$

which is the basic integrodifferential equation of circuit theory.

13–4 Elementary transient behavior. The only transient behavior to be considered here is that associated with the sudden application of a constant emf $\mathcal{E}$ to a network of resistors, capacitors, and inductors, the first example being the simple L-R circuit shown in Fig. 13–2. For this circuit, Eq. (13–3) becomes

$$\mathcal{E} = RI + L\frac{dI}{dt} \qquad (13\text{--}4)$$

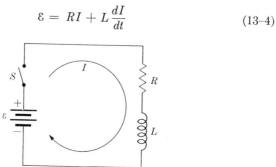

Fig. 13–2. Transient response of an R-L circuit. Circuit diagram.

---

* It is worth noting that the induced emf is written $-L(dI/dt)$; however, being an emf, it would normally be written on the other side of the equation from the counter voltages. Thus no inconsistency is introduced by writing $+L(dI/dt)$ for the counter voltage.

after the switch S is closed. Before the switch is closed the solution is trivial, being just $I = 0$. Equation (13–4) is a first-order linear differential equation with constant coefficients, hence can always be solved with one arbitrary constant in the solution. The solution is

$$I(t) = \frac{\mathcal{E}}{R} - Ke^{-tR/L}, \tag{13–5}$$

with K the arbitrary constant. Since the circuit contains an inductance which prevents an abrupt change in the current, the current just after the switch is closed must be the same as the current just before the switch is closed, i.e., zero. If the switch is closed at $t = t_0$, this requires that

$$\frac{\mathcal{E}}{R} - Ke^{-t_0 R/L} = 0 \tag{13–6}$$

or

$$K = \frac{\mathcal{E}}{R} e^{t_0 R/L}. \tag{13–7}$$

The complete solution is then

$$I(t) = \frac{\mathcal{E}}{R} [1 - e^{(t_0-t)R/L}], \tag{13–8}$$

which is plotted in Fig. 13–3. There are several useful, easily obtained facts which can be found from Eq. (13–8) and Fig. 13–3. First, L/R has the dimensions of time and is called the time constant. Since $1/e \cong 0.368$, the time constant is the time required for the current to reach 0.632 times its final value, $\mathcal{E}/R$. In five time constants the current reaches 0.993 times its final value, which is conveniently remembered as 99%. The initial slope dI/dt is just the final current $\mathcal{E}/R$ divided by one time constant L/R, i.e., a slope such that if the current continued to increase at this rate it would reach its final value in one time constant. The usefulness of these facts is that, by simply sketching a standard exponential curve, they enable evaluation of the exponential function involved

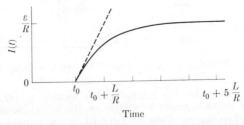

FIG. 13–3. Transient response of an R-L circuit.

in a simple transient problem to an accuracy of a few percent. Many other aspects of a resistance-inductance circuit can be explored, and a similar treatment can be applied to resistance-capacitance circuits. Several of the problems at the end of this chapter are devoted to accomplishing this end.

The second example to be considered is a series R-L-C circuit which is suddenly connected to a constant emf $\mathcal{E}$. Such a circuit is shown in Fig. 13-4. The appropriate equation after the switch is closed is

$$\mathcal{E} = RI + L\frac{dI}{dt} + \frac{1}{C}\int_{t_0}^{t} I(t)\,dt, \qquad (13\text{-}9)$$

where again t_0 is a time at which the charge on the capacitor is zero. In the interest of simplicity it will be assumed that the capacitor is initially uncharged and that the switch S is closed at $t = t_0$. Equation (13-9) is rather formidable and unfamiliar; however, by simply differentiating it once with respect to the time it becomes

$$\frac{d\mathcal{E}}{dt} = R\frac{dI}{dt} + L\frac{d^2I}{dt^2} + \frac{I}{C}, \qquad (13\text{-}10)$$

which is an ordinary second-order linear differential equation with constant coefficients. The technique for solving such equations are well known, and in fact for the case at hand, $d\mathcal{E}/dt = 0$, the solution is*

$$I = \left\{ A\exp\left[j\sqrt{\frac{1}{LC} - \frac{R^2}{4L^2}}\,t\right] + B\exp\left[-j\sqrt{\frac{1}{LC} - \frac{R^2}{4L^2}}\,t\right] \right\}\exp\left[-\frac{Rt}{2L}\right]$$

$$(13\text{-}11)$$

so long as neither L nor C is zero. If either vanishes, an indeterminacy appears in Eq. (13-11); however, Eq. (13-10) can still be solved for $L = 0$; in fact, the solution is simpler than that for Eq. (13-11). Further-

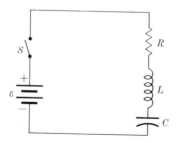

Fig. 13-4. Transient response of an R-L-C circuit. Circuit diagram.

---

* Here j is the unit imaginary number, that is, $j \equiv \sqrt{-1}$.

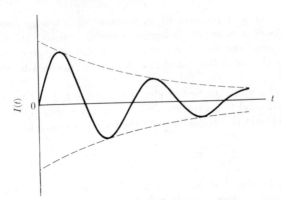

FIG. 13–5. Transient response of an *R-L-C* circuit.

more, the case $C = 0$ corresponds to the uninteresting case of an open circuit. To complete the discussion of this point, if $C = \infty$, which corresponds to short-circuiting the capacitor, Eq. (13–11) reduces to Eq. (13–5), with now two arbitrary constants to be obtained by fitting boundary conditions. This, of course, reflects the fact that all knowledge of $\mathcal{E}$ was lost in going from Eq. (13–9) to Eq. (13–10).

We return now to the solution of (13–11), where it remains to evaluate the constants A and B. For the current to be real, B must be the complex conjugate of A. Since the switch is closed at $t = t_0$, it is convenient to measure the time from $t = t_0$ by replacing t with $t - t_0$. Furthermore, at $t = t_0$ the current must be zero, which means that the two imaginary exponentials must combine to give a sine function. These observations lead to

$$I(t) = D e^{-R(t-t_0)/2L} \sin\left[\sqrt{\frac{1}{LC} - \frac{R^2}{4L^2}}\,(t - t_0)\right], \quad (13\text{–}12)$$

where D is a single real constant still to be evaluated. This evaluation is accomplished by noting that at $t = t_0$, Q and I are both zero, and hence that

$$\mathcal{E} = L\frac{dI}{dt}\bigg|_{t=t_0}. \quad (13\text{–}13)$$

Using this initial condition gives

$$D = \frac{\mathcal{E}}{\sqrt{\dfrac{L}{C} - \dfrac{R^2}{4}}}. \quad (13\text{–}14)$$

The solution is now complete. The current oscillates with a frequency

$$\omega = \sqrt{\frac{1}{LC} - \frac{R^2}{4L^2}},$$

with, however, an amplitude which decreases with time and which is given by $De^{-R(t-t_0)/2L}$. This behavior is shown in Fig. 13–5.

This completes the elementary transient analysis to be presented here. The balance of this chapter will be devoted to circuits excited by sinusoidal emf's in the steady state, i.e., sufficiently long after the excitation has been applied to ensure that the transients are negligible.

13–5 Steady-state behavior of a simple series circuit. The behavior of the circuit of Fig. 13–1, with the following excitation, will now be studied:

$$\mathcal{E}(t) = \mathcal{E}_0 \cos \omega t. \tag{13–15}$$

This could simply be written in place of $\mathcal{E}(t)$ in Eq. (13–1) or Eq. (13–10) and the resulting equation solved; however, a more fruitful procedure is to note that $\mathcal{E}_0 \cos \omega t$ is the real part of $\mathcal{E}_0 e^{j\omega t}$. If a fictitious complex voltage $\mathcal{E}_1 + j\mathcal{E}_2$ were applied to the circuit the resulting current would most certainly also be complex, $I_1 + jI_2$ (it is implied here that $\mathcal{E}_1$, $\mathcal{E}_2$, I_1, and I_2 are all real). Putting these fictitious quantities into Eq. (13–10) gives us

$$\frac{d\mathcal{E}_1}{dt} + j\frac{d\mathcal{E}_2}{dt} = \left(L\frac{d^2 I_1}{dt^2} + R\frac{dI_1}{dt} + \frac{I_1}{C} \right) + j\left(L\frac{d^2 I_2}{dt^2} + R\frac{dI_2}{dt} + \frac{I_2}{C} \right).$$
$$\tag{13–16}$$

The only way this equation can be satisfied is if the real parts on the left and right are equal and the imaginary parts on the left and right are equal. Thus I_1 satisfies Eq. (13–10) with $d\mathcal{E}_1/dt$ on the left, and I_2 satisfies Eq. (13–10) with $d\mathcal{E}_2/dt$ on the left. This means that if $\mathcal{E}(t)$ is the real part of some complex function it is sufficient to solve Eq. (13–10) with the complex function for $\mathcal{E}(t)$, and then obtain the physical current by taking the real part of the complex solution. For the excitation $\mathcal{E}_0 \cos \omega t$ it is appropriate to use $\mathcal{E}_0 e^{j\omega t}$ and take the real part of the solution to be the physical current. In some instances it may be preferable to use $e^{j(\omega t + \varphi)}$ in order to obtain the response to $\cos (\omega t + \varphi)$.

If $\mathcal{E}_0 e^{j\omega t}$ is used in Eq. (13–10), then the current will be $I_0 e^{j\omega t}$, with I_0 some complex constant. Direct substitution into the equation gives

$$j\omega \mathcal{E}_0 e^{j\omega t} = \left[-\omega^2 L + j\omega R + \frac{1}{C} \right] I_0 e^{j\omega t}. \tag{13–17}$$

Dividing by $j\omega$ changes this to

$$\mathcal{E}_0 e^{j\omega t} = \left[R + j\omega L + \frac{1}{j\omega C} \right] I_0 e^{j\omega t}, \tag{13–18}$$

which is in the form

$$\mathcal{E}_0 e^{j\omega t} = Z I_0 e^{j\omega t} \tag{13-19}$$

with

$$Z = R + j\omega L + \frac{1}{j\omega C}, \tag{13-20a}$$

or

$$Z = R + j\left(\omega L - \frac{1}{\omega C}\right). \tag{13-20b}$$

The *impedance* Z of the circuit consists of two parts: the real part or *resistance* (R), and the imaginary part or *reactance* (X). The reactance is further divided into the *inductive reactance* $X_L = \omega L$ and the *capacitive reactance* $X_C = -1/\omega C$. The fact that the impedance is complex means that the current is not in phase with the applied emf. It is sometimes convenient to write the impedance in polar form:

$$Z = |Z| e^{j\theta}, \tag{13-21}$$

with

$$|Z| = [R^2 + (\omega L - 1/\omega C)^2]^{1/2} \tag{13-22}$$

and

$$\theta = \tan^{-1}\left(\frac{\omega L - 1/\omega C}{R}\right). \tag{13-23}$$

Using this form for the impedance, the complex current may be written as

$$I(t) = \frac{\mathcal{E}_0}{|Z|} e^{j(\omega t - \theta)}, \tag{13-24a}$$

and the physical current is given by

$$\frac{\mathcal{E}_0}{|Z|} \cos(\omega t - \theta). \tag{13-24b}$$

If θ is greater than zero the current reaches a specified phase later than the voltage, and is said to lag the voltage. In the opposite case the current leads the voltage. This formally completes the study of the simple series circuit, although later we shall examine the solution with care, to enhance our physical understanding of the situation.

13–6 Series and parallel connection of impedances. If two impedances are connected in series, then the same current flows through each of them. The voltages* across the two impedances are $V_1 = Z_1 I$ and $V_2 = Z_2 I$.

---

* In this and the remaining sections of the chapter we shall use the symbol V in place of ΔU for the potential difference across an element, or group of elements.

The voltage across the combination is $V_1 + V_2 = (Z_1 + Z_2)I$. It is clear, then, that the connection of impedances in series add the impedances, that is,

$$Z = Z_1 + Z_2 + Z_3 + \cdots \qquad \text{(series connection).} \qquad (13\text{–}25)$$

It is important to note that the impedances add as complex numbers. If $Z_1 = R_1 + jX_1$ and $Z_2 = R_2 + jX_2$, then

$$Z = Z_1 + Z_2 = (R_1 + R_2) + j(X_1 + X_2). \qquad (13\text{–}26)$$

In polar form,

$$Z = |Z|e^{j\theta}, \qquad |Z| = [(R_1 + R_2)^2 + (X_1 + X_2)^2]^{1/2},$$

$$\theta = \tan^{-1}\frac{X_1 + X_2}{R_1 + R_2}. \qquad (13\text{–}27)$$

Note that the magnitude of Z is **not** the sum of the magnitudes of Z_1 and Z_2.

If impedances are connected in parallel, then the same voltage appears across each, and the currents are given by $I_1 = V/Z_1$, $I_2 = V/Z_2$, etc. The total current is

$$I = I_1 + I_2 + \cdots = \frac{V}{Z_1} + \frac{V}{Z_2} + \cdots = V\left(\frac{1}{Z_1} + \frac{1}{Z_2} + \cdots\right),$$

from which it is clear that

$$\frac{1}{Z} = \frac{1}{Z_1} + \frac{1}{Z_2} + \cdots \qquad \text{(parallel connection).} \qquad (13\text{–}28)$$

Here, too, the addition is the addition of complex numbers.

Equations (13–25) and (13–28) provide the basis for solving problems involving more complex configurations with a single emf. As an example, we now consider the circuit of Fig. 13–6. The impedance consists of a

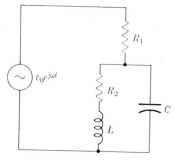

FIG. 13–6. A typical a-c circuit.

resistor in series with the parallel combination of a capacitor and an inductor. This is written as

$$Z = R_1 + \cfrac{1}{\cfrac{1}{R_2 + j\omega L} + \cfrac{1}{1/j\omega C}}. \qquad (13\text{-}29)$$

Alternatively,

$$Z = R_1 + \frac{R_2 + j\omega L}{1 + j\omega C(R_2 + j\omega L)} \qquad (13\text{-}30)$$

or

$$Z = R_1 + \frac{(R_2 + j\omega L)[(1 - \omega^2 LC) - j\omega R_2 C]}{(1 - \omega^2 LC)^2 + \omega^2 R_2^2 C^2}. \qquad (13\text{-}31)$$

The only other worth-while manipulation at this time is the separation into real and imaginary parts:

$$Z = R_1 + \frac{R_2}{(1 - \omega^2 LC)^2 + \omega^2 R_2^2 C^2} + j\frac{\omega L(1 - \omega^2 LC) - \omega R_2^2 C}{(1 - \omega^2 LC)^2 + \omega^2 R_2^2 C^2}. $$
$$(13\text{-}32)$$

Having found Z, we now determine the current by dividing Z into $\mathcal{E}_0 e^{j\omega t}$. The study of this circuit will be continued later, in connection with resonance phenomena.

13-7 Power and power factors. The power delivered to a resistor may be determined by multiplying the voltage across the resistor by the current through the resistor. However, for the more general case, such as the impedance shown in Fig. 13-7, a more subtle approach is required. If $V(t)$ and $I(t)$ are the complex voltage and current as shown, then the instantaneous power is

$$P_{\text{inst}} = \text{Re } I(t) \text{ Re } V(t). \qquad (13\text{-}33)$$

The *average* power is a more important quantity, with the average being taken over either one full period or a very long time (many periods). In Section 16-5 it is shown that

$$\overline{\text{Re } (I_0 e^{j\omega t}) \text{ Re } (V_0 e^{j\omega t})} = \tfrac{1}{2} \text{ Re } (I_0^* V_0), \qquad (13\text{-}34)$$

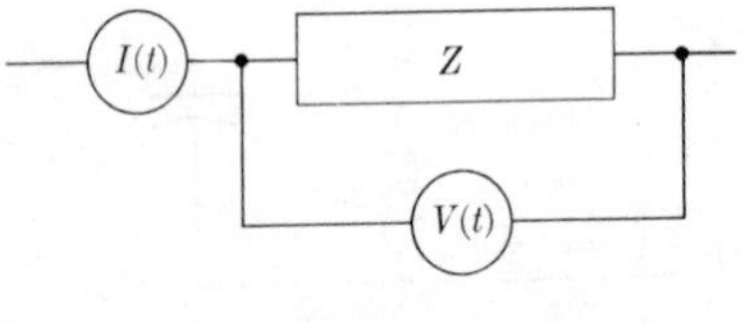

Fig. 13-7. Measurement of power.

where I_0^* is the complex conjugate of I_0. If the phases are chosen so that V_0 is real and, as usual, $Z = |Z|e^{j\theta}$, then

$$\overline{P} = \overline{\text{Re } I(t) \text{ Re } V(t)} = \tfrac{1}{2}|I_0| \, |V_0| \cos \theta. \qquad (13\text{–}35)$$

The factor one-half in Eq. (13–35) represents the fact that the average of $\sin^2 \omega t$ or $\cos^2 \omega t$ is one-half. The other interesting factor is cosine θ, which takes into account the fact that the current and voltage are not in phase. Cosine θ is frequently called the *power factor* of an alternating current (a-c) circuit.

As a final comment, we mention that the *effective values* of the voltage and current are often defined by

$$V_{\text{eff}} = \frac{\sqrt{2}}{2}|V_0|, \qquad I_{\text{eff}} = \frac{\sqrt{2}}{2}|I_0|. \qquad (13\text{–}36)$$

The virtue of these definitions is that a given V_{eff} applied to a resistance dissipates the same power as a constant voltage of the same magnitude. The specification, of effective values is very common, e.g., 115-volt a-c lines are 115 effective volt lines.

13–8 Resonance. Equation (13–22) shows that a simple series L-R-C circuit has a frequency-dependent impedance which is a minimum at $\omega^2 = \omega_0^2 \equiv 1/LC$. At this frequency the impedance is just R, the phase angle is zero, and the current is a maximum of magnitude $\mathcal{E}_0/R$. This is a resonant phenomenon much like that observed in force-damped mechanical oscillators. If the current is plotted as a function of frequency, a curve of the form shown in Fig. 13–8 is obtained. Several curves are shown; all are based on the same values of L and C, but the series resistance varies from cui ve to curve. It is clear that the curves are sharper for small than for large values of the series resistance. The

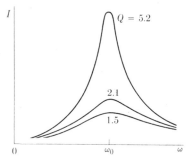

Fig. 13–8. Resonance curves for a series R-L-C circuit.

current falls to $\sqrt{2}/2$ times its maximum value at a frequency where the magnitude of the impedance is $\sqrt{2}$ times R, or where

$$\left| \omega L - \frac{1}{\omega C} \right| = R. \tag{13–37}$$

For relatively sharply peaked responses this obtains at values of ω not far removed from ω_0. We then write $\omega = \omega_0 + \Delta\omega$, and obtain

$$\left| \omega_0 L + \Delta\omega L - \frac{1}{\omega_0 C} \frac{1}{1 + \Delta\omega/\omega_0} \right| = R. \tag{13–38}$$

Using $\omega_0^2 = 1/LC$ and $(1 + \Delta\omega/\omega_0)^{-1} \cong 1 - \Delta\omega/\omega_0$ gives

$$2|\Delta\omega|L = R$$

or

$$\frac{2|\Delta\omega|}{\omega_0} = \frac{R}{\omega_0 L}. \tag{13–39}$$

The quantity

$$Q = \omega_0 L/R \qquad \text{or} \qquad Q = \frac{\omega_0}{2|\Delta\omega|} \tag{13–40}$$

characterizes the sharpness of the resonance and is known as the Q of the circuit. For elementary purposes, Q may be considered to be a property of the inductor only, since most of the unavoidable series resistance is associated with the wire with which the inductor is wound. However, a more refined treatment shows that the capacitor losses must also be included in computing Q's. The curves of Fig. 13–8 are labeled with the appropriate Q values.

As the driving frequency is varied, not only the magnitude but also the phase of the current varies. This variation is shown in Fig. 13–9 for the same Q values used in Fig. 13–8. Below resonance, the phase angle of the impedance function is negative; therefore the phase of the current is positive and it leads the voltage. Above resonance, the opposite is true and the current lags the voltage.

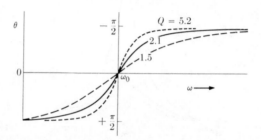

Fig. 13–9. Phase angle of the impedance in a typical R-L-C series circuit.

It is interesting to note that the usual radiofrequency resonant circuits found in communications equipment are series resonant circuits, in spite of their parallel-circuit appearance. In the most simple case this is because the driving power is inductively coupled into L and thus appears as an emf in series with L.

Resonance is not restricted to series circuits like those just discussed; parallel circuits may also exhibit resonant characteristics. The circuit of Fig. 13-6 exhibits such a resonance. Defining the resonant frequency for a parallel resonant circuit is not as simple as it is for a series circuit. Some of the possibilities are: (1) $\omega_0 = 1/\sqrt{LC}$, (2) the frequency at which the impedance [given by Eq. (13-31)] is a maximum, or (3) the frequency at which the power factor is unity. Each of these three choices gives a different frequency; however, for high Q circuits they are very nearly the same. The first choice is by far the most useful in practice because it makes many series resonance results directly applicable to the parallel resonant case. One very interesting result is obtained by using Eq. (13-31) to evaluate Z, with $R_1 = 0$ and $\omega_0 = 1/\sqrt{LC}$. The result is

$$Z = \omega_0 L \left[\frac{\omega_0 L}{R} - j \right], \qquad (\omega = \omega_0). \qquad (13\text{-}41)$$

For a high Q circuit the j can be neglected, with the result that the impedance at resonance is Q times the inductive reactance at resonance.

The subject of resonant circuits can be pursued at great length; however, to do so here is probably unwarranted. Some of the problems extend this section, and very comprehensive details are given in the work by Terman,* to which the interested reader is referred.

13-9 Mutual inductances in a-c circuits. Solving a-c circuit problems involving mutual inductances presents a minor difficulty in assigning the correct sign to the mutual inductance. This difficulty can be readily resolved by noting that the sign to be associated with the mutual inductance depends on the assumed direction of the current in the two circuits involved, and on the way in which the windings are connected. The notation M_{ij} will be used for the pure mutual inductance between two circuits.

It was shown in Chapter 9 that the emf in winding 2, due to a changing current in winding 1, is given in magnitude by

$$\mathcal{E}_2 = M_{21} \frac{dI_1}{dt}. \qquad (13\text{-}42)$$

---

* Terman, *Radio Engineers Handbook*, McGraw-Hill, New York, 1943.

For sinusoidal currents, using complex notation, we have

$$\mathcal{E}_2 = j\omega M_{21} I_{10} e^{j\omega t} \tag{13-43}$$

or

$$\mathcal{E}_2 = j\omega M_{21} I_1. \tag{13-44}$$

In what follows, the symbol M_{21} will be taken to be a positive quantity and the sign of $\mathcal{E}_2$ will be displayed explicitly; in other words, M_{21} in Eq. (13-44) will be replaced by $\pm M_{21}$, with M_{21} a positive quantity.

To demonstrate the technique for assigning signs we now consider the circuit shown in Fig. 13-10, in which two impedances Z_1 and Z_2 are combined with a mutual inductance and connected to a source of emf $\mathcal{E}(t) = \mathcal{E}_0 e^{j\omega t}$. The mutual inductance is labeled M_{12} and is taken to be a positive number. The black dots in the figure indicate the ends of the two windings, which are simultaneously positive; that is, if the lower winding is excited by a sinusoidal current which makes the left-hand terminal positive at some time t_1, then the voltage induced in the upper winding makes the left-hand terminal of the upper winding positive at t_1. The equation for the upper branch, in accordance with Kirchhoff's law, is

$$Z_1 I_1 + j\omega L_1 I_1 + j\omega M_{12} I_2 = \mathcal{E}. \tag{13-45}$$

The plus sign is used with the mutual inductance because a positive I_2 gives a voltage in the upper branch which has the same sense as an $I_1 R$ drop. The second equation is

$$j\omega M_{12} I_1 + Z_2 I_2 + j\omega L_2 I_2 = \mathcal{E}, \tag{13-46}$$

where $M_{12} = M_{21}$ has been written in the interests of symmetry.

The assignment of the sign is on the same basis as before, and may be checked by noting that M_{12} should appear in the branch-one equation with the same sign as M_{21} in the branch-two equation. Equations (13-45)

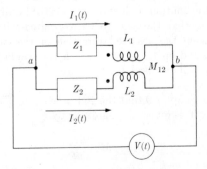

Fig. 13-10. Circuit with mutual inductance.

and (13–46) may be solved simultaneously by standard techniques to yield

$$I_1 = \mathcal{E}\frac{Z_2 + j\omega L_2 - j\omega M_{12}}{(Z_1 + j\omega L_1)(Z_2 + j\omega L_2) + \omega^2 M_{12}^2},$$

$$I_2 = \mathcal{E}\frac{Z_1 + j\omega L_1 - j\omega M_{12}}{(Z_1 + j\omega L_1)(Z_2 + j\omega L_2) + \omega^2 M_{12}^2}. \tag{13–47}$$

Combining the two to obtain the total current $I_1 + I_2$ gives

$$I = I_1 + I_2 = \mathcal{E}\frac{Z_1 + j\omega L_1 + Z_2 + j\omega L_2 - 2j\omega M_{12}}{(Z_1 + j\omega L_1)(Z_2 + j\omega L_2) + \omega^2 M_{21}^2}. \tag{13–48}$$

The coefficient of $\mathcal{E}$ on the right side is the reciprocal of the impedance presented to the generator, or the net impedance between points a and b. It is obvious that if M_{12} is zero, the impedance is the parallel combination of the two branch impedances. For the connection shown, as M_{12} increases so does the impedance.

The circuit obtained by interchanging the leads on one winding of the mutual inductance is shown in Fig. 13–11. Note that the only difference is that the black dot has been moved from the left end of the upper winding to the right end. The result is to change the sign of the M_{12} term in Eqs. (13–45) and (13–46), with the result that

and

$$\left.\begin{aligned}(Z_1 + j\omega L_1)I_1 - j\omega M_{12}I_2 &= \mathcal{E},\\ -j\omega M_{12}I_1 + (Z_2 + j\omega L_2)I_2 &= \mathcal{E}.\end{aligned}\right\} \tag{13–49}$$

The currents are easily found and combined to obtain the impedance:

$$Z_{ab} = \frac{(Z_1 + j\omega L_1)(Z_2 + j\omega L_2) + \omega^2 M_{12}^2}{Z_1 + j\omega L_1 + Z_2 + j\omega L_2 + 2j\omega M_{12}}, \tag{13–50}$$

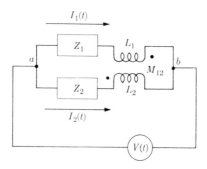

FIG. 13–11. Circuit of Fig. 13–10 with the sign of the mutual inductance reversed.

which is the same as in the previous case when the mutual inductance is zero. The relationship between Z_{ab} for finite M_{12} and Z_{ab} for $M_{12} = 0$ depends on the parameter in a rather complicated way. We will state here only that Z_{ab} may be larger or smaller than the Z_{ab} for $M_{12} = 0$.

The basic circuit for the most common mutual inductance device, the transformer, is shown in Fig. 13–12. R_1 and R_2 are the resistances of the primary (driving) and secondary (driven) windings, L_1 and L_2 are their self-inductances, and M is the (positive) mutual inductance between them. Z_L is the impedance of the load connected to the secondary winding, and $\mathcal{E}(t) = \mathcal{E}_0 e^{j\omega t}$ is the voltage across the primary winding. If currents $I_1 e^{j\omega t}$ and $I_2 e^{j\omega t}$ are assumed to be in the directions indicated, then Kirchhoff's voltage law requires that the equations

$$\mathcal{E}_0 = I_1 R_1 + j\omega L_1 I_1 + j\omega M I_2, \left.\vphantom{\begin{array}{c}1\\1\end{array}}\right\}$$

and

$$0 = I_2 R_2 + j\omega L_2 I_2 + j\omega M I_1 + I_2 Z_L, \qquad (13\text{–}51)$$

be satisfied. The solutions to these equations are

$$I_1 = \frac{Z_L + R_2 + j\omega L_2}{(R_1 + j\omega L_1)(Z_L + R_2 + j\omega L_2) + \omega^2 M^2} \mathcal{E}_0, \left.\vphantom{\begin{array}{c}1\\1\\1\\1\end{array}}\right\}$$

and

$$I_2 = \frac{-j\omega M}{(R_1 + j\omega L_1)(Z_L + R_2 + j\omega L_2) + \omega^2 M^2} \mathcal{E}_0. \qquad (13\text{–}52)$$

These relatively complex equations represent an exact solution for the circuit of Fig. 13–12.

For many purposes it is much more convenient to think in terms of an *ideal* transformer, i.e., one for which the relations

$$V_L = a\mathcal{E}_0, \qquad I_2 = -\frac{I_1}{a}, \qquad (13\text{–}53)$$

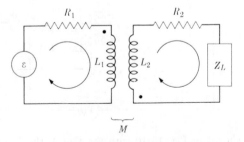

Fig. 13–12. A transformer.

are satisfied, where the constant a is independent of frequency, V_L is the voltage across Z_L, and all other quantities are as shown in Fig. 13–12. The condition that must be satisfied to ensure the second of these relations is

$$\frac{Z_L + R_2 + j\omega L_2}{j\omega M} = a, \tag{13-54}$$

which is satisfied if $\omega L_2 \gg |Z_L + R_2|$. Similar conditions can be found which will ensure that $V_L/\mathcal{E}_0 = a$.* The conditions are complex and not too easy to satisfy; however, practical transformers exist which satisfy them over relatively wide frequency ranges. For such devices,

$$I_2 = -\frac{I_1}{a}, \qquad V_L = a\mathcal{E}_0,$$

and

$$\frac{\mathcal{E}_0}{I_1} = -\frac{V_L}{a^2 I_2} = \frac{Z_L}{a^2}. \tag{13-55}$$

The last of these relationships shows that the transformer acts also as an impedance transformer, with transformation ratio a^{-2}. It is left as an exercise to show that for very close coupling of the two windings $a = N_2/N_1$, that is, the turns ratio.

13–10 Mesh and nodal equations. More complex a-c circuits may be approached in two ways: one based on Kirchhoff's voltage law and known as *mesh analysis*, and the other based on Kirchhoff's current law and known as *nodal analysis*. Each method has its advantages and disadvantages. Since choosing the expedient method can greatly simplify some problems, both methods will be considered in this section.

The first step in applying mesh analysis is the assignment of meshes. This is accomplished by assuming closed loop currents such that at least one current goes through each element. For example, in Fig. 13–13 three meshes are shown, labeled I_1, I_2, and I_3. This is, of course, not the only possible choice; several others are possible and useful. If Kirchhoff's voltage law is applied to each of these meshes, we obtain

$$
\begin{aligned}
I_1(Z_3 + Z_4) &\quad -I_2 Z_4 &\quad -I_3 Z_3 &= \mathcal{E}, \\
-I_1 Z_4 &\quad +I_2(Z_1 + Z_2 + Z_4) &\quad -I_3 Z_2 &= 0, \\
-I_1 Z_3 &\quad -I_2 Z_2 &\quad +I_3(Z_2 + Z_3 + Z_5) &= 0.
\end{aligned}
\tag{13-56}
$$

Note that the minus signs appear because in mesh one, for example, I_2

---

* The details are given in Guillemin, *loc. cit.*, Chapter VIII.

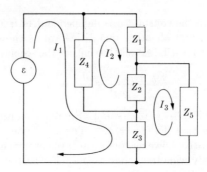

FIG. 13–13. Illustration of the use of mesh analysis in a-c circuits.

flows through Z_4 counter to the direction of I_1. Equations (13–56) can be solved most easily by determinantal techniques, resulting in expressions for the set of mesh currents in the circuit. It is useful to note that the mesh equations can be written as

$$\sum_{j=1}^{n} Z_{ij}I_j = \mathcal{E}_i \,(i = 1, 2, \ldots, n) \tag{13–57}$$

(with $n = 3$ in the circuit above). In this notation, $Z_{ij} = Z_{ji}$, which is a useful check on the mesh equations.

As a second example, consider the circuit of Fig. 13–14. The appropriate equations for this circuit are written as

$$I_1(Z_1 + Z_2) + \quad I_2Z_2 \quad = \mathcal{E}_1,$$
$$I_1Z_2 \quad + I_2(Z_2 + Z_3) = \mathcal{E}_2. \tag{13–58}$$

There is no reason why $\mathcal{E}_1$ and $\mathcal{E}_2$ must be in phase; usually they will not be, but will be expressible as $\mathcal{E}_1 = |\mathcal{E}_{10}|e^{j\omega t}$, $\mathcal{E}_2 = |\mathcal{E}_{20}|e^{j(\omega t+\varphi)}$. It is, however, very important to assign the phases correctly, and this is most conveniently accomplished by examining the relative phases at $t = 0$ and

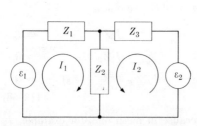

FIG. 13–14. Further use of mesh equations.

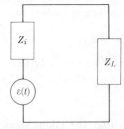

FIG. 13–15. Practical generator connected to a load Z_L.

assigning directions (senses) with respect to the assigned mesh currents. It is also important to note that unless all of the generators have the same frequency the entire technique fails (more properly, the problem reduces to the superposition of two independent problems, each involving one generator and one frequency).

Before proceeding to discuss the alternative nodal equations, it is appropriate to discuss voltage and current generators. In the preceding sections, circuit problems have been phrased in terms of pure sources of emf. Such idealized devices cannot be constructed, of course; practical devices always have a certain internal impedance. Thus a practical generator consists of a source of emf, $\varepsilon(t)$, in series with an impedance Z_i, which is the internal impedance. Such a generator is shown in Fig. 13–15 connected to a load Z_L. Several observations may be made. First, for maximum power transfer to the external load, $Z_L = Z_i^*$; that is, Z_i and Z_L should have equal resistive parts, and reactive parts which are equal in magnitude but opposite in sign. The proof of this is left as an exercise. Secondly, a voltage generator is equivalent to a current generator delivering a current $I(t) = \varepsilon(t)/Z_i$ shunted by the internal impedance. This equivalence for the circuit of Fig. 13–15, is shown in Fig. 13–16. It is easy to show this equivalence if it is noted that an ideal current generator delivers the current $I(t)$ to *any* load connected to its terminals. The equivalence further means that in any circuit problem the generators may be taken either as voltage generators or as current generators, to suit the convenience of the situation.

The nodal equations for a circuit result from the application of Kirchhoff's current laws to each of the nodes. In this context a node is a point at which three or more elements join. As a simple example of the application of the nodal equations, we refer to the circuit of Fig. 13–17. The nodal equations are obtained by requiring that the algebraic sum of the currents to each node be zero. The nodes are numbered, starting with zero for the node whose potential is the reference for the circuit. If

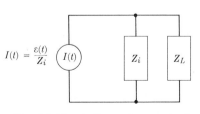

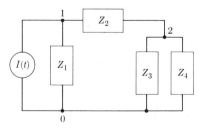

FIG. 13–16. A "current generator" which is equivalent to the voltage generator of Fig. 13–15.

FIG. 13–17. Illustrating the method of nodal analysis in a-c circuits.

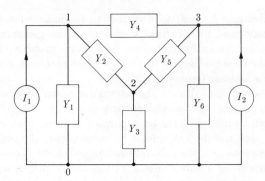

Fig. 13–18. Another circuit illustrating nodal analysis.

the potential at node 0 is taken to be zero, then at node 1

$$I(t) = \frac{V_1}{Z_1} + \frac{V_1 - V_2}{Z_2}, \qquad (13\text{–}59)$$

where V_1 and V_2 are the potentials of nodes 1 and 2 respectively. At node 2,

$$0 = \frac{V_2 - V_1}{Z_2} + \frac{V_2}{Z_3} + \frac{V_2}{Z_4}. \qquad (13\text{–}60)$$

Before proceeding, we make the observation that a quantity which is the reciprocal of an impedance would be a great convenience. Such a quantity is the *admittance*, symbolized by Y. $Y = 1/Z$. Admittances in parallel add, while admittances in series combine by adding reciprocals. In terms of admittances, Eqs. (13–59) and (13–60) become

$$I(t) = (Y_1 + Y_2)V_1 - Y_2 V_2,$$
$$\qquad (13\text{–}61)$$
$$0 = -Y_2 V_1 + (Y_2 + Y_3 + Y_4)V_2,$$

which are somewhat more convenient. The simultaneous solution of these equations yields the nodal voltages, V_1 and V_2.

We shall consider one more example of the use of nodal equations; namely, to the circuit shown in Fig. 13–18. The nodal equations are simply written down in the form

$$I_1 = Y_1 V_1 + Y_2(V_1 - V_2) + Y_4(V_1 - V_3),$$
$$0 = Y_2(V_2 - V_1) + Y_3 V_2 + Y_5(V_2 - V_3), \qquad (13\text{–}62)$$
$$I_2 = Y_6 V_3 + Y_5(V_3 - V_2) + Y_4(V_3 - V_1).$$

These equations may be solved by standard techniques to obtain the voltages at the nodes. The fact that voltages rather than currents are obtained when the equations are solved is a major advantage, particularly in communications circuits.

13–11 Driving point and transfer impedances. We shall now present simple definitions for the driving point and transfer impedance of a four-terminal network. These definitions are presented because these terms appear with increasing frequency in the technical literature, and because they are sometimes a serious stumbling block to the uninitiated. Consider a four-terminal network, and call terminals 1 and 2 the input, and 3 and 4 the output. If a generator of emf ε and internal impedance Z_i is connected between terminals 1 and 2, and an impedance Z_L between terminals 3 and 4, as shown in Fig. 13–19, there will be a current I_i in Z_i and a current I_L in Z_L. The driving point impedance Z_D is

$$Z_D = \frac{\varepsilon}{I_i},\tag{13–63}$$

and the transfer impedance is

$$Z_T = \frac{\varepsilon}{I_L}.\tag{13–64}$$

It should be noted that Z_D and Z_T both depend on Z_i and Z_L, as well as on the internal structure of the network.

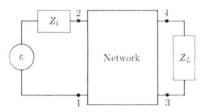

Fig. 13–19. A four-terminal network.

A brief treatment such as the above cannot do justice to the subject of network theory; classics such as that of Guillemin, as well as the multitude of more recent books, should be consulted for the details of this complex subject.

PROBLEMS

13-1. An inductance of 2 henries and a resistance of 3 ohms are connected in series with a 5-volt battery and a switch. Determine the current, and the rate of change of current (dI/dt) in the circuit at the following times after the switch is closed: (a) 0.3 sec, (b) 1 sec, (c) 4 sec.

13-2. A circuit consisting of an inductance L_0, a resistance R_0, and a battery $\mathcal{E}_0$ has a steady current $I = \mathcal{E}_0/R_0$ through it. A switch in the circuit is opened at time $t = 0$, creating an arc across the switch. If the arc resistance is given by k/I, where the constant $k < \mathcal{E}_0$, determine the current through the arc as a function of time. What is the final steady value of current through the arc?

13-3. A capacitor C, a resistor R, and a battery $\mathcal{E}_0$ are connected in series with a switch. The switch is closed at time $t = 0$. Set up the differential equation governing the charge Q on the capacitor. Determine Q as a function of time.

13-4. A capacitor C with charge Q_0 is suddenly connected in series with a resistance R and inductance L. Determine the current as a function of time. Show that there are three different types of solution, depending upon whether $R^2 - 4L/C$ is less than, equal to, or greater than zero. The first of these conditions is called underdamped, the second critically damped, and the third overdamped.

13-5. The circuit of Fig. 13-1 has an additional capacitor C' shunting the entire R-L-C combination. $R = 100$ ohms, $L = 1$ henry, $C = 100$ μf, and $C' = 10$ μf. Make a plot of the impedance $|Z|$ versus frequency from zero to $f = 10^4$ cycles/sec.

13-6. The series combination of a resistance R and an inductance L is put in parallel with the series combination of resistance R and capacitance C. Show that if $R^2 = L/C$ the impedance is independent of frequency.

13-7. A wire-wound resistor has a d-c resistance of 90.00 ohms and an inductance of 8 μhenries. What is the phase angle of the impedance at 1000 cycles/sec? A capacitor is placed in parallel with the resistor to reduce the phase angle to zero at 1000 cycles/sec without changing the resistance appreciably. Over what range of frequency is the phase angle less than it was before the capacitor was added?

13-8. An a-c generator with internal impedance Z_i is connected in series with a variable load impedance Z_L. Prove that maximum power is transferred to the load when $Z_L = Z_i^*$.

13-9. Given the circuit of Fig. 13-6, with $L = 4$ mh, $C = 2$ μf, $R_1 = 25$ ohms, $R_2 = 40$ ohms. Find the following set of frequencies: (a) where $\omega = 1/\sqrt{LC}$, (b) where the impedance is maximum, (c) where the current through R_1 is in phase with the generator voltage.

13-10. Show that the quantity Q defined in the text can be expressed as 2π times the maximum energy stored in the circuit, divided by the energy dissipated in one cycle. This statement is sometimes used as the definition of Q and is independent of specific circuit parameters.

13-11. A crossover network for a hi-fi set is to be designed so that two loudspeakers (each of resistance R) are connected to the output stage of an amplifier.

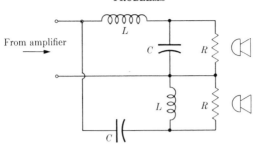

FIGURE 13–20

One speaker is to receive predominantly high frequencies, the other predominantly low frequencies. The network is as shown in Fig. 13–20. The two capacitors are each of capacitance C and the two inductors each of inductance L. (a) Find a relationship between L and C for a given R such that the network presents a purely resistive load ($=R$) to the amplifier at all frequencies. (b) The crossover frequency ω_c is defined as the frequency at which each speaker receives half of the power delivered by the amplifier. For a given R and ω_c determine L and C.

13–12. A 1-μf capacitor is first charged to 100 volts by connecting it to a battery; it is then disconnected and immediately discharged through the 300-turn winding on a ring toroid. The toroid has a mean radius of 20 cm, a 4-cm^2 cross-sectional area, and an air gap of 2 mm (see Fig. 10–15). Neglecting copper losses, hysteresis, and fringing, calculate the maximum magnetic field subsequently produced in the air gap. Take the relative permeability of the toroid equal to 5000.

13–13. A potential difference of 1 volt at a frequency $f = 10^6/\pi$ cycles/sec is impressed across the circuit of Fig. 13–21. The mutual inductance of the coils is such that they are in opposition. Find the current in the upper branch.

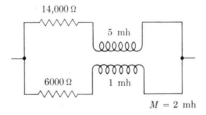

FIGURE 13–21

13–14. A 60-cycle power transformer (turns ratio 2:1) has a primary inductance of 100 henries and a d-c resistance of 20 ohms. The coupling coefficient between primary and secondary is close to unity. If 1000 volts is placed across the primary, calculate the current in the primary winding (a) when the secondary is open-circuited, (b) when a load resistance of 20 ohms is in the secondary circuit.

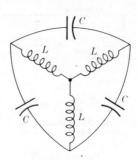

FIGURE 13-22

*13-15. Three identical capacitors and three identical inductors are connected as shown in Fig. 13-22. Find the resonant frequencies of the system. (*Hint:* Use mesh analysis, with current of an assumed frequency ω, and show that the three equations obtained are compatible for certain ω only.)

13-16. In the circuit shown in Fig. 13-14, $Z_1 = 2 + 5j$, $Z_2 = 8 - j$, $Z_3 = 4 + 3j$. The voltage generators are in phase with each other: $\mathcal{E}_1 = 10$ volts, $\mathcal{E}_2 = 2$ volts. Determine I_1 and I_2.

13-17. In the circuit shown in Fig. 13-17, $I(t) = I_1 e^{j\omega t}$ and Z_4 is *replaced* by a current generator $I_2 e^{j\omega t}$. The two current generators are in phase with each other. Z_1 and Z_3 are capacitors of reactance 40 and 60 ohms respectively. Z_2 is a pure resistance of 20 ohms. $I_1 = 5$ amp, $I_2 = 25$ amp. Determine the node voltages at 1 and 2 relative to point 0.

*CHAPTER 14

PHYSICS OF PLASMAS

Gases which are highly ionized are good conductors of electricity. The charged particles in such a gas interact with the local electromagnetic field; furthermore, the organized motion of these charge carriers (currents, fluctuations in charge density) can *produce* magnetic and electric fields. When subjected to a static electric field, an ionized gas acts like any other conductor; the charge carriers in the gas rapidly redistribute themselves in such a way that most of the gas is shielded from the field. To the relatively field-free regions of the gas where positive and negative space charges are nearly balanced, Langmuir† gave the name *plasma*, while to the space-charge or strong-field regions on the boundary of the plasma he gave the name *sheaths*.

Equivalently, we may say: an ionized gas which has a sufficiently large number of charged particles to shield itself, electrostatically, in a distance small compared with other lengths of physical interest, is a plasma. A somewhat more precise definition in terms of the shielding distance will be given in Section 14–1. The earliest interest in plasmas was in connection with gaseous electronics (electrical discharges through gases, arcs, flames); more recent interest has been directed toward problems in theoretical astrophysics, and the problem of ion containment in thermonuclear (fusion) reactors.‡

The general area of study embracing the interaction of ionized gases with time-dependent electromagnetic fields is called *plasma dynamics*. For many of the problems in this area, and these are the more important and interesting ones, it is impossible to treat a plasma adequately in terms of a purely macroscopic formulation. Instead, it is necessary to use what is known conventionally as kinetic theory. The motions of individual ions and electrons must be studied; their collisions with other particles must be taken into account through solution of the Boltzmann transport equation. Thus a rigorous formulation for plasma problems exists, but their solution is extremely difficult in general, except for situations where it is permissible to neglect some of the terms in the Boltzmann equation. There are, however, three approximate formulations which provide considerable insight into what is happening inside the plasma.

---

* This chapter may be omitted without loss of continuity.

† I. Langmuir, *Physical Review* **33**, 954 (1929).

‡ See, for example, Lyman Spitzer, *Physics of Fully Ionized Gases*, Interscience, New York (1956), and Amasa Bishop, *Project Sherwood—The U. S. Program in Controlled Fusion*, Addison-Wesley Publishing Co., Inc., Reading, Mass. (1958).

The first of these methods is *equilibrium theory*, which rests on the premise that collisions between charged particles are sufficient to maintain the well-known Maxwell-Boltzmann velocity distribution for particles in the body of the plasma:

$$N_j(\mathbf{v}) \, dv_x \, dv_y \, dv_z = N_{0j} \left(\frac{m_p}{2\pi kT} \right)^{3/2} e^{-m_p v^2/2kT} \, dv_x \, dv_y \, dv_z,$$

where N_{0j} is the number of particles of type j per unit volume in the plasma, v_x (etc.) are the components of velocity, m_p is the mass of type j particles, and T is the absolute temperature. Kinetic and transport properties may then be calculated in terms of this velocity distribution.

The second approximate method is *orbit theory*, which treats the motion of charged particles (ions and electrons) in prescribed electric and magnetic fields. These fields may be functions both of position and of time. Orbit theory is a good approximation to particle motion in a plasma when collisions between particles do *not* play the dominant role, i.e., when the mean free path for collisions is large compared with characteristic dimensions of the orbit. Under these conditions the effect of collisions can be treated as a perturbation, and the primary problem centers around making the "prescribed" electromagnetic field self-consistent; in other words, the prescribed field must be the sum of the external field and the field produced by the orbiting particles.

The third approximate treatment is the *hydromagnetic formulation*. Here one uses the classical electromagnetic equations (Maxwell's equations) in conjunction with the classical equations of fluid motion. Evidently, the hydromagnetic treatment is just a macroscopic description of the plasma; it becomes a good approximation when the mean free path for collisions is very small compared with distances of physical interest in the plasma system. The hydromagnetic picture forms a good starting point for discussing the collective motion of particles in the plasma, e.g., plasma oscillations.

The rigorous kinetic theory approach to plasma problems is beyond the scope of this book. On the other hand, many important properties of plasmas can be discussed in terms of the approximations outlined above. For simplicity we shall assume that the plasma consists of electrons (charge, $-e$) and singly charged positive ions (charge, $+e$); neutral atoms may be present, but we shall ignore such complications as ionizing collisions and recombination of electrons and ions.

In Section 14–1, and again in Section 14–7, we encounter a plasma under stationary or steady-state conditions, for which equilibrium theory is well suited. In Sections 14–2 and 14–3, on the other hand, we shall be much concerned with individual particle motion, and here orbit theory is applicable. Finally, in Sections 14–4 through 14–6 we shall treat some dynamic aspects of the plasma, and we shall do this within the hydromagnetic framework.

14–1 Electrical neutrality in a plasma. One of the most important properties of a plasma is its tendency to remain electrically neutral, i.e., its tendency to balance positive and negative space charge in each macroscopic volume element. A slight imbalance in the space-charge densities gives rise to strong electrostatic forces which act, wherever possible, in the direction of restoring neutrality. On the other hand, if a plasma is deliberately subjected to an external electric field, the space-charge densities will adjust themselves so that the major part of the plasma is shielded from the field.

Let us consider a rather simple example. Suppose a spherical charge $+Q$ is introduced into a plasma, thereby subjecting the plasma to an electric field. Actually, the charge $+Q$ would be gradually neutralized because ·of being continuously struck by charged particles from the plasma, but if the charged object is physically very small, this will take an appreciable period of time. Meanwhile, electrons find it energetically favorable to move closer to the charge, whereas positive ions tend to move away. Under equilibrium conditions (see Section 5–3), the probability of finding a charged particle in a particular region of potential energy W is proportional to the Boltzmann factor, $\exp(-W/kT)$. Thus the electron density N_e is given by

$$N_e = N_0 \exp\left(e\,\frac{U - U_0}{kT}\right), \qquad (14\text{--}1)$$

where U is the local potential, U_0 is the reference potential (plasma potential), T is the absolute temperature of the plasma, and k is Boltzmann's constant. N_0 is the electronic density in regions where $U = U_0$.

If N_0 is also the positive ion density in regions of potential U_0, then the positive ion density N_i is given by

$$N_i = N_0 \exp\left(-e\,\frac{U - U_0}{kT}\right). \qquad (14\text{--}2)$$

The potential U is obtained from the solution of Poisson's equation:

$$\frac{1}{r^2}\frac{d}{dr}\left(r^2\frac{dU}{dr}\right) = -\frac{1}{\epsilon_0}(N_i e - N_e e) = \frac{2N_0 e}{\epsilon_0}\sinh\left(e\,\frac{U - U_0}{kT}\right). \qquad (14\text{--}3\mathrm{a})$$

This differential equation is nonlinear, and hence must be integrated numerically. On the other hand, an approximate solution to (14–3a) which is rigorous at high temperature is adequate for our purposes here. If $kT > eU$, then $\sinh(eU/kT) \approx eU/kT$, and

$$\frac{1}{r^2}\frac{d}{dr}\left(r^2\frac{dU}{dr}\right) = \frac{2N_0 e^2}{\epsilon_0 kT}(U - U_0), \qquad (14\text{--}3\mathrm{b})$$

the solution of which is

$$U = U_0 + \frac{Q}{4\pi\epsilon_0 r} \exp\left(-\frac{r}{h}\right). \tag{14-4}$$

Here r is the distance from the spherical charge $+Q$, and h, the *Debye shielding distance*, is given by

$$h = \left(\frac{\epsilon_0 kT}{2N_0 e^2}\right)^{1/2} \tag{14-5}$$

Thus the redistribution of electrons and ions in the gas is such as to screen out Q completely in a distance of a few h.

An ionized gas is called a plasma if the Debye length, h, is small compared with other physical dimensions of interest. This is not much of a restriction so long as ionization of the gas is appreciable; at $T = 2000°\text{K}$ and $N_0 = 10^{18}$ electrons or ions/m³, the Debye length is 2.2×10^{-6} meter.

14-2 Particle orbits and drift motion in a plasma. The orbit of a charged particle q moving in a prescribed electric and magnetic field may be calculated directly from the force equation:

$$\mathbf{F} = q(\mathbf{E} + \mathbf{v} \times \mathbf{B}). \tag{14-6}$$

We shall find it convenient to start with relatively simple field configurations, and then to generalize to fields which are slowly varying in space.

A constant electric field applied to a plasma is not particularly interesting because the plasma adjusts itself by developing a thin sheath of space charge which shields the main body of plasma from the field. On the other hand, a constant magnetic field causes the particles to gyrate about the field lines without altering the space-charge distribution.

Case 1. Uniform magnetic field. $\mathbf{E} = 0$. This is the same motion as that described in Problem 8–1, but because it forms the basis for more complicated orbital motion in plasmas, we discuss it here in some detail. It should be emphasized, however, that Case 1 is applicable to many other situations besides plasmas, e.g., it is fundamental to the operation of particle accelerators, such as the cyclotron and betatron.

The Lorentz force is always at right angles to the velocity $\mathbf{v}$ of the charged particle; hence its kinetic energy remains constant:

$$K = \tfrac{1}{2}m_p v^2 = \text{constant}, \tag{14-7}$$

where m_p is the mass of the particle. It is convenient to resolve the velocity $\mathbf{v}$ into two components: $\mathbf{v}_{\parallel}$, parallel to $\mathbf{B}$, and $\mathbf{v}_{\perp}$, in the plane perpendicular to $\mathbf{B}$. Since $\mathbf{v}_{\parallel}$ is unaffected by the field, $K_{\parallel} = \tfrac{1}{2}m_p v_2^{\parallel}$

remains constant also. It follows that

$$K_\perp = \tfrac{1}{2}m_p v_\perp^2 = K - K_{\parallel} \qquad (14\text{–}8)$$

is also a constant of the motion.

The Lorentz force provides a centripetal acceleration. Thus

$$qv_\perp B = \frac{m_p v_\perp^2}{R},$$

and R (the radius of the orbit) is given by

$$R = \frac{m_p v_\perp}{qB}. \qquad (14\text{–}9)$$

The radius R is frequently called the *Larmor radius* of the particle. The complete motion of the charged particle is described as a gyration of the particle in an orbit (the Larmor orbit) superimposed on the uniform motion of the orbit center, or *guiding center*, along a magnetic field line. The resulting helical motion is shown in Fig. 14–1.

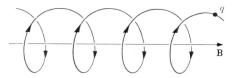

FIG. 14–1. Particle motion in a uniform magnetic field.

The magnetic field acts to confine the plasma by bending the particles in circular orbits. Of course, no confinement is observed in the field direction. For ions and electrons of the same kinetic energy $K_\perp$, the electrons gyrate in much smaller orbits, the ratio of the two Larmor radii being equal to the square root of the mass ratio.

An interesting quantity which we shall have occasion to use later is the *magnetic moment* of the gyrating particle. By definition, the magnetic moment m is given by

$$m = \text{current} \times \text{area}$$
$$= \frac{qv_\perp}{2\pi R}\pi R^2 = \frac{K_\perp}{B}. \qquad (14\text{–}10)$$

Inspection of Fig. 14–1 shows that m is directed opposite to the magnetic field and is thus a diamagnetic moment.

Case 2. Uniform electric and magnetic fields. $\mathbf{E} \perp \mathbf{B}$. If an electric and a magnetic field are simultaneously applied to a plasma, and $\mathbf{E}$ is perpendicular to $\mathbf{B}$, then there is no tendency to produce a sheath; in fact, we shall see that positive and negative space charge drift together in the same direction. For convenience, let the particle velocity $\mathbf{v}$ be written as

$$\mathbf{v} = \mathbf{u}_d + \mathbf{v}'; \qquad (14\text{--}11)$$

then Eq. (14–6) may be written as

$$\mathbf{F} = q(\mathbf{E} + \mathbf{u}_d \times \mathbf{B} + \mathbf{v}' \times \mathbf{B}). \qquad (14\text{--}12)$$

A particular choice for $\mathbf{u}_d$ causes the first two terms on the right of this equation to cancel each other:

$$\mathbf{u}_d = \frac{\mathbf{E} \times \mathbf{B}}{B^2}. \qquad (14\text{--}13)$$

The remaining force, $q\mathbf{v}' \times \mathbf{B}$, is just what was studied under Case 1.

The total motion of the particle is thus made up of three terms: (a) constant velocity $\mathbf{v}'_{\parallel}$ parallel to $\mathbf{B}$, (b) gyration about the magnetic field lines with angular frequency $v'_{\perp}/R = qB/m_p$, and (c) a constant drift velocity $u_d = E/B$ at right angles to both $\mathbf{E}$ and $\mathbf{B}$. Some examples of this motion are shown in Fig. 14–2.

The velocity $\mathbf{u}_d$ defined by Eq. (14–13) is called the *plasma drift velocity* or the *electric drift velocity*. It is important to note that $\mathbf{u}_d$ does not depend on the charge, mass, or velocity of the particle; thus all components of the plasma drift along together even though their individual gyrations may be vastly different.

Our derivation of Eq. (14–13) was obtained in a nonrelativistic fashion; if either $\mathbf{u}_d$ or $\mathbf{v}$ should approach c (the speed of light), then Eq. (14–11) must be replaced by an expression consistent with a Lorentz transformation. On the other hand, it turns out that Eq. (14–13) for the drift velocity is always correct* so long as $|\mathbf{E}| < c|\mathbf{B}|$. If $|\mathbf{E}| > c|\mathbf{B}|$, the magnetic field cannot prevent the particle from moving in the direction of $\mathbf{E}$.

Case 3. Magnetic field constant in time, but space-dependent. $\mathbf{E} = 0$. Let us suppose that a charged particle is moving in a nearly uniform magnetic field, one in which the field lines are slowly converging in space. The particle motion may be treated as a perturbation of the helical orbit in Fig. 14–1.

The motion will be something like that shown in Fig. 14–3; the reader may easily verify that there is a force tending to push the particle into the weaker magnetic field region. To specify the problem precisely it

---

* The simplest way to treat the case where $|\mathbf{E}|$ is less than but not small compared with $c|\mathbf{B}|$ is to make a Lorentz transformation, transforming both the particle velocity and the fields. The velocity of the moving system is given by $\mathbf{u}_d$ (Eq. 14–13), and the force in the moving system is given by

$$\mathbf{F}' = q(\mathbf{v}' \times \mathbf{B}) \left(\frac{c^2 - u_d^2}{c^2} \right)^{1/2}$$

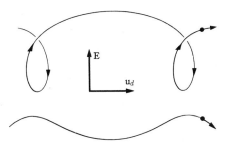

FIG. 14–2. Crossed electric and magnetic fields. Particle motion in plane perpendicular to the magnetic field. The figure shows oppositely charged ions of different initial momenta.

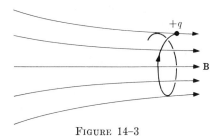

FIGURE 14–3

will be assumed that the flux line through the guiding center coincides with the z-axis, and that the magnetic field has azimuthal symmetry about the z-axis. Taking the z-component of Eq. (14–6), we obtain

$$F_z = m_p \frac{dv_z}{dt} = qv_\theta B_r|_{r=R}. \qquad (14\text{–}14)$$

But div $\mathbf{B} = 0$ or, for the case in point,

$$\frac{1}{r} \frac{\partial}{\partial r} (rB_r) + \frac{\partial B_z}{\partial z} = 0.$$

Since the field lines are converging slowly, $\partial B_z/\partial z$ may be taken constant over the orbit cross section, yielding

$$B_r|_{r=R} = -\tfrac{1}{2} R \frac{\partial B_z}{\partial z}. \qquad (14\text{–}15)$$

Furthermore, v_θ is analogous to the $v_\perp$ of Case 1. Making these substitutions in Eq. (14–14) gives

$$\begin{aligned} m_p \frac{dv_{||}}{dt} &= -\tfrac{1}{2}qRv_\perp \frac{\partial B_z}{\partial z} \\ &= -m \frac{\partial B_z}{\partial z}, \end{aligned} \qquad (14\text{–}16)$$

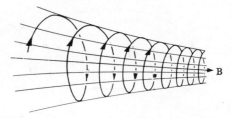

FIG. 14-4. The particle winds in a tighter and faster helix until it is reflected.

the last form being obtained through the use of Eq. (14–10).

The total kinetic energy K of the particle is unaltered in the magnetic field, since the Lorentz force, which is always at right angles to the velocity, can do no work. $K_\perp$, defined in (14–8), is not constant here; neither is $K_{||}$, but we may write

$$\frac{d}{dt}\left(\tfrac{1}{2}m_p v_{||}^2\right) = \frac{d}{dt}\left(K - K_\perp\right)$$

$$= -\frac{dK_\perp}{dt}$$

$$= -\frac{d}{dt}\left(mB_z\right), \qquad (14\text{--}17)$$

the last form coming from Eq. (14–10). On the other hand, we may multiply Eq. (14–16) by $v_{||} = \partial z/\partial t$ to obtain

$$\frac{d}{dt}\left(\tfrac{1}{2}m_p v_{||}^2\right) = -m\,\frac{\partial B_z}{\partial z}\,\frac{\partial z}{\partial t}$$

$$= -m\,\frac{dB_z}{dt}, \qquad (14\text{--}18)$$

where d/dt represents the time derivative taken along the dynamical path. By comparing (14–17) and (14–18) we see that the magnetic moment m is a constant of the motion. It should be emphasized, however, that this is an approximate result which holds only so long as B_z varies slowly. If $\mathbf{B}$ were to change substantially in distances of the order of R, the approximations used in the derivation of (14–18) would break down.

Of further interest is the fact that the particle is constrained to move on the surface of a flux tube. This follows because the magnetic flux through the orbit is

$$\Phi = B_z \pi R^2 = \pi B_z\,\frac{m_p^2 v_\perp^2}{q^2 B_z^2}$$

$$= \frac{2\pi m_p}{q^2}\,\frac{K_\perp}{B_z} = \frac{2\pi m_p}{q^2}\,m, \qquad (14\text{--}19)$$

and m is constant. The motion of the particle is depicted schematically in Fig. 14–4.

The z-component (parallel component) of the force, Eq. (14–16), is always in such a direction as to accelerate particles toward the weaker part of the field. Gyrating particles which are approaching regions of stronger magnetic field are thus slowed down, i.e., $v_\parallel$ is decreased. On the other hand, conservation of energy requires that simultaneously the orbital motion $v_\perp$ be speeded up. If the convergence of the magnetic field is sufficient, the particle will gyrate in an ever-tighter helical spiral until it is finally reflected back into the weaker field.

14–3 Magnetic mirrors. The results of the preceding section show that a slowly converging magnetic field can, in principle, confine a plasma. At right angles to the principal field direction the particles are bent into circular orbits; along the principal direction of the field the particles are slowed down and finally reflected by the converging field lines. Such a field configuration is called a *magnetic mirror*. At least two mirrors must be used in any confinement system; a system of this type is shown in Fig. 14–5.

Not all particles can be confined by the mirror system, however. The field lines cannot be made to converge to a point; thus there is a large but not infinite magnetic field B_m at the mirror. If the particle has too much "axial kinetic energy" it will not be turned back by the mirror field, and it will be able to escape.

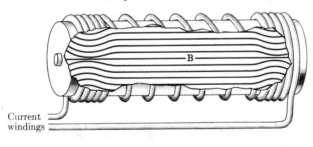

Current
windings

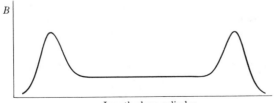

Length along cylinder

FIG. 14–5. Magnetic mirror system.

Because the magnetic moment is a constant of the motion, we find, according to Eq. (14–10), that

$$\frac{K_{0\perp}}{B_0} = \frac{K_{1\perp}}{B_{1\perp}}.$$

Here the subscript 0 refers to the central region of Fig. 14–5, and the subscript 1 to the reflection point. At the reflection point, however, $K_\perp = K$. Furthermore, K, the total kinetic energy, is a constant of the motion. In order that the particle be reflected, the mirror field B_m must be greater than B_1; that is,

$$B_m > B_1 = \frac{K}{K_{0\perp}} B_0,$$

or

$$\frac{K_{0\perp}}{K} > \frac{B_0}{B_m}. \tag{14–20a}$$

If the initial velocity v_0 makes an angle θ_0 with the field direction, then $v_{0\parallel} = v_0 \cos \theta_0$ and $v_{0\perp} = v_0 \sin \theta_0$. Equation (14–20a) then reduces to

$$\sin^2 \theta_0 > \frac{B_0}{B_m}, \tag{14–20b}$$

as the criterion for reflection. For example, if the mirror field is one hundred times as intense as B_0, then particles with velocities making an angle of less than 6° with the field direction escape from the system.

The collisions between particles in the central region of the mirror system tend to produce an isotropic velocity distribution. Thus the net result of collisions is that particles are continually scattered into a region of velocity space such that they can escape from the system. As a result of collisions particles can also "diffuse" at right angles to the field direction, and so eventually escape.

14–4 The hydromagnetic equations. Collective motions of the particles in a plasma, such as the "pinch effect" and plasma oscillations, are handled best in the hydromagnetic formulation. According to this description, the plasma is regarded as a classical fluid which obeys the conventional equations of hydrodynamics. The fluid, however, is an electrical conductor, and thus electromagnetic forces must be taken into account explicitly.

The force on a unit volume of the plasma may be written as

$$\mathbf{F}_v = \mathbf{J} \times \mathbf{B} - \mathbf{grad}\, p, \tag{14–21}$$

where $\mathbf{J}$ is the current density and p is the fluid pressure. Other forces, such as gravitational and viscous forces, may also be included, but are neglected here in the interest of simplicity. Because of the approximate electrical neutrality of the plasma, the term $\rho\mathbf{E}$ need not be included along with other force terms in (14–21). Deviations from neutrality must be considered, of course, in Poisson's equation, but they are usually ignored in the dynamical equations.

Momentum balance requires that

$$\zeta \frac{d\mathbf{v}}{dt} = \zeta \left[\frac{\partial \mathbf{v}}{\partial t} + (\mathbf{v} \cdot \mathbf{grad})\, \mathbf{v}\right]$$

$$= \mathbf{J} \times \mathbf{B} - \mathbf{grad}\, p, \tag{14–22}$$

which is the equation of motion, or the *Euler equation*, of the fluid. Here ζ is the mass density of the plasma and $\mathbf{v}$ its fluid velocity. For problems in which the hydrodynamic motion is not particularly large, the term containing $(\mathbf{v} \cdot \mathbf{grad})\, \mathbf{v}$ can usually be neglected.*

It is sometimes convenient to interpret the $\mathbf{J} \times \mathbf{B}$ term of Eq. (14–21) as arising in part from a "magnetic pressure." This can be done with the aid of Ampere's circuital law, Eq. (10–29), which, specialized to the plasma case, is

$$\mathbf{curl}\, \mathbf{B} = \mu_0 \mathbf{J}, \tag{14–23}$$

and the vector identity

$$\mathbf{B} \times \mathbf{curl}\, \mathbf{B} = \mathbf{grad}\, (\tfrac{1}{2}B^2) - (\mathbf{B} \cdot \mathbf{grad})\, \mathbf{B}. \tag{14–24}$$

Thus

$$\mathbf{J} \times \mathbf{B} = -\frac{1}{\mu_0}\, \mathbf{B} \times \mathbf{curl}\, \mathbf{B}$$

$$= -\mathbf{grad}\left(\frac{B^2}{2\mu_0}\right) + \frac{1}{\mu_0}\, (\mathbf{B} \cdot \mathbf{grad})\, \mathbf{B}. \tag{14–25}$$

The quantity $B^2/2\mu_0$, which is, of course, the magnetic energy density, thus plays the role of a magnetic pressure, p_m:

$$p_m = \frac{B^2}{2\mu_0}. \tag{14–26}$$

It should be emphasized, however, that $-\mathbf{grad}\, p_m$ gives in most cases only part of the magnetic force; the remaining force comes from the $(1/\mu_0)\, (\mathbf{B} \cdot \mathbf{grad})\mathbf{B}$ term. When $\mathbf{J} = 0$, the two terms on the right of (14–25) cancel each other.

As an example of the utility of the magnetic pressure concept, consider a *unidirectional* magnetic field. The equation div $\mathbf{B} = 0$ guarantees that

---

* Although it may not be neglected in steady-flow problems for which the term $\partial\mathbf{v}/\partial t$ vanishes explicitly.

B does not change along the field direction. Since space variations can occur only in directions at right angles to **B**, it follows that $(\mathbf{B} \cdot \mathbf{grad})\mathbf{B} = 0$ for this case. Equation (14–21) reduces, therefore, to

$$\mathbf{F}_v = -\mathbf{grad}\ (p + p_m),$$

and the condition for static equilibrium of each volume element is

$$p + p_m = \text{constant}.$$

In other words, for this example the sum of the fluid pressure and the magnetic pressure must be space-independent.

In addition to Eq. (14–22) and the macroscopic equations governing electricity and magnetism,* we require two additional relationships to complete the hydromagnetic formulation. These are: (1) the equation of continuity for the plasma fluid:

$$\frac{\partial \zeta}{\partial t} + \text{div}\ (\zeta\mathbf{v}) = 0, \qquad\qquad (14\text{–}27)$$

and (2) an equation relating **J** to the field quantities. The latter relationship is simply a generalized form of Ohm's law which, under certain conditions, may be written as†

$$\mathbf{J} = g(\mathbf{E} + \mathbf{v} \times \mathbf{B}) \qquad\qquad (14\text{–}28\text{a})$$

Here $\mathbf{v} \times \mathbf{B}$ is the motional electric field arising from hydrodynamic motion of the plasma in a magnetic field, and g is the conductivity of the plasma.

An approximation which is frequently made is that of infinite conductivity. The advantage of this approximation is that it permits a substantial simplification of the hydromagnetic equations, thus presenting a much clearer picture of the physical processes going on in the plasma. In some problems, particularly astrophysical ones, the approximation is quite good. For the case of infinite conductivity, Ohm's law reduces to

$$g \to \infty,$$

$$\mathbf{E} + \mathbf{v} \times \mathbf{B} = 0. \qquad\qquad (14\text{–}28\text{b})$$

Infinite conductivity (or, for practical purposes, high conductivity) has an important consequence, namely, that the magnetic flux is frozen

---

* The Maxwell equations are summarized in Section 15–2. The reader will note that Eq. (15–13), the original Ampere's circuital law, has been modified through inclusion of the displacement current, $\partial \mathbf{D}/\partial t$. Actually, the displacement current does not play an important role in *most* hydromagnetic phenomena.

† A more general form has been given by Spitzer, *op. cit.*

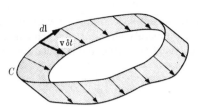

FIGURE 14-6

into the plasma. If Eq. (14–28b) is combined with the differential form of Faraday's law of induction, we obtain

$$\frac{\partial \mathbf{B}}{\partial t} = \text{curl } (\mathbf{v} \times \mathbf{B}). \qquad (14\text{–}29)$$

The normal component of this equation integrated over a fixed surface S yields

$$\frac{d}{dt} \int_S \mathbf{B} \cdot \mathbf{n} \, da = \int_S \text{curl } (\mathbf{v} \times \mathbf{B}) \cdot n \, da,$$

or

$$\frac{d\Phi}{dt} = \oint_C \mathbf{v} \times \mathbf{B} \cdot d\mathbf{l} = \oint_C \mathbf{B} \cdot (d\mathbf{l} \times \mathbf{v}), \qquad (14\text{–}30)$$

where C is a fixed contour in space through which the plasma moves due to hydrodynamic motion. From Fig. 14–6 we see that $\oint_C d\mathbf{l} \times \mathbf{v}$ may be regarded as the increase in area, per unit time, of the cap surface which is bounded by C, and $\oint_C \mathbf{B} \cdot d\mathbf{l} \times \mathbf{v}$ is the magnetic flux associated with this increased area. Equation (14–30) simply states that the flux change per unit time through the contour C is just what we should calculate geometrically on the basis that all flux lines move along with the fluid. We conclude, therefore, that the lines of magnetic induction are "frozen" into the perfectly conducting material.

14–5 The pinch effect. The tendency of a high-current discharge through a plasma to constrict itself laterally is known as the "pinch effect." The basic mechanism causing the pinch is the interaction of a current with its own magnetic field or, equivalently, the attraction between parallel current filaments. The pinch effect was first predicted by Bennett, and later independently by Tonks.[*] A somewhat different picture of the pinch, showing its inherent instability, has been given by Rosenbluth.[†]

---

[*] W. Bennett, *Physical Review* **45**, 890 (1934); L. Tonks, *Physical Review* **56**, 369 (1939).

[†] M. Rosenbluth, "Dynamics of a Pinched Gas," from *Magnetohydrodynamics*, edited by Rolf Landshoff, Stanford University Press, 1957.

Let us consider a current discharge of cylindrical symmetry through the plasma. From Ampere's circuital law, the magnetic induction at distance r from the axis of the discharge is given by

$$B(r) = \frac{\mu_0}{r} \int_0^r J(r')r' \, dr'. \tag{14-31}$$

From this it follows that

$$\frac{\partial B}{\partial r} = -\frac{\mu_0}{r^2} \int_0^r J(r')r' \, dr' + \mu_0 J(r)$$

$$= -\frac{1}{r} B(r) + \mu_0 J(r). \tag{14-32}$$

The magnetic force per unit volume is

$$\mathbf{F}_v = \mathbf{J} \times \mathbf{B} = -J(r)B(r)\mathbf{a}_r, \tag{14-33}$$

where $\mathbf{a}_r$ is a unit vector in the r-direction. Eliminating $J(r)$ between (14-32) and (14-33) yields

$$F_v = -\frac{1}{\mu_0} B \frac{\partial B}{\partial r} - \frac{1}{\mu_0 r} B^2. \tag{14-34}$$

This force can be converted to an equivalent pressure, p_{eq}, by writing $F_v = -\partial p_{eq}/\partial r$, and then integrating:

$$p_{eq} = \frac{1}{2\mu_0} B^2 + \frac{1}{\mu_0} \int_0^r \frac{B^2}{r} \, dr. \tag{14-35}$$

We are particularly interested in the pressure on the lateral boundaries of the discharge. Following Rosenbluth, we restrict our attention to the high-conductivity case where the magnetic field lines cannot penetrate appreciably into the conducting fluid.* Here the integral in (14-35) contains no contribution from the discharge region. At the boundary of the discharge, $r = R$; and the pressure is just what we have called the magnetic pressure, p_m:

$$p_m = \frac{1}{2\mu_0} B^2(R). \tag{14-36}$$

It is evident from (14-35) that the magnetic pressure is uniform in the outside region, but zero or very small inside the discharge. Thus the pinch effect can be viewed as coming about from the sudden buildup of magnetic pressure in the region external to the discharge.

---

* The nonpenetration of the field lines follows from the results of the preceding section and the fact that both the current and magnetic field are initially very small in the discharge.

The pinching of the discharge results in plasma compression. If the pinch could contract in a stable manner it would proceed until the magnetic pressure in the external region was equal to the fluid pressure in the discharge. Let us treat the plasma as a perfect gas, whose fluid pressure $p = NkT$. Then, at the final radius R of the discharge,

$$\frac{1}{2\mu_0} B^2(R) = \frac{1}{2} \frac{\mu_0}{4\pi^2 R^2} I^2 = NkT,$$

where I is the current in the discharge. This expression may be solved for the current:

$$I^2 = 2 \left(\frac{\mu_0}{4\pi}\right)^{-1} \pi R^2 NkT$$

$$= 2 \left(\frac{\mu_0}{4\pi}\right)^{-1} A_0 N_0 kT,$$

since conservation of particles requires that $A_0 N_0 = \pi R^2 N$. Here A_0 is the initial cross section of the discharge, N_0 is its initial particle density, $\mu_0/4\pi = 10^{-7}$ w/amp·m, and Boltzmann's constant $k = 1.38 \times 10^{-23}$ joule/°K. In order to achieve the temperature of 10^8 °K required for a thermonuclear (fusion) reactor, with $A_0 = 0.04\ \mathrm{m}^2$ and $N_0 = 10^{21}$ particles/m^3, a pinch current of approximately one million amperes is required.

It is easy to see that the pinch is an inherently unstable phenomenon. The magnetic pressure on the boundary of the discharge depends on its radius as well as on its detailed geometry. Small perturbations will grow if the pressure changes which result are such as to enhance these perturbations. Figure 14–7 shows that small ripples on the bounding surface of

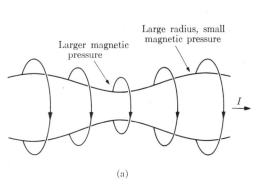

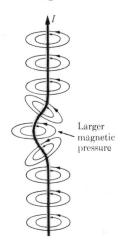

FIG. 14–7.   Instabilities in the pinched plasma: (a) sausage instability, (b) kink instability.

the discharge, as well as kinks, fall into this category, producing the so-called sausage and kink instabilities of the pinched plasma.

14–6 Plasma oscillations and wave motion. One of the interesting properties of a plasma is its ability to sustain oscillations and propagate waves. Various types of oscillatory behavior are possible, and because of the nonlinear character of the hydrodynamic equations these oscillations can be quite complex. We find it expedient to restrict our attention to some rather simple cases which, nevertheless, have been observed in controlled experiments.

Case 1. Electrostatic plasma-electron oscillations. Electrostatic oscillations in a plasma were first discussed by Tonks and Langmuir.* Actually, there are two possible types of electrostatic oscillations: high-frequency oscillations which are too rapid for the heavy ions to follow, and oscillations of the ions which are so slow that the electrons are always distributed around the ions in a statistical manner. We discuss the first case only, the so-called electron oscillations.

Let us fix our attention on a region of plasma containing a uniform density of positive ions, N. There are no negative ions. Initially, the electrons also have uniform density N, but let us suppose that each electron is displaced in the x-direction by a distance ξ which is independent of the y- and z-coordinates and is zero on the plasma boundaries. The displacement of electrons disturbs the neutral plasma, producing a charge in each volume element $\Delta x \, \Delta y \, \Delta z$:

$$\delta \rho \, \Delta x \, \Delta y \, \Delta z = -Ne \, \Delta y \, \Delta z \left[\xi - \left(\xi + \frac{\partial \xi}{\partial x} \Delta x \right) \right]$$

$$= \Delta x \, \Delta y \, \Delta z \, Ne \frac{\partial \xi}{\partial x}. \tag{14–37}$$

The motion of the electrons produces an electric field $\mathbf{E}(x, t)$ which, because of the symmetry of the problem, is in the x-direction. Thus

$$\operatorname{div} \mathbf{E} = \frac{1}{\epsilon_0} \delta \rho,$$

or

$$\frac{\partial E}{\partial x} = \frac{1}{\epsilon_0} Ne \frac{\partial \xi}{\partial x}, \tag{14–38}$$

which, when integrated, yields

$$E = \frac{Ne}{\epsilon_0} \xi. \tag{14–39}$$

---

* L. Tonks and I. Langmuir, *Physical Review* **33**, 195 (1929).

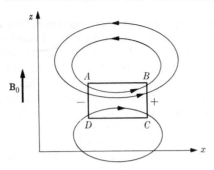

Fig. 14–8. The segment, $ABCD$, of plasma moves in the positive y-direction. The currents which are generated are depicted schematically.

Here, the constant of integration has been taken equal to zero, since sheath formation will shield the plasma from a uniform electric field.

The force on each electron is $-eE$, which, according to Eq. (14–39), is proportional to the displacement ξ. It is also seen to be a restoring force. Thus each electron oscillates about its original position with simple harmonic motion. The equation of motion for each electron is

$$m_e \frac{d^2\xi}{dt^2} + \frac{Ne^2}{\epsilon_0}\,\xi = 0. \tag{14–40}$$

The "plasma frequency," $f_p = \omega_p/2\pi$, is defined, therefore, by

$$\omega_p = \left(\frac{Ne^2}{m_e\epsilon_0}\right)^{1/2}, \tag{14–41}$$

where m_e is the electron mass. As a numerical example, we have $f_p = 9.0 \times 10^9$ sec^{-1} for a particle density $N = 10^{18}$ electrons/m^3.

Case 2. Hydromagnetic or Alfvén waves. Hydromagnetic waves represent true wave propagation in a conducting medium which is subjected to a constant magnetic field. This behavior, which was first predicted by Alfvén* in 1942, is consistent with the hydromagnetic formulation of a plasma discussed in Section 14–4.

Before proceeding to the differential equations, let us look at the physical processes in the plasma from as elementary a viewpoint as possible. Consider an infinite plasma subjected to a constant, uniform magnetic field $\mathbf{B}_0$ which is directed along the z-axis. If a segment of the plasma, the rectangular section $ABCD$ in Fig. 14–8 that extends parallel to the y-axis, is given a velocity $\mathbf{v}$ directed parallel to the positive y-axis, then the charge carriers (ions and electrons) experience forces

$$q_i(\mathbf{v} \times \mathbf{B}_0)$$

* H. Alfvén, *Cosmical Electrodynamics*, Oxford University Press, 1950.

which tend to separate the positive and negative carriers. The segment
$ABCD$ thus becomes a seat of emf, its right-hand end tending to charge
up positively, its left end negatively. But since we are dealing with a conducting medium, the plasma external to $ABCD$ completes the electrical
circuit. A few of the current lines are shown in the figure.

The induced current now interacts with the magnetic field $\mathbf{B}_0$. It is easy
to verify that the force density $\mathbf{J} \times \mathbf{B}_0$ in the segment $ABCD$ is such as
to oppose its motion, whereas the force on external parts of the plasma is
such as to accelerate it in the positive y-direction. Eventually, $ABCD$
will have slowed down, and its motion will have been transferred to
neighboring segments of the plasma. The mechanism is still operating,
however, and the whole process is repeated, thus propagating the dis-
turbance farther in the $\pm z$-direction.

We now turn to the differential equations. Let $\mathbf{B} = \mathbf{B}_0 + \mathbf{B}_1$, where
$\mathbf{B}_0$ is the constant, uniform field parallel to the z-axis and $\mathbf{B}_1$ is the magnetic
field set up by the induced currents. Using the results of the preceding
paragraphs as a guide, we look for the simplest type of wave motion,
characterized by $v_y, E_x, J_x,$ and B_{1y}, other components vanishing. From
Ampere's circuital law,

$$-\frac{\partial B_{1y}}{\partial z} = \mu_0 J_x, \tag{14-42}$$

and the Euler equation of the fluid, Eq. (14–22), gives the two relations

$$\zeta \frac{\partial v_y}{\partial t} = -J_x B_0, \tag{14-43a}$$

and

$$0 = J_x B_{1y} - \frac{\partial p}{\partial z}. \tag{14-43b}$$

Equations (14–43) may be combined with (14–42) to yield

$$\frac{\partial v_y}{\partial t} = \frac{B_0}{\mu_0 \zeta} \frac{\partial B_{1y}}{\partial z} \tag{14-44}$$

and

$$\frac{\partial p}{\partial z} = -\frac{1}{2\mu_0} \frac{\partial (B_{1y}^2)}{\partial z}. \tag{14-45}$$

The generalized Ohm's law may be written as

$$E_x = -v_y B_0 + \frac{1}{g} J_x$$

$$= -v_y B_0 - \frac{1}{g\mu_0} \frac{\partial B_{1y}}{\partial z}. \tag{14-46}$$

Finally, Faraday's law yields

$$\frac{\partial B_{1y}}{\partial t} = -\frac{\partial E_x}{\partial z}. \tag{14–47}$$

If v_y is eliminated between Eqs. (14–44) and (14–46), and E_x eliminated between the resulting equation and (14–47), we obtain, on the assumption of constant ζ,

$$\frac{\partial^2 B_{1y}}{\partial t^2} = \frac{B_0^2}{\mu_0 \zeta} \frac{\partial^2 B_{1y}}{\partial z^2} + \frac{1}{g\mu_0} \frac{\partial^3 B_{1y}}{\partial z^2 \, \partial t}, \tag{14–48}$$

which is the equation governing the propagation of Alfvén waves.

If the conductivity g of the plasma were infinite, then (14–48) would become identical with the wave equation whose solution is discussed in Sections 15–4 and 15–5. In these circumstances, Eq. (14–48) describes a plane, undamped wave moving parallel to the z-axis with phase velocity

$$v_p = \frac{B_0}{\sqrt{\mu_0 \zeta}}. \tag{14–49}$$

As a numerical example, take $B_0 = 0.01$ w/m², $\zeta = 10^{-5}$ kgm/m³ $= 10^{-8}$ gm/cm³; then $v_p = 2800$ m/sec.

In order to see what results for finite conductivity, we try a solution to (14–48) of the form

$$B_{1y} = b_1 \exp\left[\alpha z + j\omega t\right].$$

This solution is satisfactory provided

$$\alpha^2 = \frac{-\omega^2}{v_p^2 + j\omega/g\mu_0}, \tag{14–50}$$

with v_p as defined in (14–49). For small damping,

$$\alpha \approx \pm \left(j\frac{\omega}{v_p} + \frac{\omega^2}{2g\mu_0 v_p^3} \right). \tag{14–51}$$

Thus the solution to Eq. (14–48) is a damped plane wave propagating in the $\pm z$-direction. The distance z_0 in which the amplitude of the wave is reduced to $1/e$ of its original value is

$$z_0 = \frac{2g\mu_0 v_p^3}{\omega^2} = \frac{2gB_0^3}{\mu_0^{1/2}\zeta^{3/2}\omega^2}. \tag{14–52}$$

14–7 The use of probes for plasma measurements. A plasma consists of electrons, ions, and perhaps neutral atoms. The electrons gain energy from electric fields at the boundary of the plasma as well as from the ionizing collisions in which they are produced, and the velocities of the electrons become random through collisions with ions. Thus we can speak of an electron temperature, T_e. In fact, for plasmas created in the laboratory (arcs, electrical discharges), the electrons are found to have a Maxwell-Boltzmann velocity distribution, which means, of course, that they may be characterized by a temperature. Electron temperatures in typical arc plasmas range from several thousand to 50,000°K.

To a certain extent, the preceding discussion also applies to the heavy ions; however, ions do not necessarily have the same temperatures as electrons. If a substantial difference between the mean kinetic energies of ions and electrons exists, then it takes several thousand collisions per particle to equalize the energy difference, and this may require a time longer than the mean life of an ion in the system.

Interesting quantities to be determined are the particle temperatures, particle densities, and random current densities in the plasma. Langmuir and Mott-Smith* have shown that a small metal electrode or "probe" inserted into the plasma can be used to determine some of these quantities experimentally, by applying various potentials and measuring the corresponding collected currents. An electrode not at plasma potential will be enveloped by a sheath which shields the plasma from the disturbing field caused by the electrode. The sheath is, in most cases, quite thin, and if the probe is maintained negative, zero, or slightly positive with respect to plasma potential it will barely disturb the bulk plasma.

The current-voltage relationship for a typical probe is shown in Fig. 14–9. When the probe is at plasma potential, it collects both the random electron and the random ion currents. But the random electron current is so much greater than the ion current that the former dominates, the reason for this being that the electrons have much larger average velocities than do the ions. As the probe is made negative it repels electrons and the electron current drops off; at point U_F, the floating potential, the net current to the probe is zero; finally, if the probe is made negative enough, only the ion current density J_i is collected. If the probe is made slightly positive with respect to the plasma, the ions are repelled and the electron current density J_e is collected. If the probe is made even more positive, it will begin to act like a secondary anode and the current-voltage behavior will become complicated, depending in detail upon the nature of the plasma.

Let us consider a plasma consisting of positive ions (singly charged) and electrons. The ion density is equal to the electron density in the neutral region:

$$N_i = N_e = N_0. \tag{14–53}$$

If the electron distribution is characterized by the temperature T_e then, according to kinetic theory, the random electron current density is

* I. Langmuir and H. Mott-Smith, *General Electric Review* **27,** 449 (1924); *Physical Review* **28,** 727 (1926).

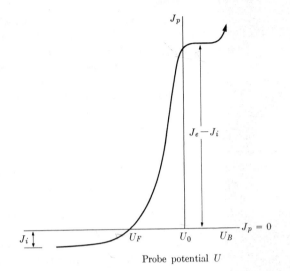

FIG. 14-9. Current-voltage characteristic of a probe inserted in a plasma. U_0 is plasma potential.

$$J_e = \tfrac{1}{4} N_0 e \bar{v} = N_0 e \left(\frac{kT_e}{2\pi m_e} \right)^{1/2}, \qquad (14\text{-}54)$$

where $\bar{v}$ is the average thermal velocity of the electrons. This is the electron current collected per unit area of the probe in the region $U = U_0$ to $U = U_B$. If the probe is made negative, the electron current density falls off, because only a fraction of the electrons has energy sufficient to penetrate the potential barrier:

$$J_e' = J_e \exp \left(e\, \frac{U - U_0}{kT_e} \right) = \tfrac{1}{4} N_e e \bar{v} \exp \left(e\, \frac{U - U_0}{kT_e} \right), \qquad \text{for } U \leq U_0. \tag{14-55}$$

The ion current density, on the other hand, is constant in the negative potential region, namely, J_i. The total probe current is thus

$$J_p = J_e \exp \left(e\, \frac{U - U_0}{kT_e} \right) - J_i,$$

and the electron temperature is found to be

$$T_e = \frac{e}{k} \left[\frac{d}{dU} \ln \left(J_p + |J_i| \right) \right]^{-1}. \qquad (14\text{-}56)$$

The particle density N_0 can now be determined from Eq. (14-54) by using the experimental value of J_p corresponding to the plateau region to the right of U_0 in the figure. It should be noted that Eq. (14–56) and the shape of the J_p-U characteristic are independent of the absolute value of U; thus the potential of the probe can be measured with respect to any fixed potential (for example, an electrode potential) in the plasma.

Probe characteristics are well understood, but before the data obtained from probe measurements can be interpreted unambiguously it is necessary that certain conditions be satisfied: (1) the probe should be small compared with the mean free paths of electrons and ions, (2) the sheath should be small compared with the dimensions of the probe, (3) the ionization in the sheath must be negligible, (4) secondary emission from the probe must be negligible, and (5) there must be no plasma oscillations. In addition to these requirements, it is tacitly assumed that there is no magnetic field present; the use of probes in plasmas containing magnetic fields has been discussed by Bohm, Burhop, and Massey.*

We end this section with a discussion of the sheath surrounding the negatively charged probe. The equation governing the potential U in the sheath region is Poisson's equation:

$$\nabla^2 U = -\frac{1}{\epsilon_0} e(N_i - N_e), \qquad (14\text{–}57)$$

where N_i and N_e are the local ion and electron densities. An approximate plot of U versus distance from the probe is given in Fig. 14–10. It is convenient to make the substitution $U = -V$, where V is a positive quantity, and since the sheath thickness is small compared with the dimensions of the probe, we may use a one-dimensional version of (14–57):

$$\frac{d^2 V}{dx^2} = \frac{1}{\mu_0} e(N_i - N_e). \qquad (14\text{–}58)$$

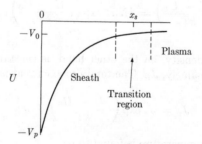

FIG. 14–10. Plot of potential versus distance from the probe.

* Chapter 2 of *Characteristics of Electrical Discharges in Magnetic Fields*, edited by A. Guthrie and R. K. Wakerling, McGraw-Hill, New York, 1949.

Electrons are distributed in the sheath in approximately a statistical fashion:

$$N_e = N_0 \exp\left[\frac{-e(V - V_0)}{kT_e}\right], \qquad (14\text{–}59)$$

where N_0 is the electron density at plasma potential $-V_0$. The ion density is related to the ion current, J_i, in accordance with

$$J_i = N_i e v_i = N_i e \sqrt{\frac{2eV}{m_i}}. \qquad (14\text{–}60\text{a})$$

In the plasma, outside the sheath, the ion current is given by

$$J_i = N_0 e v_{io} = N_0 e \sqrt{\frac{2eV_0}{m_i}}, \qquad (14\text{–}60\text{b})$$

provided the plasma potential, $-V_0$, is measured relative to the point where the positive ions are formed. Thus

$$N_i = N_0 \sqrt{\frac{V_0}{V}}. \qquad (14\text{–}61)$$

Substituting Eqs. (14–59) and (14–61) into (14–58) yields the so-called *plasma-sheath* equation:

$$\frac{d^2 V}{dx^2} = \frac{1}{\epsilon_0} N_0 e\left[V_0^{1/2} V^{-1/2} - \exp\frac{-e(V - V_0)}{kT_e}\right]. \qquad (14\text{–}62)$$

The last equation may be multiplied through by $(dV/dx)\,dx = dV$ and integrated to obtain

$$\frac{1}{2}\left(\frac{dV}{dx}\right)^2 = \frac{1}{\epsilon_0} N_0 e\left[2V_0^{1/2} V^{1/2} + \frac{kT_e}{e}\exp\frac{-e(V - V_0)}{kT_e}\right] + C, \qquad (14\text{–}63)$$

where the constant C is determined from the condition that $dV/dx = 0$ at the sheath edge, i.e., where $V = V_0$. Thus

$$C = -\frac{1}{\epsilon_0} N_0[2eV_0 + kT_e]. \qquad (14\text{–}64)$$

For all points in the sheath, $(dV/dx)^2 \geq 0$; examination of Eq. (14–63) shows that this condition is satisfied only if

$$V_0 \geq \frac{kT_e}{2e}, \qquad (14\text{–}65)$$

a relation first pointed out by Bohm.* In other words, for a stable sheath

---

* See Chapter 3 of the book edited by Guthrie and Wakerling, *op. cit.*

to form, the ions which reach the sheath from the plasma must have a kinetic energy at least half as large as kT_e. Since stable sheaths always form under these circumstances, Eq. (14–65) effectively determines V_0; in fact, the inequality in (14–65) may usually be replaced by an equality sign.

The sheath thickness may be found by integrating (14–63); we do this only for very negative probes, for which N_e may be neglected. Here

$$\left(\frac{dV}{dx}\right)^2 \approx \frac{4N_0eV_0}{\epsilon_0}\left[\left(\frac{V}{V_0}\right)^{1/2} - 1\right] \approx \frac{4N_0eV_0^{1/2}V^{1/2}}{\epsilon_0}$$

$$= 2\sqrt{\frac{2m_i}{e}}\,\frac{1}{\epsilon_0}\,J_iV^{1/2}, \tag{14–66}$$

which, when integrated, yields

$$x_s = \frac{4\epsilon_0^{1/2}V_p^{3/4}}{3(8m_i/e)^{1/4}J_i^{1/2}}. \tag{14–67}$$

PROBLEMS

14–1. The condition for orbit theory to be a good approximation to the motion of an electron in a plasma is that $\tau \gg 2\pi m_e/Be$, where τ is the mean collision time (see Chapter 7) and $2\pi m_e/Be$ is the cyclotron period in the magnetic field B. Show that this statement is equivalent to $\eta \ll \eta_H$, where $\eta_H \equiv B/N_0 e$ is the Hall resistivity.

14–2. Given a steady-flow hydromagnetic problem in which $\mathbf{v}$, $\mathbf{J}$, and $\mathbf{B}$ are mutually orthogonal. Assume that $\mathbf{v}$ is in the x-direction, and that $\mathbf{v}$, $\mathbf{J}$, and $\mathbf{B}$ are functions of x only. Assume also that the channel cross section (perpendicular to x) is independent of x. Show that

$$v = v_0 - \frac{1}{2\zeta_0 v_0}\left[2B_0\int J\,dx + \mu_0\left(\int J\,dx\right)^2\right],$$

where v_0 is the velocity when $\zeta = \zeta_0$, $B = B_0$.

14–3. Derive Eq. (14–65) by examining Eq. (14–63) relative to the neighborhood of $V \approx V_0$.

14–4. The current-voltage characteristic is measured for a probe which is inserted into the plasma of a current-discharge tube. The probe has an area of 0.05 cm^2. All voltages are with respect to a fixed reference potential:

U_p, volts	I, milliamp	U_p, volts	I, milliamp
40.0	−20.5	35.0	−0.34
39.0	−20.4	34.0	−0.096
38.0	−7.5	33.0	−0.011
37.0	−2.7	31.0	+0.033
36.0	−0.98	29.0	+0.041

Determine the electron temperature in the plasma, the electron density, and the floating potential of the probe.

CHAPTER 15

MAXWELL'S EQUATIONS

15–1 The generalization of Ampere's law. Displacement current. In Chapter 8 we found that the magnetic field due to a current distribution satisfied Ampere's circuital law,

$$\oint \mathbf{H} \cdot d\mathbf{l} = \int_S \mathbf{J} \cdot \mathbf{n} \, da. \tag{15–1}$$

We shall now examine this law, show that it fails, and find a generalization which is valid.

Consider the circuit shown in Fig. 15–1, which consists of a small parallel-plate capacitor being charged by a constant current I (we need not worry about what causes the current). If Ampere's law is applied to the contour C and the surface S_1, we find

$$\oint_C \mathbf{H} \cdot d\mathbf{l} = \int_{S_1} \mathbf{J} \cdot \mathbf{n} \, da = I. \tag{15–2}$$

If, on the other hand, Ampere's law is applied to the contour C and surface S_2, then J is zero at all points on S_2 and

$$\oint_C \mathbf{H} \cdot d\mathbf{l} = \int_{S_2} \mathbf{J} \cdot \mathbf{n} \, da = 0. \tag{15–3}$$

Equations (15–2) and (15–3) contradict each other and thus cannot both

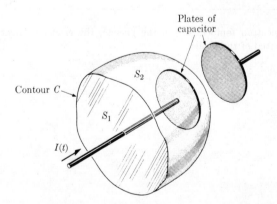

Fig. 15–1. The contour C and two surfaces, S_1 and S_2, for testing Ampere's circuital law.

be correct. If C is imagined to be a great distance from the capacitor, it is clear that the situation is not substantially different from the standard Ampere law cases considered in Chapter 8. One is thus led to think that (15–2) is correct, since it is not dependent on the new feature, namely, the capacitor. Equation (15–3), on the other hand, requires consideration of the capacitor for its deduction. It would appear, then, that (15–3) requires modification.

The proper modification can be made by noting that (15–2) and (15–3) give different results because the integrals on the right-hand sides are different. Phrased mathematically,

$$\int_{S_2} \mathbf{J} \cdot \mathbf{n}_2 \, da - \int_{S_1} \mathbf{J} \cdot \mathbf{n}_1 \, da \neq 0. \qquad (15\text{–}4)$$

S_1 and S_2 together form a closed surface (they join at C); however, $\mathbf{n}_2$ is outward drawn and $\mathbf{n}_1$ inward drawn. If this fact is taken into account, (15–4) may be written

$$\oint_{S_1 + S_2} \mathbf{J} \cdot \mathbf{n} \, da \neq 0, \qquad (15\text{–}5)$$

which is just the form of the integral in the divergence theorem. It is clear that the integral would vanish and thus remove the disparity between (15–2) and (15–3) if $\mathbf{J}$ were replaced by a vector $\mathbf{J}'$ with zero divergence. That is, since

$$\oint_{S_1 + S_2} \mathbf{J}' \cdot \mathbf{n} \, da = \int_V \operatorname{div} \mathbf{J}' \, dv, \qquad (15\text{–}6)$$

the vanishing of the divergence of $\mathbf{J}'$ ensures that the surface integral vanishes. This in turn indicates that replacing $\mathbf{J}$ and $\mathbf{J}'$ in Ampere's circuital law would be satisfactory from the standpoint of the consistency of (15–2) and (15–3).

It must be remembered, however, that the original Ampere's law is satisfactory in many cases. We then write

$$\mathbf{J}' = \mathbf{J} + \boldsymbol{\alpha}, \qquad (15\text{–}7)$$

where $\boldsymbol{\alpha}$ is a vector which is, loosely speaking, important in problems involving capacitors and not important in conduction problems. Furthermore, $\boldsymbol{\alpha}$ must be such as to make the divergence of $\mathbf{J}'$ vanish. If we take the divergence of (15–7) and set it equal to zero, we have

$$\operatorname{div} \mathbf{J}' = \operatorname{div} \mathbf{J} + \operatorname{div} \boldsymbol{\alpha}. \qquad (15\text{–}8)$$

The divergence of $\mathbf{J}$ may be replaced by $-\partial \rho / \partial t$, since differential conservation of charge requires that

$$\operatorname{div} \mathbf{J} + \frac{\partial \rho}{\partial t} = 0. \qquad (15\text{–}9)$$

Thus,

$$\text{div } \mathbf{J}' = -\frac{\partial \rho}{\partial t} + \text{div } \boldsymbol{\alpha}. \qquad (15\text{-}10)$$

But the electric displacement $\mathbf{D}$ is related to the charge density by

$$\text{div } \mathbf{D} = \rho. \qquad (15\text{-}11)$$

If $\boldsymbol{\alpha}$ is taken to be $\partial \mathbf{D}/\partial t$, div $\mathbf{J}' = 0$. We make this choice and write

$$\mathbf{J}' = \mathbf{J} + \frac{\partial \mathbf{D}}{\partial t}, \qquad (15\text{-}12)$$

which gives the modified Ampere's law:

$$\text{curl } \mathbf{H} = \mathbf{J} + \frac{\partial \mathbf{D}}{\partial t}. \qquad (15\text{-}13)$$

The introduction of the second term on the right, which is known as the displacement current, represents one of Maxwell's major contributions to electromagnetic theory.

15–2 Maxwell's equations and their empirical basis. Equation (15–13) is one of the set of equations known as Maxwell's equations. The entire set consists of (15–13) plus three equations with which we are already familiar, namely:

$$\text{curl } \mathbf{H} = \mathbf{J} + \frac{\partial \mathbf{D}}{\partial t}, \qquad (15\text{-}13)$$

$$\text{curl } \mathbf{E} = -\frac{\partial \mathbf{B}}{\partial t}, \qquad (9\text{-}6)\ (15\text{-}14)$$

$$\text{div } \mathbf{D} = \rho, \qquad (4\text{-}29)\ (15\text{-}15)$$

$$\text{div } \mathbf{B} = 0. \qquad (8\text{-}30)\ (15\text{-}16)$$

Each of these equations represents a generalization of certain experimental observations: (15–13) represents an extension of Ampere's law; (15–14) is the differential form of Faraday's law of electromagnetic induction; (15–15) is Gauss's law, which in turn derives from Coulomb's law; (15–16) is usually said to represent the fact that single magnetic poles have never been observed.

It is clear that Maxwell's equations represent mathematical expressions of certain experimental results. In this light it is apparent that they cannot be proved; however, the applicability to any situation can be verified. As a result of extensive experimental work, Maxwell's equations are now known to apply to almost all macroscopic situations and they are usually used, much like conservation of momentum, as guiding principles.

15–3 Electromagnetic energy. It was shown in Chapter 6 that the quantity

$$W_E = \tfrac{1}{2} \int_V \mathbf{E} \cdot \mathbf{D} \, dv \qquad (15\text{–}17)$$

can be identified with the electrostatic potential energy of the system of charges producing the electric field. This was done by computing the work done in establishing the field. In a similar way

$$W_M = \tfrac{1}{2} \int_V \mathbf{H} \cdot \mathbf{B} \, dv \qquad (15\text{–}18)$$

was identified, in Chapter 12, with the energy stored in the magnetic field. The question of the applicability of these expressions to nonstatic situations now arises.

If the scalar product of (15–13) with $\mathbf{E}$ is taken, and the resulting equation is subtracted from the scalar product of (15–14) with $\mathbf{H}$, the resulting equation is

$$\mathbf{H} \cdot \operatorname{curl} \mathbf{E} - \mathbf{E} \cdot \operatorname{curl} \mathbf{H} = -\mathbf{H} \cdot \frac{\partial \mathbf{B}}{\partial t} - \mathbf{E} \cdot \frac{\partial \mathbf{D}}{\partial t} - \mathbf{E} \cdot \mathbf{J}. \quad (15\text{–}19)$$

The left side of this expression can be converted into a divergence by using the identity

$$\operatorname{div} (\mathbf{A} \times \mathbf{B}) = \mathbf{B} \cdot \operatorname{curl} \mathbf{A} - \mathbf{A} \cdot \operatorname{curl} \mathbf{B}$$

to obtain

$$\operatorname{div} (\mathbf{E} \times \mathbf{H}) = -\mathbf{H} \cdot \frac{\partial \mathbf{B}}{\partial t} - \mathbf{E} \cdot \frac{\partial \mathbf{D}}{\partial t} - \mathbf{E} \cdot \mathbf{J}. \qquad (15\text{–}20)$$

If the medium to which (15–20) is applied is linear, i.e., if $\mathbf{D}$ is proportional to $\mathbf{E}$ and $\mathbf{B}$ is proportional to $\mathbf{H}$,* then the time derivatives on the right

---

* A medium is linear if $\mathbf{B} = \mu\mathbf{H}$ and $\mathbf{D} = \epsilon\mathbf{E}$, with μ and ϵ quantities which are independent of the field variables and which do not depend explicitly on the time. A notable exception to linearity occurs in the case of ferromagnetism, where the relationship between the magnetic induction and the magnetic intensity depends not only on the magnetic intensity but also on the past history of the specimen.

It should, however, be noted that anisotropy alone does not invalidate the expressions

$$\mathbf{E} \cdot \frac{\partial \mathbf{D}}{\partial t} = \frac{1}{2} \frac{\partial}{\partial t} (\mathbf{E} \cdot \mathbf{D}) \quad \text{and} \quad \mathbf{H} \cdot \frac{\partial \mathbf{B}}{\partial t} = \frac{1}{2} \frac{\partial}{\partial t} (\mathbf{H} \cdot \mathbf{B}).$$

In the case of anisotropic media, the relationship between $\mathbf{E}$ and $\mathbf{D}$ can be written as

$$D_i = \sum_{j=1}^{3} \epsilon_{ij} E_j.$$

Consequently,

can be written as

$$\mathbf{E} \cdot \frac{\partial \mathbf{D}}{\partial t} = \mathbf{E} \cdot \frac{\partial}{\partial t} \epsilon \mathbf{E} = \tfrac{1}{2}\epsilon \frac{\partial}{\partial t} \mathbf{E}^2 = \frac{\partial}{\partial t} \tfrac{1}{2}\mathbf{E} \cdot \mathbf{D}$$

and

$$\mathbf{H} \cdot \frac{\partial \mathbf{B}}{\partial t} = \mathbf{H} \cdot \frac{\partial}{\partial t} \mu \mathbf{H} = \tfrac{1}{2}\mu \frac{\partial}{\partial t} \mathbf{H}^2 = \frac{\partial}{\partial t} \tfrac{1}{2}\mathbf{H} \cdot \mathbf{B}.$$

Using this relationship, (15–20) takes the form

$$\text{div} (\mathbf{E} \times \mathbf{H}) = -\frac{\partial}{\partial t} \tfrac{1}{2}(\mathbf{E} \cdot \mathbf{D} + \mathbf{B} \cdot \mathbf{H}) - \mathbf{J} \cdot \mathbf{E}. \qquad (15\text{–}21)$$

The first term on the right is the time derivative of the sum of the electric and magnetic energy densities; the second term is, in many cases, just the negative of the Joule heating rate per unit volume. Integrating over a fixed volume V bounded by the surface S gives

$$\int_V \text{div} (\mathbf{E} \times \mathbf{H}) \, dv = -\frac{d}{dt} \int_V \tfrac{1}{2}(\mathbf{E} \cdot \mathbf{D} + \mathbf{B} \cdot \mathbf{H}) \, dv - \int_V \mathbf{J} \cdot \mathbf{E} \, dv.$$

Applying the divergence theorem to the left side, we obtain

$$\oint_S \mathbf{E} \times \mathbf{H} \cdot \mathbf{n} \, da = -\frac{d}{dt} \int_V \tfrac{1}{2}(\mathbf{E} \cdot \mathbf{D} + \mathbf{B} \cdot \mathbf{H}) \, dv - \int_V \mathbf{J} \cdot \mathbf{E} \, dv.$$

Rewriting this equation:

$$-\int_V \mathbf{J} \cdot \mathbf{E} \, dv = \frac{d}{dt} \int_V \tfrac{1}{2}(\mathbf{E} \cdot \mathbf{D} + \mathbf{B} \cdot \mathbf{H}) \, dv + \oint_S \mathbf{E} \times \mathbf{H} \cdot \mathbf{n} \, da, \qquad (15\text{–}22)$$

$$\frac{1}{2} \frac{\partial}{\partial t} (\mathbf{E} \cdot \mathbf{D}) = \frac{1}{2} \sum_{i=1}^{3} \sum_{j=1}^{3} \epsilon_{ij} \left(E_i \frac{\partial E_j}{\partial t} + \frac{\partial E_i}{\partial t} E_j \right).$$

A simple argument based on the conservation of energy (Wooster, *Crystal Physics*, Cambridge University Press, 1938, p. 277) shows that $\epsilon_{ij} = \epsilon_{ji}$. Using this result to interchange i and j in the last term, we have

$$\frac{1}{2} \frac{\partial}{\partial t} (\mathbf{E} \cdot \mathbf{D}) = \sum_{i=1}^{3} \sum_{j=1}^{3} E_i \epsilon_{ij} \frac{\partial E_j}{\partial t}.$$

If $[\epsilon_{ij}]$ is a set of constants independent of $\mathbf{E}$ and of t, then

$$\frac{1}{2} \frac{\partial}{\partial t} (\mathbf{E} \cdot \mathbf{D}) = \sum_{i=1}^{3} E_i \frac{\partial}{\partial t} \sum_{j=1}^{3} \epsilon_{ij} E_j = \sum_{i=1}^{3} E_i \frac{\partial D_i}{\partial t} = \mathbf{E} \cdot \frac{\partial \mathbf{D}}{\partial t}.$$

Thus it is seen that anisotropy alone does not restrict the derivation.

makes it clear that the $\mathbf{J} \cdot \mathbf{E}$ term is comprised of two parts: the rate of change of electromagnetic energy stored in V, and a surface integral. The left side of Eq. (15–22) is the power transferred *into* the electromagnetic field through the motion of free charge in volume V. If there are no sources of emf in V, then the left side of (15–22) is negative and equal to minus the Joule heat production per unit time. In certain circumstances, however, the left side of (15–22) may be positive. Suppose that a charged particle q moves with constant velocity $\mathbf{v}$ under the combined influence of mechanical, electric, and magnetic forces; the rate at which mechanical work is done on the particle is

$$\mathbf{F}_m \cdot \mathbf{v} = -q(\mathbf{E} + \mathbf{v} \times \mathbf{B}) \cdot \mathbf{v} = -q\mathbf{E} \cdot \mathbf{v}.$$

But according to Eq. (7–4) the current density is defined by

$$\mathbf{J} = \sum_i N_i q_i \mathbf{v}_i;$$

thus the rate at which mechanical work is done (per unit volume) is

$$\sum_i N_i \mathbf{F}_m \cdot \mathbf{v}_i = -\mathbf{E} \cdot \mathbf{J},$$

and this power density is transferred into the electromagnetic field.

Since the surface integral in (15–22) involves only the electric and magnetic fields, it is feasible to interpret this term as the rate of energy flow across the surface. It is tempting to interpret $\mathbf{E} \times \mathbf{H}$ itself as the energy flow per unit time per unit area. The latter interpretation, however, leads to certain inconsistencies; the only interpretation which survives careful scrutiny is that the integral of $\mathbf{E} \times \mathbf{H}$ over a closed surface represents the rate at which electromagnetic energy crosses the closed surface. The vector $\mathbf{E} \times \mathbf{H}$ is known as the Poynting vector, and is usually represented by the symbol $\mathbf{S}$.

Equation (15–22) thus expresses the conservation of energy in a fixed volume V.

15–4 The wave equation. One of the most important applications of Maxwell's equations is in the derivation of equations for electromagnetic waves. The wave equation for $\mathbf{H}$ is derived by taking the curl of (15–13):

$$\operatorname{curl} \operatorname{curl} \mathbf{H} = \operatorname{curl} \mathbf{J} + \operatorname{curl} \frac{\partial \mathbf{D}}{\partial t}.$$

Putting $\mathbf{D} = \epsilon \mathbf{E}$ and $\mathbf{J} = g\mathbf{E}$ and assuming g and ϵ to be constants, we obtain

$$\operatorname{curl} \operatorname{curl} \mathbf{H} = g \operatorname{curl} \mathbf{E} + \epsilon \frac{\partial}{\partial t} \operatorname{curl} \mathbf{E}.$$

The order of time and space differentiation can be interchanged if **E** is a sufficiently well-behaved function, which we assume to be the case. Equation (15–14) can now be used to eliminate **curl E**, which yields

$$\text{curl curl } \mathbf{H} = -g\mu \frac{\partial \mathbf{H}}{\partial t} - \epsilon\mu \frac{\partial^2 \mathbf{H}}{\partial t^2}, \tag{15–23}$$

where $\mathbf{B} = \mu\mathbf{H}$, with μ a constant, has been used. The vector identity

$$\text{curl curl } = \text{grad div} - \nabla^2 \tag{15–24}$$

is now used to obtain

$$\text{grad div } \mathbf{H} - \nabla^2\mathbf{H} = -g\mu \frac{\partial \mathbf{H}}{\partial t} - \epsilon\mu \frac{\partial^2 \mathbf{H}}{\partial t^2}. \tag{15–25}$$

Since μ is a constant,

$$\text{div } \mathbf{H} = \frac{1}{\mu} \text{div } \mathbf{B} = 0;$$

consequently the first term on the left side of (15–25) vanishes. The final wave equation is

$$\nabla^2\mathbf{H} - \epsilon\mu \frac{\partial^2 \mathbf{H}}{\partial t^2} - g\mu \frac{\partial \mathbf{H}}{\partial t} = 0. \tag{15–26}$$

The vector **E** satisfies the same wave equation, as is readily seen by first taking the curl of Eq. (15–14):

$$\text{curl curl } \mathbf{E} = - \text{ curl } \frac{\partial \mathbf{B}}{\partial t}.$$

Using (15–13) to eliminate the magnetic field and treating g, μ, and ϵ as constants yields

$$\text{curl curl } \mathbf{E} = -g\mu \frac{\partial \mathbf{E}}{\partial t} - \epsilon\mu \frac{\partial^2 \mathbf{E}}{\partial t^2}.$$

Applying the vector identity (15–24) and restricting the application of the equation to charge-free space so that div **D** = 0 gives

$$\nabla^2\mathbf{E} - \epsilon\mu \frac{\partial^2 \mathbf{E}}{\partial t^2} - g\mu \frac{\partial \mathbf{E}}{\partial t} = 0. \tag{15–27}$$

The wave equations derived above govern the electromagnetic field in a homogeneous, linear medium in which the charge density is zero, whether this medium is conducting or nonconducting. However, it is not enough that these equations be satisfied; Maxwell's equations must also be satisfied. It is clear that Eqs. (15–26) and (15–27) are a necessary consequence of Maxwell's equation, but the converse is not true. In solving the wave equations, special care must be used to obtain solutions to Maxwell's equations. One method which works very well for monochromatic waves is to obtain a solution for **E**. The curl of **E** then gives the time derivative of **B**, which for monochromatic waves is sufficiently simply related to **B** so that **B** can be easily found.

Monochromatic waves may be described as waves which are characterized by a single frequency. The methods of complex variable analysis afford a convenient way of treating such waves. The time dependence of the field (for definiteness we take the vector **E**) is taken to be as $e^{-j\omega t}$, so that

$$\mathbf{E}(\mathbf{r}, t) = \mathbf{E}_s(\mathbf{r})e^{-j\omega t}. \qquad (15\text{--}28)$$

It must be remembered that the physical electric field is obtained by taking the real part* of (15–28); furthermore $\mathbf{E}_s(\mathbf{r})$ is in general complex, so that the actual electric field is proportional to $\cos(\omega t + \varphi)$ where φ is the phase of $\mathbf{E}_s(\mathbf{r})$. Using (15–28) in Eq. (15–27) gives

$$e^{-j\omega t}\{\nabla^2 \mathbf{E}_s + \omega^2 \epsilon \mu \mathbf{E}_s + j\omega g \mu \mathbf{E}_s\} = 0 \qquad (15\text{--}29)$$

for the equation governing the spatial variation of the electric field (the common factor $e^{-j\omega t}$ can, of course, be dropped). The next task is to solve Eq. (15–29) in various special cases of interest to determine the spatial variation of the electromagnetic field.

15–5 Plane monochromatic waves in nonconducting media. The most easily treated solutions of Eq. (15–29) are those known as plane wave solutions. In the case of a dielectric medium with zero conductivity, Eq. (15–29) becomes

$$\nabla^2 \mathbf{E}_s + \epsilon\mu\omega^2 \mathbf{E}_s = 0. \qquad (15\text{--}30)$$

A plane wave is defined as a wave whose amplitude is the same at any point in a plane perpendicular to a specified direction. If, for example, the specified direction is the z-direction, then $\mathbf{E}_s$ must be the same at all points which have the same z value. In other words, $\mathbf{E}_s = \mathbf{E}_s(z)$. The form of (15–30) for this case is greatly simplified, becoming just

$$\frac{d^2\mathbf{E}_s(z)}{dz^2} + \epsilon\mu\omega^2 \mathbf{E}_s = 0. \qquad (15\text{--}31)$$

---

* As discussed in Chapter 13, one goes from the convenient mathematical description in terms of complex variables to the physical quantities by taking either the real or imaginary part of the complex quantity. The choice of real or imaginary part is quite arbitrary. The two choices differ only by a phase shift of $\pi/2$; however, one must always make the same choice in a given problem. In this and the following chapter the real part of complex quantities will represent the physical quantities unless otherwise explicitly noted.

The x and y derivatives have disappeared because $\mathbf{E}_s$ does not depend on either x or y; the second partial derivative has become an ordinary derivative because $\mathbf{E}_s$ is a function of a single variable. The solution to equation (15–31) is well known. It is just

$$\mathbf{E}_s(z) = \mathbf{E}_0 e^{\mp j\omega\sqrt{\epsilon\mu}\,z}, \tag{15-32}$$

with $\mathbf{E}_0$ a constant vector. Equation (15–32) gives a solution to (15–30) with wavefronts perpendicular to the z-axis; however, not all these solutions satisfy Maxwell's equations. The particular equation not satisfied in this case is (15–15) which, subject to the restrictions which have been imposed, is equivalent to

$$\operatorname{div}\mathbf{E}_s = 0. \tag{15-33}$$

Since $\mathbf{E}_s$ is independent of both x and y, (15–33) becomes

$$\frac{\partial}{\partial z} E_{sz}(z) = \mp j\omega\sqrt{\epsilon\mu}\, E_{sz}(z) = 0. \tag{15-34}$$

This can be true only if $E_{sz}(z) = 0$; in other words, if $\mathbf{E}_s$ has no z-component. This then shows that the electric vector of a plane wave must be parallel to the wavefronts. In general, the electric field for a wave with wavefronts perpendicular to the z-axis is

$$\mathbf{E}_s(z) = (\mathbf{i}E_{0x} + \mathbf{j}E_{0y})e^{\mp j\omega\sqrt{\epsilon\mu}\,z}. \tag{15-35}$$

The magnetic field to be associated with this electric field is obtained by taking the curl of Eq. (15–35):

$$\operatorname{curl}\mathbf{E}_s(z) = \mp\,[-j\omega\sqrt{\epsilon\mu}\,\mathbf{i}E_{0y} + j\omega\sqrt{\epsilon\mu}\,\mathbf{j}E_{0x}]e^{\mp j\omega\sqrt{\epsilon\mu}\,z}$$

and equating it to $j\omega\mathbf{B}_s$. This procedure derives from the Maxwell equation (15–14) through the substitution $\mathbf{E} = \mathbf{E}_s e^{-j\omega t}$, $\mathbf{B} = \mathbf{B}_s e^{-j\omega t}$. The resulting spatial portion of the magnetic induction is

$$\mathbf{B}_s = \mp\,[-E_{0y}\mathbf{i} + E_{0x}\mathbf{j}]\sqrt{\epsilon\mu}\, e^{\mp j\omega\sqrt{\epsilon\mu}\,z}, \tag{15-36}$$

or, as may be easily verified,

$$\mathbf{B}_s = \mp\sqrt{\epsilon\mu}\,\mathbf{k}\times\mathbf{E}_s. \tag{15-37}$$

Thus $\mathbf{B}_s$ is perpendicular to both $\mathbf{E}_s$ and to the z-axis. The direction of propagation is conveniently defined as the direction of the maximum rate of change of phase of $\mathbf{E}_s$ (or $\mathbf{B}_s$). In the case considered above, the direction of propagation is the z-direction if the plus sign is used, or the minus z-direction if the minus sign is used.

To recapitulate: a plane monochromatic wave propagated in the plus z-direction is described by

$$\mathbf{E}(\mathbf{r}, t) = \mathbf{E}_s(z)e^{-j\omega t} = \mathbf{E}_0 e^{j\omega(\sqrt{\epsilon\mu}\, z - t)},$$

$$\mathbf{B}(\mathbf{r}, t) = \mathbf{B}_s(z)e^{-j\omega t} = \sqrt{\epsilon\mu}\, \mathbf{k} \times \mathbf{E}_0 e^{j\omega(\sqrt{\epsilon\mu}\, z - t)}, \tag{15–38}$$

with $\mathbf{E}_0$ an arbitrary vector parallel to the xy-plane.

Plane waves traveling in the z-direction are adequate for problems in which the choice of the z-direction is arbitrary; however, in many problems a system of axes is chosen for other reasons, for example because of boundary conditions. In such cases it is necessary to construct plane waves with arbitrary directions of propagation. Suppose a plane wave solution with direction of propagation $\mathbf{u}$ is to be constructed, where $\mathbf{u}$ is a unit vector. Then $\mathbf{u}$ plays the role of $\mathbf{k}$ in the preceding discussion, and the variable z in the exponent must be replaced by $\mathbf{u} \cdot \mathbf{r}$, the projection of $\mathbf{r}$ in the $\mathbf{u}$ direction. The only other change is that $\mathbf{E}$ must be perpendicular to $\mathbf{u}$ instead of to $\mathbf{k}$. Thus a plane wave with direction of propagation parallel to $\mathbf{u}$ is described by

$$\mathbf{E}(\mathbf{r}, t) = \mathbf{E}_0 e^{j\omega[\sqrt{\epsilon\mu}\, \mathbf{u}\cdot\mathbf{r} - t]},$$

$$\mathbf{B}(\mathbf{r}, t) = \sqrt{\epsilon\mu}\, \mathbf{u} \times \mathbf{E}_0 e^{j\omega[\sqrt{\epsilon\mu}\, \mathbf{u}\cdot\mathbf{r} - t]}, \tag{15–39}$$

with $\mathbf{E}_0$ perpendicular to $\mathbf{u}$ but otherwise arbitrary. A frequently used notation puts

$$\omega\sqrt{\epsilon\mu}\, \mathbf{u} = \boldsymbol{\kappa}. \tag{15–40}$$

This vector $\boldsymbol{\kappa}$ is called the propagation vector. In terms of the propagation vector, the equation for a plane wave traveling in the $\boldsymbol{\kappa}$ direction is written as

$$\mathbf{E}(\mathbf{r}, t) = \mathbf{E}_0 e^{j(\boldsymbol{\kappa}\cdot\mathbf{r} - \omega t)},$$

$$\mathbf{B}(\mathbf{r}, t) = \frac{1}{\omega}\boldsymbol{\kappa} \times \mathbf{E}_0 e^{j(\boldsymbol{\kappa}\cdot\mathbf{r} - \omega t)}. \tag{15–41}$$

The velocity of propagation of a plane monochromatic wave is precisely the velocity with which planes of constant phase move. Constant phase means, of course, that

$$\boldsymbol{\kappa} \cdot \mathbf{r} - \omega t = \text{constant.} \tag{15–42}$$

If $\boldsymbol{\kappa} \cdot \mathbf{r}$ is written $\kappa\xi$, with κ the magnitude of $\boldsymbol{\kappa}$ and ξ the projection of $\mathbf{r}$ in the $\boldsymbol{\kappa}$ direction, then Eq. (15–42) becomes

$$\kappa\xi - \omega t = \text{constant.}$$

Differentiating with respect to the time yields

$$v_p = \frac{d\xi}{dt} = \frac{\omega}{\kappa} = \frac{1}{\sqrt{\epsilon\mu}} \tag{15–43}$$

for the velocity of surfaces of constant phase. In free space, $v_p = c = 1/\sqrt{\epsilon_0\mu_0}$, so that, in general,

$$v_p = \frac{c}{\sqrt{K_e K_m}}. \tag{15-44}$$

The expression $c = 1/\sqrt{\epsilon_0\mu_0} = 2.9979 \times 10^8$ m/sec is the velocity of light in vacuum; this, of course, is just what we expected, since light is a form of electromagnetic radiation. But when Maxwell first announced this result it was considered a great triumph of his theory, since up to that time the electromagnetic nature of light was only a speculation. The quantities K_e and K_m in Eq. (15-44) are the dielectric constant and relative permeability, respectively, of the medium.

From (15-44) it is clear that the optically defined index of refraction is

$$n = \sqrt{K_e K_m}. \tag{15-45}$$

Since for the most transparent media K_m is very close to unity, the index of refraction is just the square root of the dielectric constant for these media. With these results, it is possible to consider some extremely interesting and important optical problems. These, however, will be postponed to the next chapter.

15-6 Plane monochromatic waves in conducting media. In a conducting medium the wave equation reduces to

$$\nabla^2 \mathbf{E}_s + \omega^2 \epsilon\mu \mathbf{E}_s + j\omega g\mu \mathbf{E}_s = 0 \tag{15-29}$$

for a monochromatic wave of frequency ω. As before, plane waves with wavefronts parallel to the xy-plane are governed by

$$\frac{d^2\mathbf{E}_s}{dz^2} + \omega^2 \epsilon\mu \mathbf{E}_s + j\omega g\mu \mathbf{E}_s = 0 \tag{15-46}$$

with $\mathbf{E}_s$ a function of z only. The solution to this equation is found by writing $\mathbf{E}_s = \mathbf{E}_0 e^{j\gamma z}$. Using this in (15-46) gives

$$-\gamma^2 + \omega^2 \epsilon\mu + j\omega g\mu = 0. \tag{15-47}$$

The usual techniques of the algebra of complex numbers enable us to separate γ into real and imaginary parts, α and β, either as

$$\gamma = \alpha + j\beta = \mp(\omega^4\epsilon^2\mu^2 + \omega^2 g^2\mu^2)^{1/4}(\cos\varphi + j\sin\varphi),$$

$$\varphi = \tfrac{1}{2}\tan^{-1}\frac{g}{\omega\epsilon}, \tag{15-48a}$$

or as

$$\alpha = \mp\omega\sqrt{\epsilon\mu}\left[\tfrac{1}{2} \mp \tfrac{1}{2}\sqrt{1 + (g^2/\omega^2\epsilon^2)}\right]^{1/2}, \quad \beta = \omega g\mu/2\alpha. \tag{15-48b}$$

Both are convenient; the choice depends on the problem being considered.

Thus the plane wave traveling in the z-direction is described by

$$\mathbf{E}_s(z) = \mathbf{E}_0 e^{j(\alpha z - \omega t)} e^{-\beta z}, \tag{15–49}$$

which clearly represents an exponentially damped wave traveling in the plus z-direction. The equations above are exact but complicated; hence it is convenient to examine certain approximations. If the frequency is below the optical range, $g \gg \epsilon\omega$ for metallic conductors. In this range, $\varphi = \pi/4$ and

$$\beta = \sqrt{\omega g \mu} \sin \frac{\pi}{4} = \sqrt{\omega g \mu/2}. \tag{15–50}$$

The term $1/\beta$ measures the depth at which the electric field falls to $1/e$ of its value at the surface. This depth is known as the *skin depth*, and is usually represented by δ. The major importance of the skin depth is that it measures the depth to which an electromagnetic wave can penetrate a conducting medium. Fine silver, for example, has an effective conductivity

$$g = 3 \times 10^7 \text{ mhos/m*}$$

at microwave frequencies. At a frequency of 10^{10} cycles/sec, which is a common microwave region, the skin depth is

$$\delta = \sqrt{\frac{2}{(2\pi \times 10^{10})(3 \times 10^7)(4\pi \times 10^{-7})}} = 9.2 \times 10^{-5} \text{ cm.}$$

Thus at microwave frequencies the skin depth in silver is very small, and consequently the difference in performance between a pure silver component and a silver-plated brass component would be expected to be negligible. This is indeed the case, and the plating technique is used to reduce the material cost of high-quality waveguide components.

As a second example, we now calculate the frequency at which the skin depth in sea water is one meter. For sea water, $\mu = \mu_0$ and $g \approx 4.3$ mhos/m. The expression for the frequency corresponding to a given skin depth δ is

$$\omega = \frac{2}{g\mu\,\delta^2} = \frac{2}{4.3 \times 4\pi \times 10^{-7}\,\delta^2} \text{ sec}^{-1} = \frac{1.85 \times 10^5}{\delta^2} \text{ sec}^{-1},$$

which yields

$$f = 29.3 \times 10^3 \text{ cycles/sec,}$$

---

* One mho is one reciprocal ohm; it is a unit of conductance or reciprocal resistance (see Chapter 7).

or a frequency of 30 kc for a skin depth of one meter. If a submarine is equipped with a very sensitive receiver and if a very powerful transmitter is used, it is possible to communicate with a submerged submarine. However, a very low radiofrequency must be used, and even then an extremely severe attenuation of the signal occurs. At five skin depths (5 m in the case calculated above), only 1% of the initial electric field remains, and only 0.01% of the incident power.

*15-7 Spherical waves. As an example of a more difficult wave problem, where in fact it is not easy to find even the elementary waves, we consider the wave equation in spherical coordinates. The wave equation for the electric field in a nonconducting medium is

$$\nabla^2 \mathbf{E} - \epsilon\mu \frac{\partial^2 \mathbf{E}}{\partial t^2} = 0. \tag{15-51}$$

For monochromatic waves, the equation for the spatial portion becomes

$$\nabla^2 \mathbf{E}_s + \epsilon\mu\omega^2 \mathbf{E}_s = 0. \tag{15-52}$$

The difficulty in using spherical coordinates is that one would like to express the vector $\mathbf{E}_s$ in terms of radial, azimuthal, and meridional *components*, each expressed as functions of the radius, azimuth, and colatitude. If this is done, then it is not sufficient to use the expression for the Laplacian in spherical coordinates in Eq. (15-52); rather, it is necessary to define the Laplacian of a vector by

$$\nabla^2 \mathbf{E}_s = -\mathbf{curl\ curl\ E}_s + \mathbf{grad\ div\ E}_s. \tag{15-53}$$

The divergence of $\mathbf{E}_s$ is still zero; however, the radial component of **curl curl $\mathbf{E}_s$** involves not only the radial component of $\mathbf{E}_s$, but also its azimuthal and meridional components. The θ and ϕ components are similarly complicated, and the final result is three simultaneous partial differential equations involving the three components of $\mathbf{E}_s$. The separation which occurs for the vector Laplace equation in rectangular coordinates does not occur in spherical coordinates; it is in fact peculiar to rectangular coordinates. It should be pointed out, however, that rectangular components of $\mathbf{E}_s$ may be used; in this instance they would be written: $E_{sx}(r, \theta, \phi)$, $E_{sy}(r, \theta, \phi)$, $E_{sz}(r, \theta, \phi)$.

A simple procedure circumvents the difficulty discussed above. Consider the scalar Helmholtz equation:

$$\nabla^2 \psi + \epsilon\mu\omega^2 \psi = 0, \tag{15-54}$$

whose solutions are, as will be seen shortly, readily found. Suppose that

ψ is any one of the solutions, then $\mathbf{E}_s = \mathbf{r} \times \operatorname{grad} \psi$ satisfies the vector Helmholtz equation, Eq. (15–52):

$$-\operatorname{curl\,curl} \mathbf{E}_s + \operatorname{grad\,div} \mathbf{E}_s + \epsilon\mu\omega^2 \mathbf{E}_s = 0. \qquad (15\text{–}55)$$

To verify this, note the identity

$$\mathbf{E}_s = \mathbf{r} \times \operatorname{grad} \psi = -\operatorname{curl} (\mathbf{r}\psi), \qquad (15\text{–}56)$$

which follows from the vector identity

$$\operatorname{curl} (\mathbf{A}\varphi) = \varphi \operatorname{curl} \mathbf{A} - \mathbf{A} \times \operatorname{grad} \varphi \qquad (15\text{–}57)$$

and

$$\operatorname{curl} \mathbf{r} = 0. \qquad (15\text{–}58)$$

Since the divergence of any curl is zero, it is necessary to consider only the curl curl term in Eq. (15–55). The curl of $\mathbf{E}_s$ can be found by using the vector identity

$$\operatorname{curl} (\mathbf{A} \times \mathbf{B}) = \mathbf{A} \operatorname{div} \mathbf{B} - \mathbf{B} \operatorname{div} \mathbf{A} + (\mathbf{B} \cdot \operatorname{grad})\mathbf{A} - (\mathbf{A} \cdot \operatorname{grad})\mathbf{B} \quad (15\text{–}29)$$

to obtain

$$\operatorname{curl} (\mathbf{r} \times \operatorname{grad} \psi) = \mathbf{r}\nabla^2\psi - \operatorname{grad} \psi \operatorname{div} \mathbf{r} + (\operatorname{grad} \psi \cdot \operatorname{grad})\mathbf{r}$$
$$- (\mathbf{r} \cdot \operatorname{grad}) \operatorname{grad} \psi. \qquad (15\text{–}60)$$

As was shown in Problem 1–13, $(\mathbf{A} \cdot \operatorname{grad})\mathbf{r} = \mathbf{A}$ for any vector $\mathbf{A}$; also, the divergence of $\mathbf{r}$ is three (3). The first term of Eq. (15–60) can be reduced by using the fact that ψ satisfies the scalar Helmholtz equation, thus leaving only the last term as a possible source of complication. The vector identity

$$\operatorname{grad} (\mathbf{A} \cdot \mathbf{B}) = (\mathbf{A} \cdot \operatorname{grad})\mathbf{B} + (\mathbf{B} \cdot \operatorname{grad})\mathbf{A} + \mathbf{A} \times \operatorname{curl} \mathbf{B} + \mathbf{B} \times \operatorname{curl} \mathbf{A},$$
$$(15\text{–}61)$$

with $\mathbf{A} = \mathbf{r}$ and $\mathbf{B} = \operatorname{grad} \psi$, gives

$$\operatorname{grad} (\mathbf{r} \cdot \operatorname{grad} \psi) = (\mathbf{r} \cdot \operatorname{grad}) \operatorname{grad} \psi + (\operatorname{grad} \psi \cdot \operatorname{grad})\mathbf{r}. \quad (15\text{–}62)$$

The last two terms of Eq. (15–61) vanish because the curl of any gradient is zero, as is the curl of $\mathbf{r}$. Using these relationships in Eq. (15–60) leads to

$$\operatorname{curl} (\mathbf{r} \times \operatorname{grad} \psi) = -\epsilon\mu\omega^2\mathbf{r}\psi - 3 \operatorname{grad} \psi + \operatorname{grad} \psi$$
$$- \operatorname{grad} (\mathbf{r} \cdot \operatorname{grad} \psi) + \operatorname{grad} \psi. \quad (15\text{–}63)$$

Finally, taking the curl of Eq. (15–63), we obtain

$$\operatorname{curl\,curl} (\mathbf{r} \times \operatorname{grad} \psi) = -\epsilon\mu\omega^2 \operatorname{curl} \mathbf{r}\psi = \epsilon\mu\omega^2\mathbf{r} \times \operatorname{grad} \psi, \quad (15\text{–}64)$$

which is just the vector Helmholtz equation. No explicit use of the spherical coordinate system has been made; however, since $\mathbf{r}$ is normal to a surface of constant radius in spherical coordinates, the solution $\mathbf{r} \times \mathbf{grad}\, \psi$ would be expected to be particularly useful in this system. It is in fact not very useful in other coordinate systems.

Having found that $\mathbf{r} \times \mathbf{grad}\, \psi$ is a solution of the vector Helmholtz equation, with ψ a solution of the scalar Helmholtz equation, it becomes pertinent to find out how such solutions can be used to construct electromagnetic waves. The procedure is very simple. The spatial variation of the electric field is taken as

$$\mathbf{E}_s = \mathbf{r} \times \mathbf{grad}\, \psi. \qquad (15\text{--}56)$$

The magnetic field must be so chosen that it, together with $\mathbf{E}_s$, satisfies Maxwell's equations. To this end we write Eq. (15–14) as

$$\mathbf{curl}\, \mathbf{E}_s = j\omega \mathbf{B}_s, \qquad (15\text{--}65)$$

where the standard $e^{-j\omega t}$ time dependence has been assumed. Equation (15–63) gives the curl of $\mathbf{E}_s$ explicitly or, in a shorter form,

$$\mathbf{B}_s = -j\frac{1}{\omega} \mathbf{curl}\,(\mathbf{r} \times \mathbf{grad}\, \psi). \qquad (15\text{--}66)$$

Since the divergence of any curl vanishes, Eq. (15–16) is satisfied. That Eq. (15–13) is satisfied is obvious from the fact that $\mathbf{E}_s$ and $\mathbf{B}_s$ are both solutions of the wave equation, which in turn represents a combination of Eqs. (15–13) and (15–14).

The solution represented by Eqs. (15–56) and (15–66) is not the most general solution that can be derived from a given ψ. Another solution is obtained by putting

$$\mathbf{B}_s' = \sqrt{\epsilon\mu}\, \mathbf{r} \times \mathbf{grad}\, \psi \qquad (15\text{--}67)$$

and obtaining the electric field from Eq. (15–13) (with $\mathbf{J} = 0$),

$$\mathbf{E}_s' = \frac{j}{\omega\sqrt{\epsilon\mu}} \mathbf{curl}\,(\mathbf{r} \times \mathbf{grad}\, \psi). \qquad (15\text{--}68)$$

The considerations detailed above show that $\mathbf{E}_s'$, $\mathbf{B}_s'$ form a solution to Maxwell's equations, just as $\mathbf{E}_s$, $\mathbf{B}_s$ do. The solutions differ in that $\mathbf{E}_s$ at any point is tangent to a spherical surface through the point with center at the origin of coordinates; on the other hand, $\mathbf{B}_s'$ has the same property. These facts lead to the solution $\mathbf{E}_s$, $\mathbf{B}_s$ being sometimes called transverse electric, and $\mathbf{E}_s'$, $\mathbf{B}_s'$ transverse magnetic, transverse meaning perpendicular to the radial direction.

In the preceding sections the problem of solving the vector Helmholtz equation has been reduced to that of solving the scalar Helmholtz equation. In spherical coordinates this is accomplished by the technique of separation of variables already familiar from potential problems (Chapter 3). In terms of spherical coordinates, the scalar Helmholtz equation is

$$\frac{1}{r^2} \frac{\partial}{\partial r}\left(r^2 \frac{\partial \psi}{\partial r}\right) + \frac{1}{r^2 \sin \theta} \frac{\partial}{\partial \theta}\left(\sin \theta \frac{\partial \psi}{\partial \theta}\right) + \frac{1}{r^2 \sin^2 \theta} \frac{\partial^2 \psi}{\partial \phi^2} - \kappa^2 \psi = 0,$$
(15–69)

where $\kappa^2 = \epsilon\mu\omega^2$ and ψ is assumed to have the form

$$\psi = R(r)\Theta(\theta)\Phi(\phi).$$
(15–70)

Substituting this assumed form for ψ in (15–69) and dividing by ψ gives

$$\frac{1}{R} \sin^2 \theta \frac{d}{dr} r^2 \frac{dR}{dr} + \frac{1}{\Theta} \sin \theta \frac{d}{d\theta} \sin \theta \frac{d\Theta}{d\theta} + \frac{1}{\Phi} \frac{d^2\Phi}{d\phi^2} - \kappa^2 r^2 \sin^2 \theta = 0,$$
(15–71)

after multiplying by $r^2 \sin^2 \theta$. The third term depends only on ϕ, and this is the only term which depends on ϕ. Consequently this term must be a constant, which is chosen to be $-m^2$. In other words,

$$\frac{d^2\Phi_m}{d\phi^2} + m^2\Phi_m = 0,$$
(15–72)

where the subscript m serves to indicate that Φ depends on m. Rewriting Eq. (15–71) using (15–72) gives

$$\frac{1}{R} \frac{d}{dr} r^2 \frac{dR}{dr} - \kappa^2 r^2 + \frac{1}{\Theta} \frac{1}{\sin \theta} \frac{d}{d\theta} \sin \theta \frac{d\Theta}{d\theta} - \frac{m^2}{\sin^2 \theta} = 0. \quad (15–73)$$

The first two terms depend only on r, while the last two depend only on θ. Thus the sum of the last two must be a constant, which is chosen as $-l(l + 1)$. The sum of the first two terms must, of course, be $l(l + 1)$. Thus there result two equations:

$$\frac{1}{\sin \theta} \frac{d}{d\theta} \sin \theta \frac{d\Theta_{lm}}{d\theta} + \left[l(l + 1) - \frac{m^2}{\sin^2 \theta}\right]\Theta_{lm} = 0 \quad (15–74)$$

and

$$\frac{d}{dr} r^2 \frac{dR_l}{dr} - [l(l + 1) + \kappa^2 r^2]R_l = 0.$$
(15–75)

The solutions of Eq. (15–72) are well known:

$$\Phi_m = e^{\mp jm\phi}.$$
(15–76)

The solutions of (15–74) are less well known, but some have already been met in Chapter 3, where solutions for $m = 0$ were discussed. These solutions* are the Legendre polynomials $P_l(\cos \theta)$. The solutions of (15–74) for arbitrary $m \leq l$ are known as the associated Legendre polynomials. They may be defined by

$$P_l^m(u) = (1 - u^2)^{m/2} \frac{d^m}{du^m} P_l(u), \tag{15–77}$$

with $u = \cos \theta$. It is clear that $P_l^0(u) = P_l(u)$, the ordinary Legendre polynomial. For $m \neq 0$ the functions are given in Table 15–1.

Finally, Eq. (15–75) must be considered. The change of variable from r to $\xi = \kappa r$ is readily accomplished; the resulting equation is

$$\frac{d}{d\xi} \xi^2 \frac{d}{d\xi} R_l - [l(l + 1) + \xi^2] R_l = 0. \tag{15–78}$$

The substitution $R_l = \xi^{-1/2} Z_l$ transforms this equation into

$$\xi^2 \frac{d^2 Z_l}{d\xi^2} + \xi \frac{dZ_l}{d\xi} - [(l + \tfrac{1}{2})^2 + \xi^2] Z_l = 0. \tag{15–79}$$

TABLE 15–1

ASSOCIATED LEGENDRE POLYNOMIALS, $P_l^m(u)$, WHERE $u = \cos \theta$

Designation	Function
$P_0(u)$	1
$P_1(u)$	$u = \cos \theta$
$P_1^1(u)$	$(1 - u^2)^{1/2} = \sin \theta$
$P_2(u)$	$\tfrac{1}{2}(3u^2 - 1) = \tfrac{1}{4}(3 \cos 2\theta + 1)$
$P_2^1(u)$	$3u(1 - u^2)^{1/2} = \tfrac{3}{2} \sin 2\theta$
$P_2^2(u)$	$3(1 - u^2) = \tfrac{3}{2}(1 - \cos 2\theta)$
$P_3(u)$	$\tfrac{1}{2}(5u^3 - 3u)$
$P_3^1(u)$	$\tfrac{3}{2}(1 - u^2)^{1/2}(5u^2 - 1)$
$P_3^2(u)$	$15u(1 - u^2)$
$P_3^3(u)$	$15(1 - u^2)^{3/2}$

---

* In Chapter 3 these functions were written $P_l(\theta)$. Since, however, the Legendre polynomials are polynomials in $\cos \theta$, it is more common to write $P_l(\cos \theta)$; we follow this practice in the present chapter as well as in the succeeding one.

This equation, which is very familiar to mathematical physicists, is known as Bessel's equation. The solutions of the equation are also well known, and have been extensively investigated and indeed tabulated. The common solutions are designated $J_{l+1/2}(\kappa r)$ and $N_{l+1/2}(\kappa r)$ and are known respectively as the Bessel function and the Neumann function, of order $l + \frac{1}{2}$. For purposes of the wave equation, it is extremely convenient to define spherical Bessel functions by

$$j_l(\kappa r) = \sqrt{\pi/2\kappa r}\, J_{l+1/2}(\kappa r), \qquad n_l(\kappa r) = \sqrt{\pi/2\kappa r}\, N_{l+1/2}(\kappa r); \qquad (15\text{-}80)$$

and from these in turn we obtain

$$h_l^{(1)}(\kappa r) = j_l(\kappa r) + j n_l(\kappa r), \qquad h_l^{(2)} = j_l(\kappa r) - j n_l(\kappa r). \qquad (15\text{-}81)$$

The functions $j_l(\kappa r)$, $n_l(\kappa r)$, $h_l^{(1)}(\kappa r)$, and $h_l^{(2)}(\kappa r)$ are all solutions of the radial equation, Eq. (15–75). These functions are tabulated for $l = 0, 1,$ and 2 in Table 15–2. The h's are particularly convenient for radiation problems because for large values of r they behave as

$$h_l^{(1)}(\kappa r) \xrightarrow[\kappa r \to \infty]{} \frac{(-j)^{l+1} e^{j\kappa r}}{\kappa r},$$

$$h_l^{(2)}(\kappa r) \xrightarrow[\kappa r \to \infty]{} \frac{j^{l+1} e^{-j\kappa r}}{\kappa r},$$

and thus lead to outgoing and ingoing spherical waves.

A general form for ψ may be written as

$$\psi_{lm} = \sqrt{\pi/2\kappa r}\, Z_l(\kappa r) P_l^m (\cos \theta)\, e^{\mp jm\phi}. \qquad (15\text{-}82)$$

The corresponding vector fields are computed by using Eqs. (15–56) and (15–66) for the TE waves, and (15–67) and (15–68) for the TM waves. The simplest interesting choice of ψ is ψ_{10}, which is just

$$\psi_{10} = \frac{1}{\kappa r} e^{j\kappa r} \left[1 + \frac{j}{\kappa r} \right] \cos \theta. \qquad (15\text{-}83)$$

The gradient of ψ_{10} is

$$\mathbf{grad}\, \psi_{10} = \mathbf{a}_r e^{j\kappa r} \left[\frac{j}{r} - \frac{2}{\kappa r^2} - \frac{2j}{\kappa^2 r^3} \right] \cos \theta - \mathbf{a}_\theta e^{j\kappa r} \left[\frac{1}{\kappa r^2} + \frac{j}{\kappa^2 r^3} \right] \sin \theta. \qquad (15\text{-}84)$$

The spatial portion of the electric field is

$$\mathbf{E}_s = \mathbf{r} \times \mathbf{grad}\, \psi_{10} = -\mathbf{a}_\phi E_0 e^{j\kappa r} \left[\frac{1}{\kappa r} + \frac{j}{\kappa^2 r^2} \right] \sin \theta, \qquad (15\text{-}85)$$

where E_0 has been introduced to make the equation dimensionally correct.

The spatial dependence of the magnetic induction is given by

$$\mathbf{B}_s = -j\frac{1}{\omega}\operatorname{curl}\mathbf{E}_s = j\frac{1}{\omega}E_0 e^{j\kappa r}\left[\frac{1}{\kappa r^2} + \frac{j}{\kappa^2 r^3}\right]2\cos\theta\mathbf{a}_r$$

$$-j\frac{1}{\omega}E_0 e^{j\kappa r}\left[\frac{j}{r} - \frac{1}{\kappa r^2} - \frac{j}{\kappa^2 r^3}\right]\sin\theta\mathbf{a}_\theta. \quad (15\text{--}86)$$

As will be seen later, these are just the fields produced by a radiating magnetic dipole. It is interesting to note that only the portions of $\mathbf{E}_s$ and $\mathbf{B}_s$ which are proportional to $1/r$ contribute to the net radiation. All other terms give terms in the Poynting vector which fall off more rapidly than $1/r^2$, and which consequently have integrals over spherical surfaces which vanish as the radii of these spherical surfaces go to infinity. The spherical wave solutions are particularly important in considering the radiation from bounded sources, which will be treated in the next section.

TABLE 15–2

SPHERICAL BESSEL AND NEUMANN FUNCTIONS

Type	Function
$j_0(\rho)$	$(1/\rho)\sin\rho$
$n_0(\rho)$	$-(1/\rho)\cos\rho$
$h_0^{(1)}(\rho)$	$-(j/\rho)e^{j\rho}$
$h_0^{(2)}(\rho)$	$(j/\rho)e^{-j\rho}$
$j_1(\rho)$	$(1/\rho^2)\sin\rho - (1/\rho)\cos\rho$
$n_1(\rho)$	$-(1/\rho)\sin\rho - (1/\rho^2)\cos\rho$
$h_1^{(1)}(\rho)$	$-(1/\rho)e^{j\rho}(1 + j/\rho)$
$h_1^{(2)}(\rho)$	$-(1/\rho)e^{-j\rho}(1 - j/\rho)$
$j_2(\rho)$	$\left[\dfrac{3}{\rho^3} - \dfrac{1}{\rho}\right]\sin\rho - \dfrac{3}{\rho^2}\cos\rho$
$n_2(\rho)$	$-\dfrac{3}{\rho^2}\sin\rho - \left[\dfrac{3}{\rho^3} - \dfrac{1}{\rho}\right]\cos\rho$
$h_2^{(1)}(\rho)$	$(j/\rho)e^{j\rho}\left(1 + \dfrac{3j}{\rho} - \dfrac{3}{\rho^2}\right)$
$h_2^{(2)}(\rho)$	$-(j/\rho)e^{-j\rho}\left(1 - \dfrac{3j}{\rho} - \dfrac{3}{\rho^2}\right)$

15-8 The wave equation with sources. In the preceding sections, plane and spherical waves have been treated without inquiring how these waves were produced. The problem now is to consider prescribed charge and current distributions, $\rho(\mathbf{r}, t)$ and $\mathbf{J}(\mathbf{r}, t)$, and find the fields produced by them. There are several ways of approaching the problem, of which the most fruitful is the potential approach, which is developed analogously to the procedures used in electrostatics and magnetostatics. Since the magnetic induction has zero divergence it may always be represented as the curl of a vector potential, that is,

$$\mathbf{B} = \text{curl } \mathbf{A}. \tag{15–87}$$

Using this expression for $\mathbf{B}$ in Eq. (15–14) gives

$$\text{curl } \mathbf{E} + \frac{\partial}{\partial t} \text{ curl } \mathbf{A} = 0. \tag{15–88}$$

Assuming sufficient continuity of the fields to interchange the spatial and temporal differentiations, this can be written

$$\text{curl}\left[\mathbf{E} + \frac{\partial \mathbf{A}}{\partial t} \right] = 0. \tag{15–89}$$

The vector, $\mathbf{E} + \partial \mathbf{A}/\partial t$, thus has zero curl and can be written as the gradient of a scalar:

$$\mathbf{E} = - \text{ grad } \varphi - \frac{\partial \mathbf{A}}{\partial t}. \tag{15–90}$$

Equations (15–87) and (15–90) give the electric and magnetic fields in terms of a vector potential $\mathbf{A}$ and a scalar potential φ. These potentials satisfy wave equations which are very similar to those satisfied by the fields. The wave equation for $\mathbf{A}$ is derived by substituting the expressions given in (15–87) and (15–90) for $\mathbf{B}$ and $\mathbf{E}$ into Eq. (15–13), with the result

$$\frac{1}{\mu} \text{ curl curl } \mathbf{A} + \epsilon \frac{\partial}{\partial t}\left[\text{grad } \varphi + \frac{\partial \mathbf{A}}{\partial t} \right] = \mathbf{J}. \tag{15–91}$$

Writing **grad** div $-\nabla^2$ for **curl curl** and multiplying by μ gives

$$-\nabla^2 \mathbf{A} + \epsilon\mu \frac{\partial^2 \mathbf{A}}{\partial t^2} + \text{grad div } \mathbf{A} + \epsilon\mu \text{ grad } \frac{\partial \varphi}{\partial t} = \mu \mathbf{J}. \tag{15–92}$$

Until now only the curl of $\mathbf{A}$ has been specified; the choice of the divergence of $\mathbf{A}$ is still arbitrary. It is clear from Eq. (15–92) that imposing the Lorentz condition,

$$\text{div } \mathbf{A} + \epsilon\mu \frac{\partial \varphi}{\partial t} = 0, \tag{15–93}$$

results in a considerable simplification. If this condition is satisfied, then **A** satisfies the wave equation

$$\nabla^2 \mathbf{A} - \epsilon\mu \frac{\partial^2 \mathbf{A}}{\partial t^2} = -\mu\mathbf{J}. \tag{15-94}$$

Furthermore, using Eq. (15–90) in (15–15) gives

$$-\epsilon\left[\operatorname{div} \mathbf{grad}\ \varphi + \operatorname{div} \frac{\partial \mathbf{A}}{\partial t}\right] = \rho. \tag{15-95}$$

Interchanging the order of the divergence and the time derivative operating on **A** and using the Lorentz condition (Eq. 15–93) leads to

$$\nabla^2 \varphi - \epsilon\mu \frac{\partial^2 \varphi}{\partial t^2} = -\frac{1}{\epsilon}\rho. \tag{15-96}$$

Thus, by imposing the Lorentz condition, both the scalar and vector potentials are forced to satisfy inhomogeneous wave equations of similar forms.

The problem of finding the general solution of the inhomogeneous scalar wave equation is analogous to finding the general solution of Poisson's equation. In the latter case, it will be recalled, the general solution consists of a particular solution of the inhomogeneous equation plus a general solution of the homogeneous equation. The inclusion of the solutions of the homogeneous equation provides the means for satisfying arbitrary appropriate boundary conditions, while the particular solution ensures that the total function satisfies the inhomogeneous equation. Exactly the same considerations apply to the inhomogeneous wave equation—the general solution consists of a particular solution plus a general solution of the homogeneous equation. Methods have already been found for finding certain solutions of the homogeneous equation. These methods may be extended and supplemented to yield solutions to almost any solvable problem. Approximate methods are available for problems which cannot be solved in terms of known functions. It remains, then, to find the needed particular solution of the inhomogeneous equation.

The inhomogeneous scalar wave equation

$$\nabla^2 \varphi - \epsilon\mu \frac{\partial^2 \varphi}{\partial t^2} = -\frac{\rho}{\epsilon} \tag{15-96}$$

can be solved most readily by finding the solution for a point charge, and then later summing over all the charge elements $\rho\Delta v$ in the appropriate charge distribution. The most convenient location for the point charge is at the origin of coordinates. Thus the equation

$$\nabla^2 \varphi - \epsilon\mu \frac{\partial^2 \varphi}{\partial t^2} = 0 \tag{15-97}$$

must be satisfied everywhere except at the origin, whereas in a small volume Δv surrounding the origin,

$$\int_{\Delta v} dv \left[\nabla^2 \varphi - \epsilon\mu \frac{\partial^2 \varphi}{\partial t^2} \right] = -\frac{1}{\epsilon} q(t) \tag{15-98}$$

must be satisfied. It is clear from the symmetry of the charge distribution that the spatial dependence of φ must be only on r. With this clue, an attempt to solve Eq. (15-97) may be made. Since φ does not depend on either the azimuthal angle or the colatitude, Eq. (15-97) becomes

$$\frac{1}{r^2} \frac{\partial}{\partial r} r^2 \frac{\partial \varphi}{\partial r} - \epsilon\mu \frac{\partial^2 \varphi}{\partial t^2} = 0. \tag{15-99}$$

Now, by putting

$$\varphi(r, t) = \frac{\chi(r, t)}{r}, \tag{15-100}$$

Eq. (15-99) is converted to

$$\frac{\partial^2 \chi}{\partial r^2} - \epsilon\mu \frac{\partial^2 \chi}{\partial t^2} = 0. \tag{15-101}$$

This equation is the one-dimensional wave equation which is solved by any function of $r - t/\sqrt{\epsilon\mu}$, or $r + t/\sqrt{\epsilon\mu}$. To verify this, let

$$u = r - t/\sqrt{\epsilon\mu}$$

and let $f(u)$ be any function of u which can be twice differentiated; then

$$\frac{\partial f}{\partial r} = \frac{df}{du} \frac{\partial u}{\partial r} = \frac{df}{du}, \qquad \frac{\partial^2 f}{\partial r^2} = \frac{d^2 f}{du^2} \frac{\partial u}{\partial r} = \frac{d^2 f}{du^2} \tag{15-102}$$

and

$$\frac{\partial f}{\partial t} = \frac{df}{du} \frac{\partial u}{\partial t} = -\frac{df}{du} \frac{1}{\sqrt{\epsilon\mu}}, \qquad \frac{\partial^2 f}{\partial t^2} = \frac{1}{\epsilon\mu} \frac{d^2 f}{du^2}. \tag{15-103}$$

Substituting the results of Eqs. (15-102) and (15-103) into Eq. (15-101) verifies that any function of $(r - t/\sqrt{\epsilon\mu})$ which is twice differentiable is a solution of Eq. (15-101). A similar calculation verifies that a function of $(r + t/\sqrt{\epsilon\mu})$ is a solution. Thus

$$\chi = f(r - t/\sqrt{\epsilon\mu}) + g(r + t/\sqrt{\epsilon\mu}) \tag{15-104}$$

is a very arbitrary solution of Eq. (15-101). It is found that $g(r + t/\sqrt{\epsilon\mu})$ does not lead to physically interesting solutions of the wave equation. For this reason it will be dropped, and only the first term of Eq. (15-104) will be carried, since this procedure simplifies the ensuing equations and causes no particular omissions.

A spherically symmetric solution of Eq. (15–97),

$$\varphi = \frac{f(r - t/\sqrt{\epsilon\mu})}{r},\tag{15-105}$$

is now available; furthermore, this solution contains an arbitrary function which may be chosen so that Eq. (15–98) is also satisfied. The proper choice is obtained by noting that for a static charge the potential compatible with Eqs. (15–97) and (15–98) is

$$\varphi = \frac{q}{4\pi\epsilon r}.\tag{15-106}$$

The functions (15–105) and (15–106) may be brought into concert by choosing

$$f(r - t/\sqrt{\epsilon\mu}) = \frac{q(t - r\sqrt{\epsilon\mu})}{4\pi\epsilon}.\tag{15-107}$$

The solution to Eqs. (15–97) and (15–98) is then

$$\varphi(r,\,t) = \frac{q(t - r\sqrt{\epsilon\mu})}{4\pi\epsilon r}.\tag{15-108}$$

With this result, we readily find that Eq. (15–96) is satisfied by

$$\varphi(\mathbf{r},\,t) = \frac{1}{4\pi\epsilon}\int_V \frac{\rho[\mathbf{r}',\,t - \sqrt{\epsilon\mu}\,|\mathbf{r} - \mathbf{r}'|]}{|\mathbf{r} - \mathbf{r}'|}\,dv',\tag{15-109}$$

which is known as the retarded scalar potential.

The solution of Eq. (15–94) can be constructed in exactly the same way. The vectors **A** and **J** are first decomposed into rectangular components. The three resulting equations are closely analogous to Eq. (15–96), the x equation, for example, being

$$\nabla^2 A_x - \epsilon\mu\frac{\partial^2 A_x}{\partial t^2} = -\mu J_x.\tag{15-110}$$

Each of these equations may be solved exactly as was Eq. (15–96), giving, for example,

$$A_x(\mathbf{r},\,t) = \frac{\mu}{4\pi}\int_V \frac{J_x(\mathbf{r}',\,t - \sqrt{\epsilon\mu}\,|\mathbf{r} - \mathbf{r}'|)}{|\mathbf{r} - \mathbf{r}'|}\,dv'.\tag{15-111}$$

These components are then combined to give

$$\mathbf{A}(\mathbf{r},\,t) = \frac{\mu}{4\pi}\int_V \frac{\mathbf{J}(\mathbf{r}',\,t - \sqrt{\epsilon\mu}\,|\mathbf{r} - \mathbf{r}'|)}{|\mathbf{r} - \mathbf{r}'|}\,dv',\tag{15-112}$$

which is the retarded vector potential.

The physical interpretation of the retarded potentials is interesting. Eqs. (15–109) and (15–112) indicate that at a given point $\mathbf{r}$ and a given time t the potentials are determined by the charge and current which existed at other points in space at earlier times. The time appropriate to each source point is earlier than t by an amount equal to the time required to travel from source to field point $\mathbf{r}$ with velocity $1/\sqrt{\epsilon\mu}$. If, for example, a point charge q located at the origin of coordinates were suddenly changed, then the effect of this change would not be felt at a distance r until a time $r\sqrt{\epsilon\mu}$ after the change was accomplished. The effect of the change propagates outward roughly as a spherical wavefront. (The actual situation is somewhat more complicated because the charge density and the current density are intimately related through div $\mathbf{J} + \partial\rho/\partial t = 0$.)

Having found the scalar and vector potentials, we find the fields by applying the gradient to φ, and the time derivative and curl to $\mathbf{A}$. These operations are in principle straightforward; however, it will be seen that they are relatively complicated in practice.

With the development of the retarded potentials the basic work on radiation is completed. It remains to apply this material to the solution of practical problems. This is the concern of the next two chapters: Chapter 16 considers boundary-value problems and radiation from prescribed charge and current distributions, while Chapter 17 treats radiation from moving point charges.

PROBLEMS

15-1. A parallel-plate capacitor with plates having the shape of circular disks has the region between its plates filled with a dielectric of permittivity ϵ. The dielectric is imperfect, having a conductivity g. The capacitance of the capacitor is C. The capacitor is charged to a potential difference ΔU and isolated. (a) Find the charge on the capacitor as a function of time. (b) Find the displacement current in the dielectric. (c) Find the magnetic field in the dielectric.

15-2. The Q of a dielectric medium is defined as the ratio of displacement current density to conduction current density. For monochromatic wave propagation, this reduces to $Q = \omega\epsilon/g$. Determine Q for glass and for sulfur, at the following frequencies: $f = 1, 10^6, 10^9$ cycles/sec.

15-3. Given the one-dimensional wave equation

$$\frac{\partial^2 E}{\partial z^2} = \epsilon\mu \frac{\partial^2 E}{\partial t^2},$$

where E is the magnitude of the electric field vector. Assume that $\mathbf{E}$ has a constant direction, namely, the y-direction. By introducing the change of variables

$$\xi = t + \sqrt{\epsilon\mu}\, z,$$

$$\eta = t - \sqrt{\epsilon\mu}\, z,$$

show that the wave equation assumes a form which is easily integrated. Integrate the equation to obtain

$$E(z, t) = E_1(\xi) + E_2(\eta),$$

where E_1 and E_2 are arbitrary functions.

15-4. Given a plane monochromatic wave traveling in a linear, isotropic, homogeneous dielectric. Show that the time-averaged electric and magnetic energy densities, W_E and W_M, are equal.

15-5. Given the electromagnetic wave

$$\mathbf{E} = \mathbf{i}E_0 \cos \omega(\sqrt{\epsilon\mu}\, z - t) + \mathbf{j}E_0 \sin \omega(\sqrt{\epsilon\mu}\, z - t),$$

where E_0 is a constant. Find the corresponding magnetic field $\mathbf{B}$ and the Poynting vector.

15-6. A straight metal wire of conductivity g and cross-sectional area A carries a steady current I. Determine the direction and magnitude of the Poynting vector at the surface of the wire. Integrate the normal component of the Poynting vector over the surface of the wire for a segment of length L, and compare your result with the Joule heat produced in this segment.

15-7. The earth receives about 1300 watts/m^2 radiant energy from the sun. Assuming the energy to be in the form of a plane polarized monochromatic wave, and assuming normal incidence, compute the magnitude of the electric and magnetic field vectors in the sunlight.

*15–8. Starting with an expression for the force per unit volume on a region of *free space* containing charges and currents:

$$\mathbf{F}_v = \rho\mathbf{E} + \mathbf{J} \times \mathbf{B},$$

and using the Maxwell equations and the vector identity of Eq. (14–24), show that

$$\mathbf{F}_v = -\epsilon_0 \frac{\partial}{\partial t} (\mathbf{E} \times \mathbf{B}) + \epsilon_0 \mathbf{E} \text{ div } \mathbf{E} - \frac{1}{2} \epsilon_0 \text{ grad } (E^2)$$

$$+ \epsilon_0 (\mathbf{E} \cdot \mathbf{grad})\mathbf{E} + \frac{1}{\mu_0} \mathbf{B} \text{ div } \mathbf{B} - \frac{1}{2\mu_0} \text{ grad } (B^2)$$

$$+ \frac{1}{\mu_0} (\mathbf{B} \cdot \mathbf{grad})\mathbf{B}.$$

(The quantity $\epsilon_0 \mathbf{E} \times \mathbf{B}$ is sometimes referred to as the momentum density of the electromagnetic field.)

15–9. Given a plane wave characterized by an E_x, B_y propagating in the positive z-direction,

$$\mathbf{E} = \mathbf{i}E_0 \sin \frac{2\pi}{\lambda} (z - ct).$$

Show that it is possible to take the scalar potential $\varphi = 0$, and find a possible vector potential $\mathbf{A}$. Be certain that the Lorentz condition is satisfied.

*15–10. The quantities (x, y, z, jct), $(A_x, A_y, A_z, j\varphi/c)$ are four-dimensional vectors. Show that terms of the form

$$F_{ij} \equiv \frac{\partial A_j}{\partial x_i} - \frac{\partial A_i}{\partial x_j}$$

represent the components of $\mathbf{B}$ and $(j/c)\mathbf{E}$. Show further that

$$\sum_i \frac{\partial F_{ij}}{\partial x_i} = 0$$

and

$$\frac{\partial F_{jk}}{\partial x_i} + \frac{\partial F_{ki}}{\partial x_j} + \frac{\partial F_{ij}}{\partial x_k} = 0$$

represent the Maxwell equations in vacuum.

15–11. Show that in free space with $\rho = 0$, $\mathbf{J} = 0$, the Maxwell equations are correctly obtained from a single vector function $\mathbf{A}$ satisfying

$$\text{div } \mathbf{A} = 0, \qquad \nabla^2 \mathbf{A} - \frac{1}{c^2} \frac{\partial^2 \mathbf{A}}{\partial t^2} = 0.$$

15–12. Given a medium in which $\rho = 0$, $\mathbf{J} = 0$, $\mu = \mu_0$, but where the polarization $\mathbf{P}$ is a given function of position and time: $\mathbf{P} = \mathbf{P}(x, y, z, t)$. Show that the Maxwell equations are correctly obtained from a single vector function

Z (the Hertz vector), where Z satisfies the equation

$$\nabla^2 Z - \frac{1}{c^2} \frac{\partial^2 Z}{\partial t^2} = -\frac{P}{\epsilon_0},$$

and

$$E = \text{curl curl } Z - \frac{1}{\epsilon_0} P, \qquad B = \frac{1}{c^2} \text{curl } \frac{\partial Z}{\partial t}.$$

15–13. Given a medium in which $\rho = 0$, $J = 0$, $\epsilon = \epsilon_0$, but where the magnetization $M(x, y, z, t)$ is a given function. Show that the Maxwell equations are correctly obtained from a single vector function Y, where Y satisfies the equation

$$\nabla^2 Y - \frac{1}{c^2} \frac{\partial^2 Y}{\partial t^2} = -\mu_0 M$$

and where

$$B = \text{curl curl } Y, \qquad E = -\text{curl } \frac{\partial Y}{\partial t}.$$

15–14. Show that Maxwell's equation for an isotropic, homogeneous, non-conducting, charge-free medium can be satisfied by taking either

(1) $E = $ real part of $\text{curl curl } (F\mathbf{a})$,

$B = $ real part of $\epsilon\mu \dfrac{\partial}{\partial t} \text{curl } (F\mathbf{a})$,

or

(2) $B = $ real part of $\text{curl curl } (F\mathbf{a})$,

$E = $ real part of $-\dfrac{\partial}{\partial t} \text{curl } (F\mathbf{a})$,

where $\mathbf{a}$ is a constant unit vector and F satisfies the scalar wave equation.

CHAPTER 16

APPLICATIONS OF MAXWELL'S EQUATIONS

The solutions of Maxwell's equations found in the preceding chapter will now be used to solve problems of practical interest. Two general classes of problems will be considered: boundary-value problems, and radiation from prescribed charge-current distributions. In the first class of problems, solutions of the homogeneous wave equation are so combined as to satisfy the appropriate boundary conditions. In the second class, solutions of the inhomogeneous wave equation with specified sources are required and boundary conditions are largely ignored, except for such things as insistence on outgoing waves and that the fields fall off as $1/r$ at large distances.

A third class of problems might prescribe a charge-current distribution that would produce a radiation field which must satisfy certain boundary conditions. However, in spite of its practical importance, this possibility will not be considered here. Enough difficulty will be encountered in the simpler problems already mentioned.

16–1 Boundary conditions. The boundary conditions which must be satisfied by the electric and magnetic fields at an interface between two media are deduced from Maxwell's equations exactly as in the static case. The most straightforward and universal boundary condition applies to the magnetic induction **B**, which satisfies the Maxwell equation

$$\operatorname{div} \mathbf{B} = 0. \qquad (16\text{–}1)$$

At any interface between two media a pillbox-like surface may be constructed as shown in Fig. 16–1. The divergence theorem may be applied to the divergence of **B** over the volume enclosed by this surface, to obtain

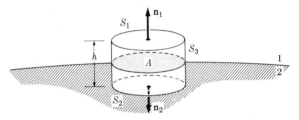

Fig. 16–1. A pillbox-shaped surface at the interface between two media may be used to obtain boundary conditions on the field vectors.

$$\oint_S \mathbf{B} \cdot \mathbf{n} \, da = \int_{S_1} \mathbf{B} \cdot \mathbf{n}_1 \, da + \int_{S_2} \mathbf{B} \cdot \mathbf{n}_2 \, da + \int_{S_3} \mathbf{B} \cdot \mathbf{n}_3 \, da = 0. \quad (16\text{-}2)$$

If $\mathbf{B}$ is bounded, letting h approach zero causes the last term to vanish and S_1 to approach S_2 geometrically. Taking account of the opposite directions of $\mathbf{n}_1$ and $\mathbf{n}_2$, it is quickly concluded that

$$B_{1n} = B_{2n}, \quad (16\text{-}3)$$

exactly as in the static case.

The tangential component of the electric field can be treated in an equally simple way. The basic equation is again one of Maxwell's equations,

$$\operatorname{curl} \mathbf{E} + \frac{\partial \mathbf{B}}{\partial t} = 0. \quad (16\text{-}4)$$

Integration of this equation over the surface bounded by a rectangular loop such as that shown in Fig. 16–2 yields

$$\int_S \operatorname{curl} \mathbf{E} \cdot \mathbf{n} \, da = -\int_S \frac{\partial \mathbf{B}}{\partial t} \cdot \mathbf{n} \, da, \quad (16\text{-}5)$$

and applying Stokes' theorem to the left side gives

$$lE_{1t} - lE_{2t} + h_1 E_{1n} + h_2 E_{2n} - h_1 E'_{1n} - h_2 E'_{2n} = -\int_S \frac{\partial \mathbf{B}}{\partial t} \cdot \mathbf{n} \, da. \quad (16\text{-}6)$$

If the loop is now shrunk by letting h_1 and h_2 go to zero, the last four terms on the left vanish, as does the right-hand side, provided only that $\partial \mathbf{B}/\partial t$ is bounded. The resulting equation contains l as a common factor; dropping this gives

$$E_{1t} = E_{2t}. \quad (16\text{-}7)$$

Thus the tangential component of $\mathbf{E}$ must be continuous across the interface.

The boundary condition on the normal component of the electric displacement is more complex; however, it too is derived from one of Max-

FIG. 16–2. The rectangular path shown at the interface between two media may be used to obtain boundary conditions on the field vectors.

well's equations. The appropriate equation in this case is

$$\text{div } \mathbf{D} = \rho. \tag{16-8}$$

If we construct a pillbox-shaped volume, as shown in Fig. 16–1, and integrate (16–8) over this volume, we obtain

$$\int_V \text{div } \mathbf{D} \, dv = \int_V \rho \, dv.$$

Applying the divergence theorem and letting h go to zero, we find

$$(D_{1n} - D_{2n})A = \sigma A, \tag{16-9}$$

where σ is the surface charge density on the interface. The fact that, in general, σ is not zero introduces some complexity in this boundary condition; however, noting that charge must be conserved, that is, that

$$\text{div } \mathbf{J} = -\frac{\partial \rho}{\partial t}, \tag{16-10}$$

makes possible certain simplifications. If we integrate this equation as we did Eq. (16–8), and shrink the pillbox in the same way, we obtain

$$J_{1n} - J_{2n} = -\frac{\partial \sigma}{\partial t}. \tag{16-11}$$

If only monochromatic radiation is considered, the surface charge density must vary as $e^{-j\omega t}$; therefore the right side of Eq. (16–11) can be written as $j\omega\sigma$. Using the constitutive relations $\mathbf{D} = \epsilon\mathbf{E}$, $\mathbf{J} = g\mathbf{E}$ puts equations (16–9) and (16–11) in the form

$$\epsilon_1 E_{1n} - \epsilon_2 E_{2n} = \sigma, \tag{16-12}$$

$$g_1 E_{1n} - g_2 E_{2n} = j\omega\sigma. \tag{16-13}$$

Several cases of practical interest may be noted. If σ is zero, then

$$\frac{\epsilon_1}{g_1} = \frac{\epsilon_2}{g_2}$$

which can be true for appropriately chosen materials or, alternatively, if $g_1 = g_2 = 0$, or ∞. The case where both conductivities are infinite is not of great interest; however, the case where both conductivities vanish is approximately realized at the boundary between two good dielectrics. If σ is not zero, which is perhaps a more common case, then it may be eliminated from Eqs. (16–12) and (16–13). The result of this elimination is

$$\left(\epsilon_1 - \frac{g_1}{j\omega}\right) E_{1n} - \left(\epsilon_2 - \frac{g_2}{j\omega}\right) E_{2n} = 0. \tag{16-14}$$

Equation (16–14) is useful as it stands in providing a boundary condition; however, it sometimes appears in the form obtained by multiplying by $\omega^2 \mu_1 \mu_2$, which is

$$\mu_2 \gamma_1^2 E_{1n} - \mu_1 \gamma_2^2 E_{2n} = 0, \qquad (16\text{–}15)$$

where γ is the propagation constant given by

$$\gamma^2 = \omega^2 \epsilon \mu + j\omega g \mu, \qquad (16\text{–}16)$$

as in Eq. (15–47). A final interesting case occurs when one conductivity, say g_2, is infinite. In this case E_{2n} must vanish and E_{1n} must equal σ/ϵ_1 in order for (16–13) and (16–12) to be satisfied.

The final boundary condition is that imposed on the tangential component of the magnetic intensity $\mathbf{H}$. This boundary condition is obtained by integrating the Maxwell equation

$$\operatorname{curl} \mathbf{H} = \frac{\partial \mathbf{D}}{\partial t} + \mathbf{J} \qquad (16\text{–}17)$$

over the area enclosed by a loop such as that shown in Fig. 16–2. If this is done and the loop is shrunk as before, the resulting boundary condition is

$$H_{1t} - H_{2t} = j_{s\perp}, \qquad (16\text{–}18)$$

where $j_{s\perp}$ is the component of the surface current density perpendicular to the direction of the $\mathbf{H}$-component which is being matched. The idea of a surface current density is closely analogous to that of a surface charge density—it represents a finite current in an infinitesimal layer. The surface current density is zero unless the conductivity is infinite; hence, for finite conductivity,

$$H_{1t} = H_{2t}. \qquad (16\text{–}19)$$

That is, unless one medium has infinite conductivity the tangential component of $\mathbf{H}$ is continuous. If the conductivity of medium 2 is infinite, then, as has already been shown, $E_{2n} = 0$. A more general result can be obtained by considering the Maxwell equation (16–17) as applied to medium 2:

$$\operatorname{curl} \mathbf{H}_2 - \frac{\partial \mathbf{D}_2}{\partial t} = \mathbf{J}_2. \qquad (16\text{–}20)$$

Using the constitutive relations and assuming that $\mathbf{E}_2$ varies with time as $e^{-j\omega t}$ yields

$$\mathbf{E}_2 = \frac{1}{g_2 - j\omega\epsilon_2} \operatorname{curl} \mathbf{H}_2. \qquad (16\text{–}21)$$

If the reasonable assumption that $\mathbf{H}_2$ is both bounded and differentiable is made, then Eq. (16–21) implies that $\mathbf{E}_2$ is zero in a medium of infinite conductivity. With the same assumptions as were made above,

$$\mathbf{H}_2 = \frac{1}{j\omega\mu_2}\,\mathbf{curl}\,\mathbf{E}_2, \qquad (16\text{–}22)$$

and the vanishing of $\mathbf{E}_2$ also implies the vanishing of $\mathbf{H}_2$. If $\mathbf{H}_2$ vanishes, then the boundary condition on the tangential component of $\mathbf{H}$ at an interface at which one medium has infinite conductivity is

$$H_{1t} = j_{s\perp}. \qquad (16\text{–}23)$$

The boundary conditions needed to solve the problems considered in this chapter have now been obtained; for convenient reference they are tabulated in Table 16–1 for $g = 0$, $g = \infty$, and arbitrary g.

16–2 Reflection and refraction at the boundary of two nonconducting media. Normal incidence. An interesting and instructive application of the boundary conditions derived in the preceding paragraph is the derivation of the reflection and transmission coefficients for plane waves normally incident on a dielectric interface. The situation is described in Fig. 16–3.

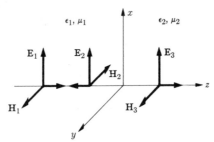

Fig. 16–3. Reflection and transmission at normal incidence.

In this figure $\mathbf{E}_1$, $\mathbf{H}_1$ describe the incident wave traveling in the plus z-direction, $\mathbf{E}_2$, $\mathbf{H}_2$ describe the reflected wave traveling in the minus z-direction, and $\mathbf{E}_3$, $\mathbf{H}_3$ describe the transmitted wave. The interface is taken as coincident with the xy-plane at $z = 0$, with medium 1 on the left and medium 2 on the right. The electric fields, which are polarized in the x-direction, are described by

$$\mathbf{E}_1 = \mathbf{i}E_{10}e^{j(\kappa_1 z - \omega t)},$$
$$\mathbf{E}_2 = \mathbf{i}E_{20}e^{-j(\kappa_1 z + \omega t)}, \qquad (16\text{–}24)$$
$$\mathbf{E}_3 = \mathbf{i}E_{30}e^{j(\kappa_2 z - \omega t)},$$

where

$$\kappa_1 = \omega\sqrt{\epsilon_1\mu_1} \quad \text{and} \quad \kappa_2 = \omega\sqrt{\epsilon_2\mu_2} \qquad (16\text{–}25)$$

TABLE 16-1

BOUNDARY CONDITIONS

g	E_t	D_n	H_t	B_n
$g_1 = g_2 = 0$	$E_{1t} = E_{2t}$	$D_{1n} = D_{2n}$	$H_{1t} = H_{2t}$	$B_{1n} = B_{2n}$
$g_2 = \infty$	$E_{2t} = 0$	$D_{2n} = 0$	$H_{2t} = 0$	$B_{2n} = 0$
	$E_{1t} = 0$	$D_{1n} = \sigma$	$H_{1t} = j_{s\perp}$	$B_{1n} = 0$
g_1, g_2 arb. $\neq \infty$	$E_{1t} = E_{2t}$	$\left(\epsilon_1 - \dfrac{g_1}{j\omega}\right) E_{1n}$ $= \left(\epsilon_2 - \dfrac{g_2}{j\omega}\right) E_{2n}$	$H_{1t} = H_{2t}$	$B_{1n} = B_{2n}$

(cf. Eqs. 15–39). The appropriate magnetic fields are obtained from the Maxwell equation

$$\text{curl } \mathbf{E} = -\frac{\partial \mathbf{B}}{\partial t}. \tag{16-26}$$

For electric fields of the type indicated in (16–24), Eq. (16–26) is equivalent to

$$\mathbf{j}\frac{\partial E_x}{\partial z} = j\omega\mu\mathbf{H} = j\omega\mu H_y\mathbf{j}; \tag{16-27}$$

hence the magnetic fields to be associated with the electric fields given above are

$$\mathbf{H}_1 = \mathbf{j}\sqrt{\epsilon_1/\mu_1}\, E_{1,0} e^{j(\kappa_1 z - \omega t)},$$
$$\mathbf{H}_2 = -\mathbf{j}\sqrt{\epsilon_1/\mu_1}\, E_{2,0} e^{-j(\kappa_1 z + \omega t)}, \tag{16-28}$$
$$\mathbf{H}_3 = \mathbf{j}\sqrt{\epsilon_2/\mu_2}\, E_{3,0} e^{j(\kappa_2 z - \omega t)}.$$

Since the normal components of the fields vanish, only the tangential components of the electric and magnetic fields need be considered, and these according to the zero conductivity line of Table 16–1. Applying these conditions at $z = 0$, we find

$$E_{1,0} + E_{2,0} = E_{3,0} \quad \text{and} \quad \sqrt{\epsilon_1/\mu_1}\,(E_{1,0} - E_{2,0}) = \sqrt{\epsilon_2/\mu_2}\, E_{3,0}. \tag{16-29}$$

Solving these equations for $E_{2,0}$ and $E_{3,0}$, we obtain

$$E_{2,0} = \frac{\sqrt{\epsilon_1/\mu_1} - \sqrt{\epsilon_2/\mu_2}}{\sqrt{\epsilon_1/\mu_1} + \sqrt{\epsilon_2/\mu_2}}\, E_{1,0}; \qquad E_{3,0} = \frac{2\sqrt{\epsilon_1/\mu_1}}{\sqrt{\epsilon_1/\mu_1} + \sqrt{\epsilon_2/\mu_2}}\, E_{1,0}. \tag{16-30}$$

Equation (16–30) determines the electric fields of the reflected and transmitted waves in terms of the incident wave and the parameters describing the medium; these amplitudes in turn determine the amplitudes of the magnetic fields through equations (16–28).

It is interesting to apply the results obtained above to the case of optically transparent materials. For such materials μ is very nearly μ_0, consequently the index of refraction is essentially given by

$$n = \sqrt{\epsilon/\epsilon_0}.$$

In terms of n, taking $\mu_1 = \mu_2 = \mu_0$, Eq. (16–30) becomes

$$\frac{E_{2,0}}{E_{1,0}} = \frac{n_1 - n_2}{n_1 + n_2}; \qquad \frac{E_{3,0}}{E_{1,0}} = \frac{2n_1}{n_1 + n_2}. \qquad (16\text{--}31)$$

The reflected wave intensity is proportional to the reflected Poynting vector, and the transmitted intensity is proportional to the transmitted Poynting vector. The transmission coefficient T_n and the reflection coefficient R_n are defined by

$$R_n = \frac{\overline{\mathbf{E}_2 \times \mathbf{H}_2}}{\overline{\mathbf{E}_1 \times \mathbf{H}_1}} = \left(\frac{n_1 - n_2}{n_1 + n_2}\right)^2, \qquad (16\text{--}32)$$

where the bars over the Poynting vectors mean that the quantity is to be averaged over many cycles in time. Similarly,

$$T_n = \frac{\overline{\mathbf{E}_3 \times \mathbf{H}_3}}{\overline{\mathbf{E}_1 \times \mathbf{H}_1}} = \frac{n_2}{n_1}\left(\frac{2n_1}{n_1 + n_2}\right)^2. \qquad (16\text{--}33)$$

For a typical air-glass interface, where $n_2 = 1.5$ and $n_1 = 1$, the reflection and transmission coefficients are

$$R_n = 0.04 \qquad \text{and} \qquad T_n = 0.96.$$

Thus, as would be expected, all of the incident energy is either reflected or transmitted—there is no place to store energy in the interface.

A further interesting fact is obtained by examining Eq. (16–31); namely, if n_1 is greater than n_2 the first ratio is negative. This is precisely the familiar statement from optics that there is no phase change on reflection from a "less dense" medium but that there is a phase change of π radians on reflection from a "more dense" medium.

*16–3 Reflection and refraction at the boundary of two nonconducting media. Oblique incidence. A more general case than that discussed in the preceding section is that of reflection of obliquely incident plane waves by a plane dielectric interface. Consideration of this case leads to three well-known optical laws: Snell's law, the law of reflection, and Brewster's law governing polarization by reflection.

The general situation is described by Fig. 16–4. To simplify the following derivation it has been assumed that the propagation vectors κ_1, κ_2, and κ_3 are coplanar and lie in the xz-plane. Furthermore, the electric field vectors $\mathbf{E}_1$, $\mathbf{E}_2$, and $\mathbf{E}_3$ have also been assumed to lie in this plane.* The electric fields of the incident, reflected, and transmitted waves are given by

$$\mathbf{E}_1 = \mathbf{E}_{1,0} e^{j(\kappa_1 \cdot \mathbf{r} - \omega t)},$$

$$\mathbf{E}_2 = \mathbf{E}_{2,0} e^{j(\kappa_2 \cdot \mathbf{r} - \omega t)}, \tag{16-34}$$

$$\mathbf{E}_3 = \mathbf{E}_{3,0} e^{j(\kappa_3 \cdot \mathbf{r} - \omega t)},$$

where

$$\mathbf{E}_{1,0} = E_{1,0}(\mathbf{i} \cos \theta_1 - \mathbf{k} \sin \theta_1),$$

$$\mathbf{E}_{2,0} = E_{2,0}(\mathbf{i} \cos \theta_2 + \mathbf{k} \sin \theta_2), \tag{16-35}$$

$$\mathbf{E}_{3,0} = E_{3,0}(\mathbf{i} \cos \theta_3 - \mathbf{k} \sin \theta_3),$$

and

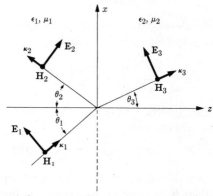

FIG. 16–4. Reflection and refraction—oblique incidence. The xz-plane is the plane of incidence. The vectors $\mathbf{H}_1$ and $\mathbf{H}_3$ are directed out of the paper, and $\mathbf{H}_2$ is directed in.

---

* It can be proved that the propagation vectors are always coplanar. The most general electric field vector can be resolved into a component in the xz-plane (plane of incidence) and a component perpendicular to this plane. The reflection and transmission of these two components are governed by different laws. The choice made above is made in order to obtain Brewster's law. The derivation for the case where the electric field is perpendicular to the plane of incidence is left as an exercise.

$$\kappa_1 = \omega\sqrt{\epsilon_1\mu_1} \ (\mathbf{i} \sin \theta_1 + \mathbf{k} \cos \theta_1),$$

$$\kappa_2 = \omega\sqrt{\epsilon_1\mu_1} \ (\mathbf{i} \sin \theta_2 - \mathbf{k} \cos \theta_2), \qquad (16\text{--}36)$$

$$\kappa_3 = \omega\sqrt{\epsilon_2\mu_2} \ (\mathbf{i} \sin \theta_3 + \mathbf{k} \cos \theta_3).$$

The magnetic intensity of each wave can be obtained, as in the case of normal incidence, from the Maxwell equation

$$\text{curl } \mathbf{E} = -\frac{\partial \mathbf{B}}{\partial t} = +j\omega\mu\mathbf{H}. \qquad (16\text{--}37)$$

The curl appearing in Eq. (16–37) can be evaluated from the definition of the curl and the explicit forms of the electric fields as given by Eqs. (16–34), (16–35), and (16–36). However, the curl of vectors of the general form of equations (16–34) occurs so frequently that it is convenient to derive a general expression. If $\mathbf{A}$ is an arbitrary vector function, then

$$\text{curl } (\mathbf{A}e^{j\kappa\cdot\mathbf{r}}) = e^{j\kappa\cdot\mathbf{r}} \text{ curl } \mathbf{A} + \text{grad} \ (e^{j\kappa\cdot\mathbf{r}}) \times \mathbf{A}. \qquad (16\text{--}38)$$

But

$$\text{grad } e^{j\kappa\cdot\mathbf{r}} = j\kappa e^{j\kappa\cdot\mathbf{r}}; \qquad (16\text{--}39)$$

hence

$$\text{curl } \mathbf{A}e^{j\kappa\cdot\mathbf{r}} = e^{j\kappa\cdot\mathbf{r}} \text{ curl } \mathbf{A} + j\kappa \times \mathbf{A}e^{j\kappa\cdot\mathbf{r}}. \qquad (16\text{--}40)$$

Using this identity and Eq. (16–37), and noting that each of the vectors in (16–35) is constant, we find

$$\mathbf{H}_1 = \frac{\kappa_1 \times \mathbf{E}_{1,0}}{\omega\mu_1} e^{j(\kappa_1\cdot\mathbf{r}-\omega t)},$$

$$\mathbf{H}_2 = \frac{\kappa_2 \times \mathbf{E}_{2,0}}{\omega\mu_1} e^{j(\kappa_2\cdot\mathbf{r}-\omega t)}, \qquad (16\text{--}41)$$

$$\mathbf{H}_3 = \frac{\kappa_3 \times \mathbf{E}_{3,0}}{\omega\mu_2} e^{j(\kappa_3\cdot\mathbf{r}-\omega t)}.$$

Having obtained this mathematical description of the waves, we next turn to the boundary conditions at the $z = 0$ interface.

As the first boundary condition to be matched, consider the tangential component (x-component) of the electric field at $z = 0$. Continuity of this component of the electric field gives (since $\kappa_1 = \kappa_2$).

$$E_{1,0} \cos \theta_1 e^{j(\kappa_1 x \sin \theta_1 - \omega t)} + E_{2,0} \cos \theta_2 e^{j(\kappa_1 x \sin \theta_2 - \omega t)}$$

$$= E_{3,0} \cos \theta_3 e^{j(\kappa_3 x \sin \theta_3 - \omega t)}. \qquad (16\text{--}42)$$

The common factor $e^{-j\omega t}$ can be cancelled from all three terms, leaving

$$E_{1,0} \cos \theta_1 e^{j\kappa_1 x \sin \theta_1} + E_{2,0} \cos \theta_2 e^{j\kappa_1 x \sin \theta_2} = E_{3,0} \cos \theta_3 e^{j\kappa_3 x \sin \theta_3}.$$

$$(16\text{--}43)$$

Each term in Eq. (16–43) depends on x through an exponential factor. The only way in which Eq. (16–43) can be satisfied for all values of x is if the three exponential factors are all the same, that is, if

$$\kappa_1 x \sin \theta_1 = \kappa_1 x \sin \theta_2 = \kappa_3 x \sin \theta_3. \qquad (16\text{--}44)$$

This result can be broken up into two equations:

$$\sin \theta_1 = \sin \theta_2, \qquad \kappa_1 \sin \theta_1 = \kappa_3 \sin \theta_3. \qquad (16\text{--}45)$$

The first of these is clearly equivalent to $\theta_1 = \theta_2$, which is the law of reflection. Since $\kappa = \omega\sqrt{\epsilon\mu}$ and $n = \sqrt{K_e K_m}$, the second equation can be written $n_1 \sin \theta_1 = n_2 \sin \theta_3$, which is Snell's law. Thus two important results have been obtained by applying the boundary condition on the tangential component of the electric field. Still more information is contained in this boundary condition, as can be seen by putting Eq. (16–44) into Eq. (16–43) and cancelling common factors, to obtain

$$E_{1,0} \cos \theta_1 + E_{2,0} \cos \theta_1 = E_{3,0} \cos \theta_3. \qquad (16\text{--}46)$$

Equation (16–46) represents one equation which must be satisfied by $E_{1,0}$, $E_{2,0}$, and $E_{3,0}$; in addition there are two other conditions, obtained from continuity of the normal component of the electric displacement and continuity of the tangential component of the magnetic intensity. Continuity of the normal component of the electric displacement gives

$$-\epsilon_1 \sin \theta_1 E_{1,0} + \epsilon_1 \sin \theta_1 E_{2,0} = -\epsilon_2 \sin \theta_3 E_{3,0}, \qquad (16\text{--}47)$$

while continuity of the tangential component of the magnetic intensity gives

$$\sqrt{\epsilon_1/\mu_1}\, E_{1,0} - \sqrt{\epsilon_1/\mu_1}\, E_{2,0} = \sqrt{\epsilon_2/\mu_2}\, E_{3,0}. \qquad (16\text{--}48)$$

These two equations are actually identical, as may be seen by writing Eq. (16–47) in the form

$$-\sqrt{\epsilon_1/\mu_1}\, \sqrt{\epsilon_1\mu_1} \sin \theta_1 E_{1,0} + \sqrt{\epsilon_1/\mu_1}\, \sqrt{\epsilon_1\mu_1} \sin \theta_1 E_{2,0}$$
$$= -\sqrt{\epsilon_2/\mu_2}\, \sqrt{\epsilon_2\mu_2} \sin \theta_3 E_{3,0}. \qquad (16\text{--}49)$$

Since $\sqrt{\epsilon_1\mu_1} = n_1\sqrt{\epsilon_0\mu_0}$, Snell's law makes possible the reduction of Eq. (16–49) to the form given in Eq. (16–48).

Equations (16–46) and (16–47) must now be solved for $E_{2,0}$ and $E_{3,0}$ in terms of $E_{1,0}$. This is easily done, with the result

$$\frac{E_{3,0}}{E_{1,0}} = \frac{2\epsilon_1 \sin \theta_1 \cos \theta_1}{\epsilon_2 \sin \theta_3 \cos \theta_1 + \epsilon_1 \sin \theta_1 \cos \theta_3} \qquad (16\text{--}50)$$

for the transmitted electric field, and

$$\frac{E_{2,0}}{E_{1,0}} = \frac{\epsilon_1 \sin \theta_1 \cos \theta_3 - \epsilon_2 \sin \theta_3 \cos \theta_1}{\epsilon_2 \sin \theta_3 \cos \theta_1 + \epsilon_1 \sin \theta_1 \cos \theta_3} \qquad (16\text{--}51)$$

for the field of the reflected wave. For most dielectric materials $\mu = \mu_0$ and $n^2 = \epsilon/\epsilon_0$. Assuming this to be the case and using Snell's law, Eq. (16–51) becomes

$$\frac{E_{2,0}}{E_{1,0}} = \frac{\sin \theta_3 \cos \theta_3 - \sin \theta_1 \cos \theta_1}{\sin \theta_3 \cos \theta_3 + \sin \theta_1 \cos \theta_1}. \qquad (16\text{--}52)$$

The trigonometric identities $\sin (\theta_1 + \theta_3) \cos (\theta_1 - \theta_3) = \sin \theta_1 \cos \theta_1 + \sin \theta_3 \cos \theta_3$, and $\sin (\theta_1 - \theta_3) \cos (\theta_1 + \theta_3) = \sin \theta_1 \cos \theta_1 - \sin \theta_3 \cos \theta_3$, reduce Eq. (16–52) to

$$\frac{E_{2,0}}{E_{1,0}} = - \frac{\tan (\theta_1 - \theta_3)}{\tan (\theta_1 + \theta_3)}. \qquad (16\text{--}53)$$

If $\theta_1 = \theta_3$, then $\tan (\theta_1 - \theta_3) = 0$ and there is no reflected wave. Unfortunately, this can occur only if $n_1 = n_2$, that is, if the two media are optically indistinguishable. If, on the other hand, $\theta_1 + \theta_3 = \pi/2$, then $\tan (\theta_1 + \theta_3)$ is infinite and the amplitude of the reflected wave is again zero. In this case the media are optically distinguishable. Since it can be shown that the other polarization, **E** perpendicular to the plane of incidence, is partially reflected, unpolarized light incident at an angle satisfying $\theta_1 + \theta_3 = \pi/2$ will be polarized by reflection. Snell's law,

$$n_1 \sin \theta_1 = n_2 \sin \theta_3,$$

provides a means for determining the value of θ_1. Using $\theta_3 = \pi/2 - \theta_1$ in Snell's law gives

$$n_1 \sin \theta_{1p} = n_2 \cos \theta_{1p},$$

or

$$\tan \theta_{1p} = \frac{n_2}{n_1}. \qquad (16\text{--}54)$$

The quantity θ_{1p} is known as Brewster's angle; the relationship between it and the indices of refraction as given in Eq. (16–54) is known as Brewster's law.

Equations (16–50) and (16–51) are two equations of the set known as the Fresnel equations, which in their totality describe the reflection and refraction of electromagnetic waves of the two possible polarizations at a plane dielectric interface. From these equations it is a simple matter to obtain the reflection and transmission coefficients for power; they are

$$R = \frac{\overline{\mathbf{E}_2 \times \mathbf{H}_2}}{\overline{\mathbf{E}_1 \times \mathbf{H}_1}} = \left(\frac{\epsilon_1 \sin \theta_1 \cos \theta_3 - \epsilon_2 \sin \theta_3 \cos \theta_1}{\epsilon_1 \sin \theta_1 \cos \theta_3 + \epsilon_2 \sin \theta_3 \cos \theta_1} \right)^2 \tag{16-55}$$

and

$$T = \frac{\overline{\mathbf{E}_3 \times \mathbf{H}_3}}{\overline{\mathbf{E}_1 \times \mathbf{H}_1}} = \frac{\sqrt{\epsilon_2/\mu_2}}{\sqrt{\epsilon_1/\mu_1}} \left(\frac{2\epsilon_1 \sin \theta_1 \cos \theta_1}{\epsilon_1 \sin \theta_1 \cos \theta_3 + \epsilon_2 \sin \theta_3 \cos \theta_1} \right)^2 \tag{16-56}$$

for a wave polarized as discussed above. If the media are dielectrics with $\mu = \mu_0$ and consequently $n^2 = \epsilon/\epsilon_0$, then these equations may be put in the forms

$$R = \frac{\tan^2 (\theta_1 - \theta_3)}{\tan^2 (\theta_1 + \theta_3)} \tag{16-57}$$

and

$$T = \frac{4 \sin \theta_3 \cos^2 \theta_1 \sin \theta_1}{\sin^2 (\theta_1 + \theta_3) \cos^2 (\theta_1 - \theta_3)}, \tag{16-58}$$

in which form they give the ratios of the transmitted and reflected intensities to the incident intensity. As written, the equations do not seem to involve the indices of refraction; however, it must be remembered that θ_1 and θ_3 are related through Snell's law.

16-4 Reflection from a conducting plane. Normal incidence. The reflection and transmission of normally incident plane waves at a plane interface between a conducting material and a nonconducting material will now be considered. The situation is essentially that described by Fig. 16–3, with the additional feature that g_2, the conductivity of medium 2, is not zero. The electric and magnetic fields $\mathbf{E}_1$, $\mathbf{H}_1$, $\mathbf{E}_2$, and $\mathbf{H}_2$ have the forms given by Eqs. (16–24) and (16–28), namely,

$$\mathbf{E}_1 = \mathbf{i}E_{1,0}e^{j(\kappa_1 z - \omega t)}, \qquad \mathbf{H}_1 = \mathbf{j}\sqrt{\epsilon_1/\mu_1}\, E_{1,0}e^{j(\kappa_1 z - \omega t)},$$

$$\mathbf{E}_2 = \mathbf{i}E_{2,0}e^{-j(\kappa_1 z + \omega t)}, \qquad \mathbf{H}_2 = -\mathbf{j}\sqrt{\epsilon_1/\mu_1}\, E_{2,0}e^{-j(\kappa_1 z + \omega t)}. \tag{16-59}$$

The wave in the conducting medium has the form

$$\mathbf{E}_3 = \mathbf{i}E_{3,0}e^{j(\gamma_2 z - \omega t)}, \qquad \mathbf{H}_3 = \mathbf{j}\frac{\gamma_2 E_{3,0}}{\omega \mu_2} e^{j(\gamma_2 z - \omega t)}. \tag{16-60}$$

with, however, γ_2 given by

$$\gamma_2 = \alpha_2 + j\beta_2 = \sqrt{\omega^2 \epsilon_2 \mu_2 + j\omega g_2 \mu_2}, \tag{16-61}$$

as in Eq. (15–48). Alpha and beta are given by

$$\alpha = \mp \omega\sqrt{\epsilon\mu} \left[\tfrac{1}{2} \mp \tfrac{1}{2}\sqrt{1 + (g^2/\omega^2\epsilon^2)} \right]^{1/2}, \qquad \beta = \frac{\omega g\mu}{2\alpha}. \tag{16-62}$$

Once again the appropriate boundary conditions are continuity of the tangential components of $\mathbf{E}$ and $\mathbf{H}$. The results are

$$E_{1,0} + E_{2,0} = E_{3,0} \tag{16–63}$$

and

$$\sqrt{\epsilon_1/\mu_1}\,(E_{1,0} - E_{2,0}) = \frac{\gamma_2}{\omega\mu_2}\,E_{3,0}. \tag{16–64}$$

Since γ_2 is complex, $E_{2,0}$ and $E_{3,0}$ cannot both be real; this fact indicates that phase shifts different from zero and π are possible for the reflected and transmitted waves. Formally, Eqs. (16–63) and (16–64) may be solved to give

$$E_{2,0} = \frac{1 - (\gamma_2/\omega\mu_2)\sqrt{\mu_1/\epsilon_1}}{1 + (\gamma_2/\omega\mu_2)\sqrt{\mu_1/\epsilon_1}}\,E_{1,0},$$

and
$$\tag{16–65}$$

$$E_{3,0} = \frac{2}{1 + (\gamma_2/\omega\mu_2)\sqrt{\mu_1/\epsilon_1}}\,E_{1,0}.$$

The apparent similarity of these results to those obtained in the dielectric case is misleading, for again it must be noted that γ_2 is a complex number and thus gives rise to phase shifts.

The special case of infinite conductivity is particularly simple. In this case γ_2 is infinite, thus reducing equations (16–65) to

$$E_{2,0} = -E_{1,0}, \qquad E_{3,0} = 0, \qquad (g_2 = \infty) \tag{16–66}$$

so that all of the incident energy is reflected and no energy penetrates into the conductor. The general case is rather cumbersome; however, the next approximation for good conductors is relatively straightforward and has some utility. For a good conductor,

$$\frac{g_2}{\omega\epsilon_2} \gg 1.$$

In this case,

$$\alpha_2 = \sqrt{\omega g_2 \mu_2/2} \qquad \text{and} \qquad \beta = \sqrt{\omega g_2 \mu_2/2}. \tag{16–67}$$

The reflected electric field amplitude is then given by

$$E_{2,0} = \frac{1 - \left(\dfrac{1+j}{\omega\mu_2}\right)\sqrt{\dfrac{\omega g_2 \mu_2}{2}\,\dfrac{\mu_1}{\epsilon_1}}}{1 + \left(\dfrac{1+j}{\omega\mu_2}\right)\sqrt{\dfrac{\omega g_2 \mu_2}{2}\,\dfrac{\mu_1}{\epsilon_1}}}\,E_{1,0} = \frac{1 - (1+j)\sqrt{\dfrac{\mu_1 g_2}{2\mu_2\epsilon_1\omega}}}{1 + (1+j)\sqrt{\dfrac{\mu_1 g_2}{2\mu_2\epsilon_1\omega}}}\,E_{1,0}.$$

$$\tag{16–68}$$

If along with Eq. (16–68) we have $g_2/\omega\epsilon_1 \gg 1$, then the radicals in Eq.

(16–68) are the dominant parts of the numerator and denominator. Dividing numerator and denominator by $(1 + j)$ times the radical gives

$$E_{2,0} = - \frac{1 - \left(\dfrac{1-j}{2}\right)\sqrt{2\dfrac{\mu_2\omega\epsilon_1}{\mu_1 g_2}}}{1 + \left(\dfrac{1-j}{2}\right)\sqrt{2\dfrac{\mu_2\omega\epsilon_1}{\mu_1 g_2}}} E_{1,0}. \qquad (16\text{–}69)$$

Recognition of the radical as a small quantity leads to the approximation

$$E_{2,0} = - \left[1 - (1 - j)\sqrt{2\frac{\mu_2}{\mu_1}\frac{\omega\epsilon_1}{g_2}}\right] E_{1,0}. \qquad (16\text{–}70)$$

The reflection coefficient is obtained by comparing the reflected Poynting vector with the incident Poynting vector. Since both the incident and reflected waves are in the same medium, this is equivalent to comparing the square of the magnitude of $E_{2,0}$ to the square of the magnitude of $E_{1,0}$. Thus

$$R = \frac{|E_{2,0}|^2}{|E_{1,0}|^2}. \qquad (16\text{–}71)$$

Using the approximation given in Eq. (16–70), we obtain

$$R = \left[1 - (1 - j)\sqrt{\frac{2\mu_2\omega\epsilon_1}{\mu_1 g_2}}\right]\left[1 - (1 + j)\sqrt{\frac{2\mu_2\omega\epsilon_1}{\mu_1 g_2}}\right]. \qquad (16\text{–}72)$$

To the same approximation as used above, we find that

$$R = 1 - 2\sqrt{2(\mu_2/\mu_1)(\omega\epsilon_1/g_2)}. \qquad (16\text{–}73)$$

Taking $g_2 = 5.6 \times 10^7$ mhos/m, the value for copper, and assuming $\mu_2 = \mu_1$ and $\epsilon_1 = \epsilon_0$, we find that for $f = 10^{10}$ sec^{-1} (3-cm wavelength) $R = 0.9997$; for lower frequencies the situation is even closer to the perfect reflection case. It is only for radiation of very short wavelength that the deviation of R from unity becomes significant for such good conductors as copper, silver, and aluminum. Since the skin depth for these materials is small, it is easy to see why thin sheets of good conductors provide excellent shielding for radiofrequencies.

16–5 Propagation between parallel conducting plates. As a preliminary to the study of waveguides, we now consider the propagation of electromagnetic waves in the region between two parallel, perfectly conducting plates. The region in which wave propagation is to be treated is that shown in Fig. 16–5. Since the x- and z-directions are physically indistinguishable, no generality is lost by considering only waves with wave vectors in the yz-plane—in particular, those making an angle θ with the

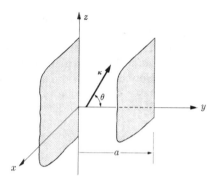

FIG. 16–5. Wave propagation between two parallel, perfectly conducting planes.

y-axis. Such waves will impinge on the perfectly conducting surface at $y = a$ and will be reflected as waves whose propagation vectors make the angle θ with the minus y-axis. When these waves are reflected a second time, by the surface at $y = 0$, they become waves of the first type again. Thus it is seen that the propagation between two parallel conducting planes can be described in terms of the exponential factors

$$e^{j[\kappa(y \cos \theta + z \sin \theta) - \omega t]}$$

and

$$e^{j[\kappa(-y \cos \theta + z \sin \theta) - \omega t]}.$$

(16–74)

For such waves there are two possible polarizations, which may be described by saying for one that $\mathbf{E}$ is parallel to the x-axis, and for the other that $\mathbf{H}$ is parallel to the x-axis. These are known respectively as TE, transverse electric, and TM, transverse magnetic, waves. Only TE waves will be considered here. The treatment of TM waves will be left to an exercise.

The electric field in the region between the two conducting planes in the TE case is given by

$$\mathbf{E} = \mathbf{i}\{E_1 e^{j[\kappa(y \cos \theta + z \sin \theta) - \omega t]} + E_2 e^{j[\kappa(-y \cos \theta + z \sin \theta) - \omega t]}\}. \quad (16\text{–}75)$$

This electric field must vanish at $y = 0$, since E_t vanishes at the boundary of a perfect conductor. This condition is clearly satisfied for all z and all t if $E_1 = -E_2 = E$. Then $\mathbf{E}$ is given by

$$\mathbf{E} = \mathbf{i}E(e^{j\kappa y \cos \theta} - e^{-j\kappa y \cos \theta})e^{j(\kappa z \sin \theta - \omega t)}. \quad (16\text{–}76)$$

In addition $\mathbf{E}$ must vanish at $y = a$ for all z and all t. This requirement imposes the condition

$$\kappa a \cos \theta = n\pi. \quad (16\text{–}77)$$

Thus for a given frequency ω, $\kappa = \omega/c$ and the angle that the waves make with the y-axis is fixed by Eq. (16–77). With this angle fixed, the apparent velocity in the z-direction is $v_p = c/\sin\,\theta$, which is always greater than the velocity of light in free space. This apparent contradiction of the special theory of relativity will be discussed in more detail later.

It is convenient to express the variation of the electric field in the y- and z-directions in terms of wavelengths. These wavelengths are

$$\lambda_g = \frac{2\pi}{\kappa \sin\,\theta} = \frac{\lambda_0}{\sin\,\theta} \quad \left(\lambda_0 = \frac{2\pi}{\kappa} = \frac{2\pi c}{\omega}\right) \tag{16–78}$$

for the z-direction, and

$$\lambda_c = \frac{2\pi}{\kappa \cos\,\theta} = \frac{\lambda_0}{\cos\,\theta} \tag{16–79}$$

for the y-direction. In terms of these wavelengths, the electric field, Eq. (16–75), is*

$$\mathbf{E} = \mathbf{i}E' \sin \frac{2\pi y}{\lambda_c}\, e^{j[(2\pi z/\lambda_g)-\omega t]}, \tag{16–80}$$

while Eq. (16–77) takes the form

$$\frac{a}{\lambda_c} = \frac{n}{2}. \tag{16–81}$$

From Eqs. (16–78) and (16–79) it follows immediately that

$$\frac{1}{\lambda_g^2} + \frac{1}{\lambda_c^2} = \frac{1}{\lambda_0^2}. \tag{16–82}$$

If the value $\lambda_c = 2a$, corresponding to $n = 1$ in Eq. (16–81), is considered, then as λ_0 increases, that is, as ω decreases, a point is reached where $1/\lambda_g^2$ must be negative in order to satisfy Eq. (16–82). In this case the coefficient of z in Eq. (16–80) is imaginary, and the exponential, instead of oscillating in z, becomes a decreasing exponential. To say this another way: if $\lambda_0 > 2a$ the electromagnetic wave will be exponentially damped in z, instead of propagating. If n is taken as 2, then $\lambda_c = 2a/2 = a$ and the longest wavelength propagated is a. The reason for the subscript c is now clear; it means "cutoff." The cutoff wavelength is the longest wavelength that can be propagated for a given mode (n value).

The velocity v_p, which was found earlier, always exceeds the velocity of light and, in fact, becomes infinite when the wavelength in free space equals λ_c, that is, when $\theta = 0$. This velocity is the phase velocity, by which is meant the velocity of a point of constant phase on the wave. Without

---

* E' has been written for $2jE$.

dwelling on the relativistic aspects of the question, this represents an apparent contradiction of the postulate that no signal can be propagated with a velocity greater than the velocity of light. The resolution of this apparent difficulty is that energy is propagated down the guide with a smaller velocity than the velocity of light, namely, with the so-called group velocity. Signals are transmitted with the group velocity; they are not transmitted with the phase velocity.

To determine the velocity of energy propagation, we shall calculate the energy density. This energy density times the group velocity gives the energy flux, or Poynting vector. Thus by dividing the Poynting vector by the energy density, the velocity of energy propagation can be obtained.

The magnetic induction in the guide is readily obtained from

$$\text{curl } \mathbf{E} = -\frac{\partial \mathbf{B}}{\partial t}. \tag{16–83}$$

By using Eq. (16–80) for $\mathbf{E}$, and assuming that $\mathbf{B}(\mathbf{r}, t) = \mathbf{B}(\mathbf{r})e^{-j\omega t}$, we quickly find

$$\mathbf{B}(\mathbf{r}, t) = \mathbf{j}E' \frac{2\pi}{\omega\lambda_g} \sin\frac{2\pi y}{\lambda_c} e^{j[(2\pi z/\lambda_g)-\omega t]} + \mathbf{j}\mathbf{k}E' \frac{2\pi}{\omega\lambda_c} \cos\frac{2\pi y}{\lambda_c} e^{j[(2\pi z/\lambda_g)-\omega t]}. \tag{16–84}$$

The energy density is

$$w = \tfrac{1}{2}(\mathbf{E} \cdot \mathbf{D} + \mathbf{B} \cdot \mathbf{H}), \tag{16–85}$$

while the Poynting vector is

$$\mathbf{S} = \mathbf{E} \times \mathbf{H}. \tag{16–86}$$

Complex notation has been used for $\mathbf{E}$ and $\mathbf{B}$, with the tacit assumption that the real part of each expression is to be taken. In calculating w and $\mathbf{S}$ then, the real parts should be taken and multiplied together. However, since the quantities to be used in calculating the group velocity are the time averages of Eq. (16–85) and (16–86), a theorem from complex variables may be used to circumvent the taking of real parts.

If $f = f_0 e^{j\omega t}$ and $g = g_0 e^{j\omega t}$, where f_0 and g_0 may depend on other variables but not on the time, then

$$\overline{\text{Re} f \, \text{Re} g} = \tfrac{1}{2} \text{Re} f^*g. \tag{16–87}$$

The bar indicates time averaging. To prove this relationship, let $f_0 = u + jv$ and $g_0 = \xi + j\eta$. Then

$$\text{Re} f \, \text{Re} g = (u \cos \omega t - v \sin \omega t)(\xi \cos \omega t - \eta \sin \omega t), \tag{16–88}$$

while

$$\text{Re} f^*g = u\xi + v\eta. \tag{16–89}$$

The following integrals are easily verified:

$$
\left.
\begin{aligned}
\lim_{T \to \infty} \frac{1}{T} \int_0^T \sin^2 \omega t\, dt &= \tfrac{1}{2}, \\[2mm]
\lim_{T \to \infty} \frac{1}{T} \int_0^T \cos^2 \omega t\, dt &= \tfrac{1}{2}, \\[2mm]
\lim_{T \to \infty} \frac{1}{T} \int_0^T \sin \omega t \cos \omega t\, dt &= 0.
\end{aligned}
\right\} \tag{16-90}
$$

By means of these integrals, it is easy to see that the time average of Eq. (16–88) is

$$
\overline{\mathrm{Re}\, f\, \mathrm{Re}\, g} = \tfrac{1}{2}(u\xi + v\eta). \tag{16-91}
$$

Comparison of (16–91) with (16–89) proves the theorem of Eq. (16–87).

The time average energy density is

$$
\overline{w} = \tfrac{1}{4}\,\mathrm{Re}\,[\mathbf{E}^* \cdot \mathbf{D} + \mathbf{B}^* \cdot \mathbf{H}] = \tfrac{1}{4}\,\mathrm{Re}\left[\epsilon_0 E'^* E' \sin^2\left(\frac{2\pi y}{\lambda_c}\right) \right.
$$
$$
\left. + \frac{1}{\mu_0} E'^* E' \left(\frac{2\pi}{\omega \lambda_g}\right)^2 \sin^2\left(\frac{2\pi y}{\lambda_c}\right) + \frac{1}{\mu_0} E'^* E' \left(\frac{2\pi}{\omega \lambda_c}\right)^2 \cos^2\left(\frac{2\pi y}{\lambda_c}\right) \right]. \tag{16-92}
$$

Integrating in the y-direction, across the guide, effectively replaces each $\sin^2 (2\pi y/\lambda_c)$ and $\cos^2 (2\pi y/\lambda_c)$ by $a/2$. Thus

$$
\int_0^a \overline{w}\, dy = \tfrac{1}{4} E'^* E' \frac{a}{2}\left[\epsilon_0 + \frac{1}{\mu_0} \frac{4\pi^2}{\omega^2}\left(\frac{1}{\lambda_g^2} + \frac{1}{\lambda_c^2}\right) \right]
$$
$$
= \tfrac{1}{4} E'^* E' \epsilon_0 a. \tag{16-93}
$$

The time average of the z-component of the Poynting vector is

$$
\overline{S}_z = \tfrac{1}{2}\,\mathrm{Re}\, E_x^* H_y
$$
$$
= \tfrac{1}{2}\,\mathrm{Re}\left[E'^* \sin\left(\frac{2\pi y}{\lambda_c}\right) \frac{1}{\mu_0} E' \frac{2\pi}{\omega \lambda_g} \sin\left(\frac{2\pi y}{\lambda_c}\right) \right] \tag{16-94}
$$
$$
= \tfrac{1}{2} E'^* E' \frac{2\pi}{\mu_0 \omega \lambda_g} \sin^2\left(\frac{2\pi y}{\lambda_c}\right).
$$

Integrating this expression from $y = 0$ to $y = a$ yields the total average power (per unit length in the x-direction) traveling down the guide:

$$
\int_0^a \overline{S}_z\, dy = \tfrac{1}{4} E'^* E' \frac{2\pi}{\mu_0 \omega \lambda_g} a. \tag{16-95}
$$

The velocity of energy propagation is the quotient of Eq. (16–95) divided by (16–93). Thus

$$v_g = \frac{2\pi}{\epsilon_0\mu_0\omega\lambda_g} = \frac{2\pi c^2}{\omega\lambda_g} = c\frac{\lambda_0}{\lambda_g}. \qquad (16\text{–}96)$$

From Eq. (16–78), we note that λ_g is greater than λ_0, and hence $\omega\lambda_g/2\pi$ is greater than c, which makes it clear that v_g is less than c.

Our understanding of the difference between the group velocity, v_g, and the phase velocity, v_p, can be enhanced by noting that from Eq. (16–78) $\lambda_g = \lambda_0/\sin\theta$. Using this result in Eq. (16–96), we find

$$v_g = c\sin\theta, \qquad (16\text{–}97)$$

and we have already seen that

$$v_p = \frac{c}{\sin\theta}. \qquad (16\text{–}98)$$

It is readily apparent that

$$v_g v_p = c^2, \qquad (16\text{–}99)$$

which is generally true for propagation in a waveguide. [Note that Eq. (16–99) does not necessarily apply to other kinds of wave propagation, in particular it does not apply to plane waves in nondispersive media where the phase and group velocities are identical.] Recalling that θ is the angle between the direction of propagation of one of the component waves and the y-axis makes it a simple matter to draw Fig. 16–6, which shows a section in the yz-plane of the region between the conducting planes. The intersection of a wavefront with the z-axis moves with the velocity $v_p = c/\sin\theta$; however, the component of c along the z-axis is $c\sin\theta = v_g$.

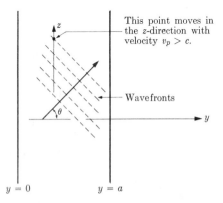

FIG. 16–6.   Detailed motion of the wavefronts during wave propagation between conducting planes.

Many of the results obtained for the simple parallel plate waveguide persist for more complex cases. In particular, the common rectangular waveguide has very similar properties. In the next section some general aspects of other waveguides will be considered, with particular reference to rectangular guides.

16-6 Waveguides. In Section 15-4 it was shown that $\mathbf{E}$ and $\mathbf{H}$ both satisfy the wave equation in free space, that is,

$$\nabla^2 \mathbf{E} - \epsilon_0\mu_0 \frac{\partial^2 \mathbf{E}}{\partial t^2} = 0, \qquad \nabla^2 \mathbf{H} - \epsilon_0\mu_0 \frac{\partial^2 \mathbf{H}}{\partial t^2} = 0. \qquad (16\text{--}100)$$

For monochromatic waves, that is, waves of the form $\mathbf{E}(\mathbf{r}, t) = \mathbf{E}(\mathbf{r})e^{-j\omega t}$, these equations become

$$\nabla^2 \mathbf{E} + \omega^2\epsilon_0\mu_0\mathbf{E} = 0, \qquad \nabla^2 \mathbf{H} + \omega^2\epsilon_0\mu_0\mathbf{H} = 0. \qquad (16\text{--}101)$$

In addition to these wave equations, Maxwell's equations must be satisfied. For the transverse electric (TE) case propagating in the z-direction, $E_z = 0$; furthermore, waves propagating in the z-direction have the remaining five field quantities proportional to $e^{j2\pi z/\lambda_g}$. Maxwell's curl equations in this case are

curl $\mathbf{E} - j\mu_0\omega\mathbf{H} = 0$:

$$\frac{\partial E_y}{\partial x} - \frac{\partial E_x}{\partial y} - j\mu_0\omega H_z = 0, \qquad \text{(a)} \left.\vphantom{\begin{array}{c}1\\1\\1\end{array}}\right\}$$

$$E_x = +\frac{\mu_0\omega\lambda_g}{2\pi} H_y, \qquad \text{(b)} \left.\vphantom{\begin{array}{c}1\\1\end{array}}\right\} \quad (16\text{--}102)$$

$$E_y = -\frac{\mu_0\omega\lambda_g}{2\pi} H_x. \qquad \text{(c)} \left.\vphantom{\begin{array}{c}1\end{array}}\right.$$

curl $\mathbf{H} + j\mu_0\omega\mathbf{E} = 0$:

$$\frac{\partial H_z}{\partial y} - \frac{2\pi j}{\lambda_g} H_y + j\epsilon_0\omega E_x = 0, \qquad \text{(a)} \left.\vphantom{\begin{array}{c}1\\1\\1\end{array}}\right\}$$

$$\frac{2\pi j}{\lambda_g} H_x - \frac{\partial H_z}{\partial x} + j\epsilon_0\omega E_y = 0, \qquad \text{(b)} \left.\vphantom{\begin{array}{c}1\\1\end{array}}\right\} \quad (16\text{--}103)$$

$$\frac{\partial H_y}{\partial x} - \frac{\partial H_x}{\partial y} = 0. \qquad \text{(c)} \left.\vphantom{\begin{array}{c}1\end{array}}\right.$$

It is clear that (a) of Eq. (16-103) and (b) of Eq. (16-102) imply

$$\frac{\partial H_z}{\partial y} = \left(\frac{2\pi j}{\lambda_g} - j\frac{\epsilon_0\mu_0\omega^2\lambda_g}{2\pi}\right) H_y, \qquad (16\text{--}104)$$

and therefore that H_y can be found if H_z is known. Similarly, from (c) of

(16-102) and (b) of (16-103), H_x can be found from H_z. Finally, E_x and E_y are simply related to H_y and H_x by (b) and (c) of (16-102). Thus if H_z is found, all the other field quantities may be found by differentiation. H_z itself must satisfy Eq. (16-100); therefore, taking cognizance of the $e^{j2\pi z/\lambda_g}$ z-dependence, we write

$$\frac{\partial^2 H_z}{\partial x^2} + \frac{\partial^2 H_z}{\partial y^2} + \left(\omega^2 \epsilon_0 \mu_0 - \frac{4\pi^2}{\lambda_g^2}\right) H_z = 0. \qquad (16\text{-}105)$$

It remains only to determine the boundary conditions to be imposed on the solutions of Eq. (16-105).

If a general cylindrical guide with perfectly conducting walls, such as that shown in Fig. 16-7, is under consideration, then the appropriate boundary conditions are that the tangential component of **E** and the normal component of **B** should vanish on S. The tangential component of **H** and the normal component of **D** are arbitrary. Imposing these conditions gives rise to a relationship connecting λ_g, ω, and the dimensions of the guide, exactly as Eq. (16-82) does for the parallel plane case.

To better understand the procedure, consider the rectangular waveguide shown in Fig. 16-8. Equation (16-105) can be separated by the usual method of separation of variables. The general solution consists of a sum of terms of the form

$$H_z(x, y, z) = (A \cos \kappa_x x \cos \kappa_y y + B \cos \kappa_x x \sin \kappa_y y$$
$$+ C \sin \kappa_x x \cos \kappa_y y + D \sin \kappa_x x \sin \kappa_y y)e^{2\pi j z/\lambda_g}, \qquad (16\text{-}106)$$

with

$$-(\kappa_x^2 + \kappa_y^2) + [\omega^2 \epsilon_0 \mu_0 - (4\pi^2/\lambda_g^2)] = 0. \qquad (16\text{-}107)$$

From this H_z, we obtain E_x:

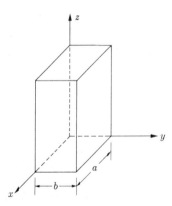

FIG. 16-7. Wave propagation inside a conducting cylinder.

FIG. 16-8. A rectangular waveguide.

$$E_x = -\frac{\mu_0 \omega \lambda_g}{2\pi} \left(\frac{2\pi j}{\lambda_g} - j \frac{\epsilon_0 \mu_0 \omega^2 \lambda_g}{2\pi} \right)^{-1} \frac{\partial H_z}{\partial y}. \qquad (16\text{--}108)$$

The partial differentiation changes every $\cos \kappa_y y$ to a $\sin \kappa_y y$, and conversely. However, since E_x must vanish at $y = 0$ and at $y = b$, only terms involving $\sin \kappa_y y$ may survive in E_x, and these terms must have $\kappa_y = n\pi/b$. Thus only $\cos \kappa_y y$ terms survive in Eq. (16–106). A similar argument shows that only $\cos \kappa_x x$ terms may survive, and that these must have $\kappa_x = m\pi/a$. The allowed solutions for H_z, that is, those which give vanishing tangential components of **E** at the boundary, have the form

$$H_z = A \cos \frac{m\pi x}{a} \cos \frac{n\pi y}{b} e^{2\pi j z/\lambda_g}. \qquad (16\text{--}109)$$

Each possible pair of values of m and n is referred to as a mode. The notation TE_{mn} is used for modes of the form (16–109); TE means transverse electric, n and m count the number of half-waves in the narrower (n) and wider (m) dimensions.

Returning now to Eq. (16–107) and using $\kappa_x = m\pi/a$ and $\kappa_y = n\pi/b$, we obtain

$$\left(\frac{2\pi}{\lambda_g} \right)^2 = \left(\frac{2\pi}{\lambda_0} \right)^2 - \left(\frac{n\pi}{b} \right)^2 - \left(\frac{m\pi}{a} \right)^2, \qquad (16\text{--}110)$$

which clearly indicates that for fixed λ_0 the guide wavelength, and consequently the guide velocity $v_g = c\lambda_0/\lambda_g$, depend on the mode. We also see that there are maximum wavelengths for the propagation of various modes. Clearly, if λ_0 is sufficiently large $(2\pi/\lambda_0)^2$ will be smaller than $(n\pi/b)^2 + (m\pi/a)^2$. In this case, the right side of Eq. (16–110) becomes negative and consequently the value of λ_g is imaginary. This leads to attenuation rather than propagation.

Rectangular waveguides are extensively used for the transmission of microwave power. It is usual to choose a waveguide size such that only the TE_{10} mode at the desired frequency propagates in the guide. A common size of waveguide is 0.4 in. $\times$ 0.9 in., inside dimensions. The maximum wavelength that will propagate in the TE_{10} mode is found by putting $m = 1$, $n = 0$, $a = 0.9$ in. $= 2.28$ cm and, $b = 0.4$ in. $= 1.01$ cm into Eq. (16–110). · The result: $\lambda_{0,\text{max}} = 4.57$ cm is obtained by putting $\lambda_g = \infty$; wavelengths longer than this will not propagate, but shorter wavelengths will. The mode with the next shorter cutoff wavelength is TE_{11} or TE_{20}, depending on the dimensions of the guide. If $b < a/\sqrt{3}$, the TE_{20} cutoff wavelength is greater than the TE_{11}. Calculation of the TE_{20} wavelength is very simple; it is just one-half the TE_{10} cutoff wavelength, or 2.28 cm. Imperfections in manufactured waveguides and high losses close to the TE_{10} cutoff wavelength make it necessary to restrict the TE_{10} band of commercial waveguides to the practical limits of 2.42 to 4.35 cm.

16–7 Cavity resonators. Another type of device closely related to waveguides and of considerable practical importance is the cavity resonator. Cavity resonators display the properties typical of resonant circuits in that they can store energy in oscillating electric and magnetic fields; furthermore, practical cavity resonators dissipate a fraction of the stored energy in each cycle of oscillation. In this latter respect, however, cavity resonators are usually superior to conventional L-C circuits by a factor of about twenty, that is, the fraction of the stored energy dissipated per cycle in a cavity resonator is about $1/20$ the fraction dissipated per cycle in an L-C circuit. An additional advantage is that cavity resonators of practical size have resonant frequencies which range upward from a few hundred megacycles—just the region where it is almost impossible to construct ordinary L-C circuits.

The simplest cavity resonator is a rectangular parallelepiped with perfectly conducting walls. For such a cavity, the appropriate boundary conditions are the vanishing of the tangential component of $\mathbf{E}$ and the normal component of $\mathbf{B}$ at the boundary. The tangential component of $\mathbf{H}$ and the normal component of $\mathbf{D}$ are arbitrary. The electric and magnetic fields must satisfy the wave equations (16–100); thus E_x must satisfy

$$\frac{\partial^2 E_x}{\partial x^2} + \frac{\partial^2 E_x}{\partial y^2} + \frac{\partial^2 E_x}{\partial z^2} + \frac{\omega^2}{c^2} E_x = 0. \tag{16–111}$$

If the cavity consists of the region bounded by the six planes $x = 0$, $x = a$; $y = 0$, $y = b$; $z = 0$, $z = d$, then E_x must have the form

$$E_x = E_1 f_1(x) \sin \kappa_y y \sin \kappa_z z\, e^{-j\omega t}, \tag{16–112}$$

with $\kappa_y = m\pi/b$ and $\kappa_z = n\pi/d$, in order that E_x vanish at $y = 0$, at $z = 0$, at $y = b$, and at $z = d$. Furthermore, E_x alone cannot be a solution unless $f_1(x)$ is a constant, since div $\mathbf{E}$ must vanish to satisfy one of Maxwell's equations. For E_y and E_z the situation is similar, and the solutions take the forms

$$E_y = E_2 \sin \kappa_x x\, f_2(y) \sin \kappa_z z\, e^{-j\omega t},$$

$$E_z = E_3 \sin \kappa_x x \sin \kappa_y y\, f_3(z) e^{-j\omega t}, \tag{16–113}$$

with κ_y and κ_z as in Eq. (16–112), and $\kappa_x = l\pi/a$. If the divergence of $\mathbf{E}$ is to vanish, then the equation

$$\left(E_1 \frac{df_1}{dx} \sin \kappa_y y \sin \kappa_z z + E_2 \sin \kappa_x x \frac{df_2}{dy} \sin \kappa_z z \right.$$

$$\left. + E_3 \sin \kappa_x x \sin \kappa_y y \frac{df_3}{dz} \right) e^{-j\omega t} = 0 \tag{16–114}$$

must be satisfied. This is accomplished if $f_1 = \cos \kappa_x x$, $f_2 = \cos \kappa_y y$, $f_3 = \cos \kappa_z z$, and

$$\kappa_x E_1 + \kappa_y E_2 + \kappa_z E_3 = 0, \tag{16-115}$$

which is just the condition that $\boldsymbol{\kappa}$ be perpendicular to $\mathbf{E}$. Returning to the wave equation, it is apparent that the resonant frequencies of the cavity are given by

$$\kappa_x^2 + \kappa_y^2 + \kappa_z^2 - \frac{\omega^2}{c^2} = 0, \tag{16-116}$$

or

$$\frac{l^2}{a^2} + \frac{m^2}{b^2} + \frac{n^2}{d^2} - \frac{4f^2}{c^2} = 0. \tag{16-117}$$

A typical cavity constructed from a waveguide 0.4 in. $\times$ 0.9 in. in size is characterized by $l = 1$, $m = 0$, $n = 2$ (a so-called TE_{102} cavity). The resonant frequency of such a cavity is clearly determined by the z-dimension, d. Many other aspects of the rectangular cavity resonator problem can be treated in detail; some of these are left as exercises.

Other forms of cavity resonators may be constructed; however, only the right circular cylinder and the rectangular parallelepiped are easily fabricated and amenable to an exact mathematical treatment. The treatment of the right circular cylinder involves functions which are more complicated than the sines and cosines, specifically the Bessel functions. Satisfying the boundary conditions requires finding the zeros of these functions in the same way the zeros of the sines entered the rectangular problem. Rather than enter into the elaborate discussion which results, we refer the interested reader to Montgomery, *Technique of Microwave Measurements* (McGraw-Hill, New York, 1947), p. 297 ff., where a brief but very useful treatment of the cylindrical cavity resonator is given.

16–8 Radiation from an oscillating dipole. A simple example of radiation from a prescribed time-dependent charge-current distribution is provided by calculation of the radiation from an oscillating electric dipole. The dipole will be assumed to consist of spheres located at $z = \pm l/2$ connected by a wire of negligible capacitance, as shown in Fig. 16–9. The charge on the upper sphere is q, and that on the lower sphere is $-q$. Conservation of charge requires that the current in the connecting wire be given by

$$I = +\dot{q}, \tag{16-118}$$

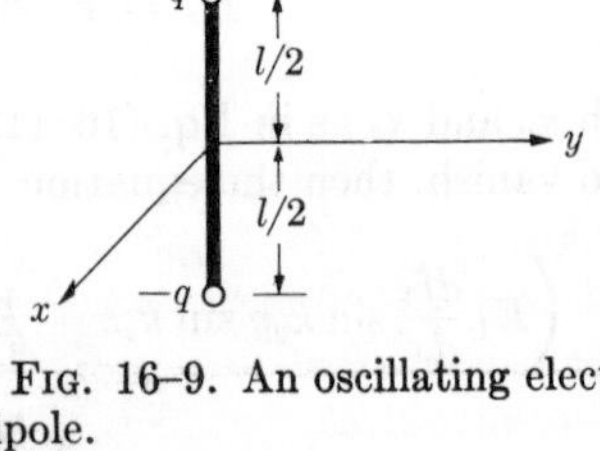

FIG. 16–9. An oscillating electric dipole.

where I is positive in the plus z-direction. It must be noted that the condition of negligible capacitance of the wire and its concomitant uniform current can be satisfied only if the length l of the dipole is small compared with the wavelength of the radiation (see the discussion at the beginning of Chapter 13).

The vector potential due to the current distribution specified by Eq. (16–118) is

$$A_z(\mathbf{r}, t) = \frac{\mu}{4\pi} \int_{-l/2}^{l/2} \frac{I(z', t - \sqrt{\epsilon\mu}|\mathbf{r} - z'\mathbf{k}|)\, dz'}{|\mathbf{r} - z'\mathbf{k}|}. \qquad (16\text{–}119)$$

This rather cumbersome expression can be quickly simplified if we examine the quantity $|\mathbf{r} - \mathbf{k}z'|$. It is clear that

$$|\mathbf{r} - \mathbf{k}z'| = (r^2 - 2z'\mathbf{k} \cdot \mathbf{r} + z'^2)^{1/2}. \qquad (16\text{–}120)$$

If l is small compared with r, that is, if we consider the field only at large distances from the dipole, the right side of (16–119) can be expanded in the form

$$|\mathbf{r} - \mathbf{k}z'| = r - z'\cos\theta, \qquad (16\text{–}121)$$

where θ is the angle between $\mathbf{r}$ and the z-axis. The quantity in (16–121) is involved twice in the expression for $\mathbf{A}$. In the denominator, $z'\cos\theta$ can simply be neglected if r is large enough. In the retardation term, however, $z'\cos\theta$ can be neglected only if $z'\cos\theta\sqrt{\epsilon\mu}$ is negligible compared with the time during which the current changes significantly, e.g., compared with the period for harmonically varying currents. Since $(\epsilon\mu)^{-1/2} = v$, the velocity of electromagnetic waves, and $z'\cos\theta \lesssim l/2$, this means that $z'\cos\theta/v$ can be neglected in the retardation term only if

$$\frac{l}{2} \ll vT = \lambda. \qquad (16\text{–}122)$$

Thus, if the dipole is small compared with one wavelength, and the observation point is far, compared with l, from the dipole, then $\mathbf{A}$ is given by

$$A_z(\mathbf{r}, t) = \frac{\mu}{4\pi} \frac{1}{r} l\, I\left(t - \frac{r}{v}\right). \qquad (16\text{–}123)$$

The scalar potential φ can be found either by applying the Lorentz condition or by using the appropriate expression for the retarded potential. Both methods give the same final result; however, because the electric potential due to a dipole is the difference between two large terms, great care must be used in approximating the retarded potential. Since this difficulty is circumvented in the Lorentz condition calculation, the scalar potential will be obtained by solving

$$\operatorname{div} \mathbf{A} + \epsilon\mu \frac{\partial\varphi}{\partial t} = 0, \qquad (16\text{--}124)$$

with $\mathbf{A}$ as given by Eq. (6–123). Thus

$$\frac{\partial\varphi}{\partial t} = -\frac{l}{4\pi\epsilon} \frac{\partial}{\partial z} \frac{1}{r} I\left(t - \frac{r}{v}\right)$$

$$= \frac{l}{4\pi\epsilon}\left[\frac{z}{r^3} I\left(t - \frac{r}{v}\right) + \frac{z}{r^2 v} I'\left(t - \frac{r}{v}\right)\right], \qquad (16\text{--}125)$$

where I' represents the derivative of I with respect to its argument. This equation is readily integrated by noting that $I = +q'$ and thus that

$$\varphi(\mathbf{r}, t) = \frac{l}{4\pi\epsilon} \frac{z}{r^2}\left[\frac{q(t - r/v)}{r} + \frac{I(t - r/v)}{v}\right]. \qquad (16\text{--}126)$$

Having obtained the scalar and vector potentials, we now need only to differentiate them to obtain the electromagnetic field. Before doing this, it is convenient to specialize the charge-current distribution to one which varies harmonically with the time. The particular choice

$$q\left(t - \frac{r}{v}\right) = q_0 \cos\omega\left(t - \frac{r}{v}\right),$$

$$I = I_0 \sin\omega\left(t - \frac{r}{v}\right) = -\omega q_0 \sin\omega\left(t - \frac{r}{v}\right) \qquad (16\text{--}127)$$

will be made. Resolving $\mathbf{A}$ into spherical components, we obtain

$$A_r = \frac{\mu}{4\pi} \frac{I_0 l}{r} \cos\theta \sin\omega\left(t - \frac{r}{v}\right),$$

$$A_\theta = -\frac{\mu}{4\pi} \frac{I_0 l}{r} \sin\theta \sin\omega\left(t - \frac{r}{v}\right), \qquad (16\text{--}128)$$

$$A_\phi = 0,$$

and it becomes obvious that only the ϕ-component of $\mathbf{B}$ is different from zero. This component is

$$B_\phi = \frac{1}{r} \frac{\partial}{\partial r}(rA_\theta) - \frac{1}{r} \frac{\partial A_r}{\partial \theta}$$

$$= \frac{\mu}{4\pi} \frac{I_0 l}{r} \sin\theta\left[\frac{\omega}{v} \cos\omega\left(t - \frac{r}{v}\right) + \frac{1}{r} \sin\omega\left(t - \frac{r}{v}\right)\right]. \qquad (16\text{--}129)$$

The computation of the electric field is somewhat more complex, since not only $\mathbf{A}$ but also φ is involved. The result of performing the differentiations is

$$E_r = -\frac{\partial \varphi}{\partial r} - \frac{\partial A_r}{\partial t} = \frac{2lI_0 \cos \theta}{4\pi\epsilon}\left[\frac{\sin \omega(t - r/v)}{r^2 v} - \frac{\cos \omega(t - r/v)}{\omega r^3}\right],$$

$$E_\theta = -\frac{1}{r}\frac{\partial \varphi}{\partial \theta} - \frac{\partial A_\theta}{\partial t}$$

$$= -\frac{lI_0 \sin \theta}{4\pi\epsilon}\left[\left(\frac{1}{\omega r^3} - \frac{\omega}{rv^2}\right)\cos \omega\left(t - \frac{r}{v}\right) - \frac{1}{r^2 v}\sin \omega\left(t - \frac{r}{v}\right)\right],$$

$$E_\phi = -\frac{1}{r \sin \theta}\frac{\partial \varphi}{\partial \phi} - \frac{\partial A_\phi}{\partial t} = 0. \tag{16-130}$$

It is interesting to compute the rate at which the dipole radiates energy. This is done by integrating the normal component of the Poynting vector over a sphere of radius R. Thus

$$\oint \mathbf{S} \cdot \mathbf{n}\, da = \frac{1}{\mu} R^2 \int_0^\pi E_\theta B_\phi 2\pi \sin \theta\, d\theta. \tag{16-131}$$

Equations (16-129) and (16-130) make it possible to evaluate completely the integral which appears in Eq. (16-131); however, it is perhaps more instructive to evaluate only the portion which does not vanish as $R \to \infty$. This is done by selecting the term proportional to $1/r$ in E_θ and B_ϕ. The result is

$$\oint \mathbf{S} \cdot \mathbf{n}\, da = \frac{(I_0 l)^2}{6\pi\epsilon}\frac{\omega^2}{v^3}\cos^2 \omega\left(t - \frac{r}{v}\right). \tag{16-132}$$

This is the instantaneous radiated power; the average radiated power (since the average of $\cos^2$ is one-half) is

$$\overline{P} = \frac{l^2\omega^2}{6\pi\epsilon v^3}\frac{I_0^2}{2}. \tag{16-133}$$

A more conventional form of Eq. (16-133) is obtained by introducing $\lambda = 2\pi v/\omega$ and $v = 1/\sqrt{\epsilon\mu}$. The result is

$$\overline{P} = \frac{2\pi}{3}\sqrt{\frac{\mu}{\epsilon}}\left(\frac{l}{\lambda}\right)^2 \frac{I_0^2}{2}. \tag{16-134}$$

A resistance R carrying a current $I_0 \cos \omega t$ dissipates energy at an average rate $\overline{P} = RI_0^2/2$. Comparing this with Eq. (16-134), we see that it is sensible to define the *radiation resistance* of a dipole by

$$R_r = \frac{2\pi}{3}\sqrt{\frac{\mu}{\epsilon}}\left(\frac{l}{\lambda}\right)^2. \tag{16-135}$$

In free space, $\mu = \mu_0$, $\epsilon = \epsilon_0$ and

$$R_r = 787 \left(\frac{l}{\lambda}\right)^2 \text{ ohms}, \qquad \text{(free space)}.$$

One might be tempted to use Eq. (16–135) to describe the radiation from a radio antenna. Unfortunately, several defects prevent obtaining good results in this way. The principal defects are (1) the effect of the proximity of the earth is neglected, (2) ordinarily antennas are not capacitively loaded at the ends, and (3) antennas are very seldom short compared with the wavelength they radiate. Removal of the last two defects will be discussed in the next section; however, discussion of the perturbing effect of the earth is beyond the scope of this text.

16–9 Radiation from a half-wave antenna. The restriction to lengths small compared with one wavelength can be removed in some cases by relatively simple means. In particular, a wire which is just one-half wavelength in length can be broken into infinitesimal elements, to each of which the method of the preceding section can be applied. Let the wire lie along the z-axis from $-\lambda/4$ to $+\lambda/4$ and carry a current

$$I(z', t) = I_0 \sin \omega t \cos\left(\frac{2\pi z'}{\lambda}\right). \tag{16–136}$$

An element dz' at z' contributes

$$dE_\theta = I_0 \frac{\sin \theta}{4\pi \epsilon R v^2} \omega \cos\left(\omega t - \frac{R\omega}{v}\right) \cos\left(\frac{2\pi z'}{\lambda}\right) dz' \tag{16–137}$$

to E_θ. Here R is the distance from dz' to the point of observation, and terms of order $1/R^2$ have been neglected. In the same way,

$$dB_\phi = \frac{\mu}{4\pi} \frac{I_0 \omega}{Rv} \sin \theta \cos \omega\left(t - \frac{R}{v}\right) \cos\left(\frac{2\pi z'}{\lambda}\right) dz'. \tag{16–138}$$

The problem in calculating E_θ and B_ϕ is reduced to evaluating

$$K = \int_{-\pi/2}^{\pi/2} \frac{1}{R} \cos \omega\left(t - \frac{R}{v}\right) \cos u \, du, \tag{16–139}$$

where $u = 2\pi z'/\lambda$. As before, $R = r - z' \cos \theta$, and hence by choosing r sufficiently large $z' \cos \theta$ can be made negligible. In the argument of the cosine, however, more care is required, and K is written as

$$K = \frac{1}{r} \int_{-\pi/2}^{\pi/2} \cos\left[\omega\left(t - \frac{r}{v}\right) + u \cos \theta\right] \cos u \, du.$$

The cosine can be expanded to give

$$K = \frac{1}{r} \cos \omega \left(t - \frac{r}{v} \right) \int_{-\pi/2}^{\pi/2} \cos \left(u \cos \theta \right) \cos u \, du$$

$$- \frac{1}{r} \sin \omega \left(t - \frac{r}{v} \right) \int_{-\pi/2}^{\pi/2} \sin \left(u \cos \theta \right) \cos u \, du.$$

The second integral vanishes, and the first can be evaluated by expressing the cosines as exponentials or by using standard tables. The result is

$$K = \frac{2}{r} \cos \omega \left(t - \frac{r}{v} \right) \frac{\cos \left[(\pi/2) \cos \theta \right]}{\sin^2 \theta}. \tag{16-140}$$

Having evaluated K, we find that

$$E_\theta = \frac{I_0}{2\pi \epsilon r v} \cos \omega \left(t - \frac{r}{v} \right) \frac{\cos \left[(\pi/2) \cos \theta \right]}{\sin \theta}$$

$$B_\phi = \frac{\mu I_0}{2\pi r} \cos \omega \left(t - \frac{r}{v} \right) \frac{\cos \left[(\pi/2) \cos \theta \right]}{\sin \theta}. \tag{16-141}$$

The integrated average Poynting vector is

$$\overline{P} = \frac{1}{4\pi} \sqrt{\frac{\mu}{\epsilon}} I_0^2 \int_0^\pi \frac{\cos^2 \left[(\pi/2) \cos \theta \right]}{\sin^2 \theta} \sin \theta \, d\theta. \tag{16-142}$$

The remaining integral can be evaluated only as an infinite series, but we simply note that for a half-wave antenna the result is

$$\overline{P} = 73.1 \text{ ohms} \frac{I_0^2}{2}. \tag{16-143}$$

This method can be applied to more complicated problems; however, the technical details become rather formidable.

PROBLEMS

16–1. A beam of monochromatic light (frequency ω) in vacuum is incident normally on a dielectric film of refractive index $n = \sqrt{\epsilon/\epsilon_0}$. The thickness of the film is d. Calculate the reflection coefficient for the reflected wave as a function of d and n. [*Hint:* Assume two waves traveling in opposite directions inside the film.]

16–2. Find the surface charge density and the current per unit width on the surface of a perfect conductor on which plane electromagnetic waves are incident, when the electric vector is (1) perpendicular to the plane of incidence, and (2) parallel to the plane of incidence.

16–3. A plane wave is incident obliquely on the interface between two nonconducting, dielectric media (1, 2). The electric field vectors E_1, E_2, and E_3 are all perpendicular to the plane of incidence. Apply the boundary conditions, and show that two independent equations are obtained in addition to Snell's law and the law of reflection.

16–4. Obtain the Fresnel equations [analogous to Eqs. (16–50) and (16–51)] for the case described in the preceding problem.

16–5. (a) Assuming $\mu_1 = \mu_2 = \mu_0$, and using Snell's law, rewrite Eqs. (16–50) and (16–51) in terms of the indices of refraction and functions of θ_1 only; in other words, eliminate θ_3 from the equations. (b) Use the results of part (a) to discuss reflection and transmission at the interface between two dielectrics for the case where $n_2 < n_1$ and $\sin \theta_1 = n_2/n_1$.

16–6. Show that for a vacuum-conductor interface the reflection coefficient R may be written as

$$R = 1 - 4\pi \frac{\mu}{\mu_0} \frac{\delta}{\lambda_0},$$

where δ is the skin depth.

16–7. Determine E and B for TM waves propagating in the yz-plane between two parallel, perfectly conducting plates, at $y = 0$ and at $y = a$.

16–8. Write down the E and H fields for the TE_{101} mode of a cubic cavity of side a. Sketch the nature of the field distributions throughout the cube.

16–9. Determine the limiting values of the width a of a waveguide of square cross section which will transmit a wave of length λ in the TE_{10} mode but not in the TE_{11} or TM_{11} modes.

16–10. (a) Determine, as a function of the angles θ and ϕ, the average power density radiated into vacuum by an oscillating dipole. (b) Calculate the total power radiated by a dipole of length 10 ft at a frequency of 500 kc/sec if the current in the dipole is 2 amp (effective value). (c) What is the radiation resistance of the dipole oscillator in part (b)?

16–11. A circular loop of wire carrying the current $I = I_0 \cos \omega t$ constitutes an *oscillating magnetic dipole*. Determine the radiation fields E and B for this oscillator, and the total power radiated.

16–12. As sources of electromagnetic radiation, determine the relative efficiency of an electric dipole of length 2 m compared with a magnetic dipole of the same diameter at a frequency of 1 Mc/sec.

CHAPTER 17

ELECTRODYNAMICS*

The retarded potentials calculated in Chapter 15 can be used to investigate the fields produced by moving charges. There are, however, certain difficulties involved here which do not appear in the "prescribed-charge, current distribution" type of problem considered in Chapter 16. These new difficulties are related to the retardation, and reflect the fact that the present charge distribution (in space) must be extrapolated back to the appropriate retarded time. This procedure would be essentially trivial except that different portions of the charge distribution require different retarded times. Although one might expect this effect to disappear for point charges, it actually does not. The appropriate scalar and vector potentials for a moving point charge are the Lienard-Wiechert potentials,. which will now be derived.

17-1 The Lienard-Wiechert potentials. The Lienard-Wiechert potentials are, as noted above, the scalar and vector potentials produced by a moving point charge. One might think that $q/4\pi\epsilon_0 R$, with R the appropriate retarded radius, would give the scalar potential due to a moving point charge. This, however, is not the case, as can be shown in several ways. One of the most instructive procedures is to consider a moving volume carrying with it a fixed charged distribution, for example a uniformly charged spherical volume, moving through space along a prescribed trajectory. The field due to a point charge is the properly taken limit of the field due to such a distribution.

The scalar potential due to a moving charge distribution, at point $\boldsymbol{\xi}$ and time t, is given by the retarded potential†

$$\varphi(\boldsymbol{\xi}, t) = \frac{1}{4\pi\epsilon_0} \int \frac{\rho(\mathbf{r}', t')}{|\boldsymbol{\xi} - \mathbf{r}'|} \, dv'. \tag{17-1}$$

The crux of the difficulty is now apparent; namely, t' is not fixed and hence the volume of integration, i.e., the volume in which ρ is different from zero, cannot be readily specified. To obviate the difficulty some fixed time t_1 may be chosen and the integration over $\mathbf{r}'$ changed to an integration over $\mathbf{r}_1$. The most convenient choice for t_1 is the retarded time for some point in the interior of the charge distribution. If at time t_1 the charged

---

* This chapter provides a brief introduction to the electromagnetic fields and radiation from moving charges.

† Throughout this chapter only free space is considered.

volume is moving with a velocity $\mathbf{v}(t_1)$ then the important relationships are

$$\rho(\mathbf{r}', t') = \rho(\mathbf{r}_1, t_1), \tag{17-2}$$

$$\mathbf{r}_1 = \mathbf{r}' - \mathbf{v}(t')(t' - t_1) - \tfrac{1}{2}\dot{\mathbf{v}}(t')(t' - t_1)^2 + \cdots, \tag{17-3}$$

where $\dot{\mathbf{v}}$ is the time derivative of $\mathbf{v}$. It is important to understand that t' in Eq. (17-3) is not constant, but depends on $\mathbf{r}'$. The remaining problem is that of relating dv' to dv_1, which is, of course, accomplished through the Jacobian determinant. The relationship is

$$dv_1 = \frac{\partial(x_1, y_1, z_1)}{\partial(x', y', z')} \, dv', \tag{17-4}$$

where the Jacobian, $\partial(x_1, y_1, z_1)/\partial(x', y', z')$, is given by

$$\frac{\partial(x_1, y_1, z_1)}{\partial(x', y', z')} = \begin{vmatrix} \dfrac{\partial x_1}{\partial x'} & \dfrac{\partial x_1}{\partial y'} & \dfrac{\partial x_1}{\partial z'} \\[2mm] \dfrac{\partial y_1}{\partial x'} & \dfrac{\partial y_1}{\partial y'} & \dfrac{\partial y_1}{\partial z'} \\[2mm] \dfrac{\partial z_1}{\partial x'} & \dfrac{\partial z_1}{\partial y'} & \dfrac{\partial z_1}{\partial z'} \end{vmatrix}. \tag{17-5}$$

The derivatives are

$$\frac{\partial x_1}{\partial x'} = 1 - v'_x \frac{\partial t'}{\partial x'} - \dot{v}'_x(t' - t_1) \frac{\partial t'}{\partial x'} + \cdots,$$

and $\tag{17-6}$

$$\frac{\partial x_1}{\partial y'} = -v'_x \frac{\partial t'}{\partial y'} - \dot{v}'_x(t' - t_1) \frac{\partial t'}{\partial y'} + \cdots,$$

where v'_x is $v_x(t')$, the x-component of the velocity at the retarded time t'. The retarded time t' is related to the retarded position simply by

$$t' = t - \frac{|\mathbf{r}' - \boldsymbol{\xi}|}{c}; \tag{17-7}$$

hence

$$\frac{\partial t'}{\partial x'} = -\frac{n'_x}{c}, \tag{17-8}$$

where $\mathbf{n}'$ is a unit vector in the direction $\mathbf{r}' - \boldsymbol{\xi}$. A straightforward, though tedious, expansion of the Jacobian, using Eqs. (17-6) and (17-8), gives

$$\frac{\partial(x_1, y_1, z_1)}{\partial(x', y', z')} = 1 + \frac{\mathbf{v}' \cdot \mathbf{n}'}{c} + \frac{\dot{\mathbf{v}}' \cdot \mathbf{n}'(t' - t_1)}{c} + \cdots, \tag{17-9}$$

where the higher terms involve the second and higher derivatives of $\mathbf{v}'$.

Equation (17–9) can be used in Eq. (17–1) to obtain the scalar potential. However, since the principal interest is in small charged volumes (point charges), it is appropriate to note that if

$$\frac{\dot{\mathbf{v}}' \cdot \mathbf{n}'}{c} (t' - t_1) \cong \frac{\dot{v}d}{c^2} \ll 1,$$

where d measures the size of the charge distribution, then this term can certainly be neglected in the limiting point charge case. Similar criteria exist for the terms involving higher derivatives; however, we need not consider these. Finally, then,

$$\varphi(\xi, t) = \frac{1}{4\pi\epsilon_0} \int \frac{\rho(\mathbf{r}_1, t_1)}{|\xi - \mathbf{r}'|} \frac{dv_1}{1 + \mathbf{v}' \cdot \mathbf{n}'/c} . \qquad (17\text{–}10)$$

Again, if $d \ll |\xi - \mathbf{r}'|$, then $|\xi - \mathbf{r}'|$ can be replaced by R_{t_1}, the distance from the interior point (chosen earlier) to the observation point at time t_1. Thus*

$$\varphi(\xi, t) = \frac{1}{4\pi\epsilon_0} \frac{1}{R_{t_1}(1 + \mathbf{v}' \cdot \mathbf{n}'/c)} \int \rho(\mathbf{r}_1, t_1)\, dv_1 \qquad (17\text{–}11)$$

or, since the integral is now over a well-defined volume,

$$\varphi(\xi, t) = \frac{1}{4\pi\epsilon_0} \frac{q}{R_{t_1}[1 + (\mathbf{v}' \cdot \mathbf{n}'/c)]} , \qquad (17\text{–}12)$$

which is the scalar Lienard-Wiechart potential. The vector potential is found to be

$$\mathbf{A}(\xi, t) = \frac{\mu_0}{4\pi} \frac{q\mathbf{v}'}{R_{t_1}(1 + \mathbf{v}' \cdot \mathbf{n}'/c)} . \qquad (17\text{–}13)$$

These expressions are often written as

$$\varphi(\xi, t) = \frac{q}{4\pi\epsilon_0} \left\{ \frac{1}{R[1 + (\mathbf{v} \cdot \mathbf{n}/c)]} \right\}_{\text{ret}} ,$$

and

$$\mathbf{A}(\xi, t) = \frac{\mu_0 q}{4\pi} \left\{ \frac{\mathbf{v}}{R[1 + (\mathbf{v} \cdot \mathbf{n}/c)]} \right\}_{\text{ret}} ,$$

(17–14)

which simply means that the quantities in braces must be evaluated at our t_1.

17–2 The field of a uniformly moving point charge. The most direct application of the Lienard-Wiechert potentials is to the calculation of the field of a point charge moving in a straight line with constant velocity.

---

* Note that $\mathbf{v}' \cdot \mathbf{n}' = \mathbf{v}(t_1) \cdot \mathbf{n}(t_1)$ to the approximation involved in Eq. (17–11).

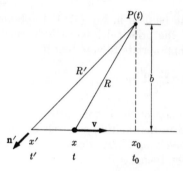

Fig. 17–1. Diagram for calculating the electric field of a moving point charge.

The geometry of such a situation is shown in Fig. 17–1. The field at point P is to be calculated at time t, at which time the charge is at x. The retarded position x' and the retarded time t' are determined by

$$R'^2 = c^2(t - t')^2 = (x_0 - x')^2 + b^2. \tag{17–15}$$

The scalar potential is given by

$$\varphi(P, t) = \frac{q}{4\pi\epsilon_0} \frac{1}{R'[1 + (\mathbf{v}' \cdot \mathbf{n}'/c)]}. \tag{17–16}$$

From the diagram it is clear that

$$R' \frac{\mathbf{v} \cdot \mathbf{n}'}{c} = -R' \frac{v}{c} \frac{x_0 - x'}{R'} = -\frac{v(x_0 - x')}{c}. \tag{17–17}$$

Even after Eq. (17–17) is substituted in Eq. (17–16), a multitude of variables appear in the expression for φ. In calculating the electric field by taking the gradient of φ, etc., these variables would have to be differentiated very carefully and would cause the calculation to be quite cumbersome. Rather than follow this procedure, it is preferable to eliminate the undesirable variables in φ and obtain an expression which involves only the coordinates of P, the present time t, and parameters which describe the path of the charged particle.

Since the charge moves from x' to x_0 in time $t_0 - t'$, it is clear that

$$c^2(t - t')^2 = v^2(t_0 - t')^2 + b^2. \tag{17–18}$$

If this equation is solved for t' the result is

$$t' = \frac{c^2 t - v^2 t_0 \pm \sqrt{v^2 c^2(t_0 - t)^2 + b^2(c^2 - v^2)}}{c^2 - v^2}. \tag{17–19}$$

The minus sign must be used in this equation to ensure that t' is retarded with respect to t. To verify this, it is only necessary to observe that at $t = t_0 = 0$, $t' = \pm\sqrt{b^2(c^2 - v^2)}/(c^2 - v^2)$ and hence only the negative sign gives an earlier time. Having found t', we find $x_0 - x'$ from

$$x_0 - x' = v(t_0 - t')$$

$$= v\left(\frac{t_0(c^2 - v^2) - c^2t + v^2t_0 + \sqrt{v^2c^2(t_0 - t)^2 + b^2(c^2 - v^2)}}{c^2 - v^2}\right),$$

$$(17\text{–}20)$$

while R' is shown to be

$$R' = c\left(\frac{t(c^2 - v^2) - c^2t + v^2t_0 + \sqrt{v^2c^2(t_0 - t)^2 + b^2(c^2 - v^2)}}{c^2 - v^2}\right).$$

$$(17\text{–}21)$$

Equations (17–20) and (17–21) may be used to evaluate the denominator which appears in Eq. (17–16). This denominator becomes

$$R^* = R' - \frac{v(x_0 - x')}{c} \qquad (17\text{–}22)$$

through the use of Eq. (17–17), and subsequently, it becomes

$$R^* = (c^2 - v^2)^{-1}\left[v^2c(t_0 - t) + c\sqrt{v^2c^2(t_0 - t)^2 + b^2(c^2 - v^2)}\right.$$

$$\left. - v^2c(t_0 - t) - \frac{v^2}{c}\sqrt{v^2c^2(t_0 - t)^2 + b^2(c^2 - v^2)}\right]$$

$$= \sqrt{v^2(t_0 - t)^2 + b^2(1 - v^2/c^2)} \qquad (17\text{–}23)$$

through Eqs. (17–21) and (17–22). The scalar potential is

$$\varphi(P, t) = \frac{q}{4\pi\epsilon_0}\frac{1}{\sqrt{v^2(t_0 - t)^2 + b^2(1 - v^2/c^2)}}, \qquad (17\text{–}24)$$

while the vector potential is

$$\mathbf{A}(P, t) = \frac{\mu_0 q}{4\pi}\frac{\mathbf{v}}{\sqrt{v^2(t_0 - t)^2 + b^2(1 - v^2/c^2)}}. \qquad (17\text{–}25)$$

It is important to realize that Eqs. (17–24) and (17–25) contain only the position and time of the observation point, and the parameters $(\mathbf{v}, t_0)$ which describe the path of the charged particle.

To make this statement more concrete and to put the potentials in a form more suitable for calculating the fields, the coordinate system must be fixed more carefully. Since the charge moves along the x-axis, and since this is an axis of symmetry for the problem, it is only necessary to specify the origin on the x-axis. This is conveniently accomplished by taking $x = 0$ to be the position of the charge at $t = 0$. Then $x = vt$ and, in particular, $x_0 = vt_0$.

If the point P is specified by the cartesian coordinates ξ, η, ζ, then

$$\xi = x_0 = vt_0 \quad \text{and} \quad \eta^2 + \zeta^2 = b^2. \tag{17-26}$$

Using these results in Eq. (17–25) and letting $\boldsymbol{\xi} = (\xi, \eta, \zeta)$, we obtain

$$\varphi(\boldsymbol{\xi}, t) = \frac{q}{4\pi\epsilon_0} \frac{1}{\sqrt{(\xi - vt)^2 + (\eta^2 + \zeta^2)(1 - v^2/c^2)}}$$

and

$$\tag{17-27}$$

$$\mathbf{A}(\boldsymbol{\xi}, t) = \frac{\mu_0 q}{4\pi} \frac{\mathbf{v}}{\sqrt{(\xi - vt)^2 + (\eta^2 + \zeta^2)(1 - v^2/c^2)}}.$$

It must be remembered that these equations apply only if $\mathbf{v}$ is along the x-axis; other directions require modification of the formulas.

The important thing about equations (17–27) is that they are in a form ideally suited for the calculation of the fields. Thus

$$\mathbf{E}(\boldsymbol{\xi}, t) = -\frac{\partial \mathbf{A}}{\partial t} - \mathbf{grad}_{\xi}\, \varphi$$

$$= -\frac{\mu_0 q}{4\pi} \mathbf{v} \frac{v(\xi - vt)}{R^{*3}}$$

$$+ \frac{q}{4\pi\epsilon_0} \frac{1}{R^{*3}}[(\xi - vt)\mathbf{i} + \eta(1 - v^2/c^2)\mathbf{j} + \zeta(1 - v^2/c^2)\mathbf{k}].$$

$$\tag{17-28}$$

Noting that $\mathbf{v} = v\mathbf{i}$, $\epsilon_0\mu_0 = 1/c^2$, and $\xi - vt = x_0 - x$ makes it possible to rewrite Eq. (17–28) in the form

$$\mathbf{E}(\boldsymbol{\xi}, t) = \frac{q}{4\pi\epsilon_0} \frac{\mathbf{R}}{R^{*3}} (1 - v^2/c^2), \tag{17-29}$$

where $\mathbf{R}$ is a vector from the position of the charge at time t to the point P.

The magnetic induction can be found by simply evaluating $\mathbf{B} = \mathbf{curl\,A}$; however, a much simpler procedure is to note that

$$\mathbf{A} = \mu_0 \epsilon_0 \mathbf{v} \varphi \tag{17-30}$$

and hence that

$$\mathbf{B} = \mu_0 \epsilon_0\, \mathbf{curl}\ (\mathbf{v}\varphi) = -\mu_0 \epsilon_0 \mathbf{v} \times \mathbf{grad}\ \varphi \tag{17-31}$$

Since $\mathbf{v}$ is along the x-axis, only the y- and z-components of $\mathbf{grad}\ \varphi$ are important in the cross product. These components are just the negatives of the y- and z-components of $\mathbf{E}$. In this way we find

$$\mathbf{B} = \mu_0 \epsilon_0 \mathbf{v} \times \mathbf{E}, \qquad (17\text{–}32)$$

which completes the computation of the fields.

It is interesting to note that although the radiation source is the retarded position, lines of $\mathbf{E}$ are directed away from the instantaneous position of the charge. The lines of $\mathbf{B}$ are circles with centers on the charge path. The field is not spherically symmetric as it is in the static case, but is stronger in the direction perpendicular to the velocity.

Having obtained the field vectors, we are in a position to calculate other electromagnetic quantities; however, rather than pursue these possibilities, we refer the reader to more advanced texts* that deal at length with such problems.

17–3 Radiation from an accelerated point charge. If an accelerated point charge is to be considered, certain simplifications which appear in the constant velocity case are no longer possible. The major difficulty here is a direct result of the fact that the Lienard-Wiechert potentials can no longer be expressed in terms of the present position of the charge; instead, the retarded position and time appear explicitly. The potentials

$$\varphi = \frac{q}{4\pi\epsilon_0} \left[\frac{1}{R(1 + \mathbf{v} \cdot \mathbf{n}/c)} \right]_{\text{ret}}$$

and $\qquad\qquad\qquad\qquad\qquad\qquad\qquad\qquad\qquad (17\text{–}33)$

$$\mathbf{A} = \frac{q}{4\pi\epsilon} \left[\frac{\mathbf{v}/c^2}{R(1 + \mathbf{v} \cdot \mathbf{n}/c)} \right]_{\text{ret}}$$

are still correct; however, in differentiating them to obtain the fields it must be noted that derivatives with respect to the position of the field point must be taken at constant observation time, and derivatives with respect to the observation time at fixed field points. Since the retarded time appears explicitly in the potentials, care must be used to obtain the correct derivatives.

To clarify the differentiation problem, we note that the potentials are functions of the field point $\boldsymbol{\xi}$, the observation time t, the retarded position $\mathbf{r}'$ of the charge, and the retarded time t'. The trajectory of the particle is specified by giving $\mathbf{r}'$ as a function of t', so that the dependence on $\mathbf{r}'$ can be removed. Furthermore, the retardation condition

$$(\xi - x')^2 + (\eta - y')^2 + (\zeta - z')^2 = c^2(t - t')^2 \qquad (17\text{–}34)$$

---

* For example: Panofsky and Phillips, *Classical Electricity and Magnetism*, Addison-Wesley, 1955.

provides a single relationship among the remaining variables. Thus it is clear that although the potentials depend superficially on eight variables, only four of these are really independent. In computing the fields $\mathbf{E}$ and $\mathbf{B}$ it is necessary to differentiate the potentials with respect to each of ξ, η, ζ, and t, holding the other three fixed; for example, $\mathbf{A}$ must be differentiated with respect to t holding ξ, η, and ζ constant. Since it is t' that appears explicitly in the potentials, the calculation of these derivatives causes some difficulty.

To keep track of the variables which are being "held constant" during various differentiations, the following notation will be adopted: A partial derivative in which all other variables, dependent or independent, are "held constant" will be designated by the usual partial derivative symbol. If not all other variables are held constant, then those that are will be indicated by subscripts. Thus the derivative of $\mathbf{A}$ which is needed in computing $\mathbf{E}$ is $(\partial A/\partial t)_\xi$, while those of φ are $(\partial\varphi/\partial\xi)_{\eta,\zeta,t}$, etc. To transform $(\partial A/\partial t)_\xi$ into a derivative with respect to t', we write

$$\left(\frac{\partial \mathbf{A}}{\partial t}\right)_\xi = \left(\frac{\partial \mathbf{A}}{\partial t}\right) + \left(\frac{\partial \mathbf{A}}{\partial t'}\right)\left(\frac{\partial t'}{\partial t}\right)_\xi \qquad (17\text{–}35)$$

and

$$\left(\frac{\partial \mathbf{A}}{\partial t'}\right)_\xi = \left(\frac{\partial \mathbf{A}}{\partial t'}\right) + \left(\frac{\partial \mathbf{A}}{\partial t}\right)\left(\frac{\partial t}{\partial t'}\right)_\xi. \qquad (17\text{–}36)$$

The retardation condition, Eq. (17–34), together with the equation specifying the trajectory, $\mathbf{x}' = \mathbf{x}'(t')$, is equivalent to an equation of the form $f(\xi, t, t') = 0$. This relationship implies that $(\partial t/\partial t')_\xi = 1/(\partial t'/\partial t)_\xi$, which, when combined with Eqs. (17–35) and (17–36), gives

$$\left(\frac{\partial \mathbf{A}}{\partial t}\right)_\xi = \left(\frac{\partial \mathbf{A}}{\partial t'}\right)_\xi \left(\frac{\partial t'}{\partial t}\right)_\xi. \qquad (17\text{–}37)$$

In calculating the time derivatives of the potentials, this equation is just what is required to get the electric and magnetic fields. The other derivatives are all of the form $(\partial\varphi/\partial\xi)_t$. Such derivatives are readily evaluated by noting that

$$\left(\frac{\partial \varphi}{\partial \xi}\right)_t = \left(\frac{\partial \varphi}{\partial \xi}\right)_{t,t'} + \left(\frac{\partial \varphi}{\partial t'}\right)_{\xi,t}\left(\frac{\partial t'}{\partial \xi}\right)_t, \qquad (17\text{–}38)$$

in which all of the subscripts have been included to avoid any possibility of confusion.

From Eqs. (17–37) and (17–38) it is clear that the calculation of $\mathbf{E}$ requires that the derivatives $(\partial t'/\partial t)_\xi$ and $(\partial t'/\partial \xi)_t$ must be evaluated. Each of these may be easily evaluated by differentiating the square root of Eq. (17–34),

$$[(\xi - x')^2 + (\eta - y')^2 + (\zeta - z')^2]^{1/2} = c(t - t'), \quad (17\text{–}39)$$

in the appropriate way. If the derivative with respect to t (holding ξ constant) is taken, the equation

$$-\frac{1}{R'}\mathbf{R}' \cdot \left(\frac{\partial \mathbf{r}'}{\partial t}\right)_{\xi} = c\left[1 - \left(\frac{\partial t'}{\partial t}\right)_{\xi}\right] \quad (17\text{–}40)$$

results. In this equation, $\mathbf{r}' = \mathbf{i}x' + \mathbf{j}y' + \mathbf{k}z'$ and $\mathbf{R}' = \xi - \mathbf{r}'$. Since $\mathbf{r}'$ depends explicitly only on t', the derivative on the left is easily changed, to give

$$-\frac{1}{R'}\mathbf{R}' \cdot \mathbf{v}'\left(\frac{\partial t'}{\partial t}\right)_{\xi} = c\left[1 - \left(\frac{\partial t'}{\partial t}\right)_{\xi}\right], \quad (17\text{–}41)$$

where $\mathbf{v}' = \partial \mathbf{r}'/\partial t'$ is the velocity of the charge at the retarded time t'. Solving this for $(\partial t'/\partial t)_{\xi}$ leads to

$$\left(\frac{\partial t'}{\partial t}\right)_{\xi} = \frac{R'}{R' - \mathbf{R}' \cdot \mathbf{v}'/c} = \frac{R'}{R^*}. \quad (17\text{–}42)$$

A similar calculation in which Eq. (17–39) is differentiated with respect to ξ at constant (η, ζ, t) gives

$$\left(\frac{\partial t'}{\partial \xi}\right)_t = -\frac{(\xi - x')}{(R' - \mathbf{R}' \cdot \mathbf{v}'/c)c}. \quad (17\text{–}43)$$

Computing the other two components, and writing the result as a vector equation, we obtain

$$(\mathbf{grad}_{\xi}\, t')_t = -\frac{\mathbf{R}'/c}{R' - \mathbf{R}' \cdot \mathbf{v}'/c} = -\frac{\mathbf{R}'}{R^*c}. \quad (17\text{–}44)$$

With these derivatives at hand, the electric field due to an accelerated point charge is readily computed from the Lienard-Wiechert potentials. Thus

$$\mathbf{E}(\xi, t) = -(\mathbf{grad}_{\xi}\, \varphi)_t - \left(\frac{\partial \mathbf{A}}{\partial t}\right)_{\xi}$$

$$= -(\mathbf{grad}_{\xi}\, \varphi)_{tt'} - \left(\frac{\partial \varphi}{\partial t'}\right)_{\xi t}(\mathbf{grad}_{\xi}\, t')_t - \left(\frac{\partial \mathbf{A}}{\partial t'}\right)_{\xi}\left(\frac{\partial t'}{\partial t}\right)_{\xi}. \quad (17\text{–}45)$$

The derivatives of the potentials which appear in this equation are easily found to be

$$(\mathbf{grad}_{\xi}\, \varphi)_{tt'} = -\frac{q}{4\pi\epsilon_0}\frac{\mathbf{R}'/R' - \mathbf{v}'/c}{(R' - \mathbf{R}' \cdot \mathbf{v}'/c)^2}, \quad (17\text{–}46)$$

$$\left(\frac{\partial \varphi}{\partial t'}\right)_{\xi t} = \frac{q}{4\pi\epsilon_0}\left[\frac{\mathbf{R}' \cdot \mathbf{v}'}{R'} - \frac{v'^2}{c} + \frac{\mathbf{R}' \cdot \dot{\mathbf{v}}'}{c}\right]\frac{1}{R^{*2}}, \quad (17\text{–}47)$$

$$\left(\frac{\partial \mathbf{A}}{\partial t'}\right)_{\xi} = \frac{q}{4\pi\epsilon_0}\left[\frac{\dot{\mathbf{v}}'}{R^*c^2} + \frac{\mathbf{v}'}{c^2}\frac{1}{R^{*2}}\left(\frac{\mathbf{R}'\cdot\mathbf{v}'}{R'} - \frac{v'^2}{c} + \frac{\mathbf{R}'\cdot\dot{\mathbf{v}}'}{c}\right)\right]\frac{1}{R^{*2}}.$$

(17–48)

Using these results in Eq. (17–45), we find

$$\mathbf{E}(\xi, t) =$$

$$= \frac{q}{4\pi\epsilon_0}\left[\frac{1}{R^{*3}}\left(\mathbf{R}' - \frac{\mathbf{R}'v'}{c}\right)\left(1 - \frac{v'^2}{c^2}\right) + \left(\mathbf{R}' - \frac{\mathbf{R}'v'}{c}\right)\frac{\dot{\mathbf{v}}'\cdot\mathbf{R}'}{R^{*3}c^2} - \frac{\dot{\mathbf{v}}'R'}{R^{*2}c^2}\right].$$

(17–49)

A similar calculation gives

$$\mathbf{B}(\xi, t) =$$

$$= \frac{q}{4\pi\epsilon_0 c^2}\left\{\frac{\mathbf{v}'\times\mathbf{R}'}{R^{*3}}\left(1 - \frac{v^{*2}}{c^2}\right) + \frac{1}{R^{*3}c}\frac{\mathbf{R}'}{R'}\times\left[\mathbf{R}'\times\left(\left[\mathbf{R}' - \frac{\mathbf{R}'v'}{c}\right]\times\dot{\mathbf{v}}'\right)\right]\right\}.$$

(17–50)

These results may be used to explain many such important phenomena as radiation damping and the classical Bremsstrahlung. Most of these calculations are readily available in various texts on electrodynamics and except for one example will be omitted here in the interest of brevity.

17–4 Radiation fields for small velocities. If the velocity of the charge is small compared with the velocity of light, that is, if $v'/c \ll 1$, then the approximations

$$\mathbf{R}' - \frac{R'\mathbf{v}'}{c} \approx \mathbf{R}'$$

(17–51)

and

$$R^* = R' - \frac{\mathbf{R}'\cdot\mathbf{v}'}{c} \approx R'$$

(17–52)

may be made in Eqs. (17–49) and (17–50). If, in addition, only the so-called radiation field, i.e., the part of the field proportional to $1/R'$, is considered, then Eqs. (17–49) and (17–50) become

$$\mathbf{E}(\xi, t) = \frac{q}{4\pi\epsilon_0}\frac{\mathbf{R}'(\dot{\mathbf{v}}'\cdot\mathbf{R}') - \dot{\mathbf{v}}'R'^2}{R'^3 c} = \frac{q}{4\pi\epsilon_0}\frac{\mathbf{R}'\times(\mathbf{R}'\times\dot{\mathbf{v}}')}{R'^3 c^2}$$

(17–53)

and

$$\mathbf{B}(\xi, t) = \frac{q}{4\pi\epsilon_0 c^2}\frac{\mathbf{R}'\times[\mathbf{R}'\times(\mathbf{R}'\times\dot{\mathbf{v}}')]}{R'^4 c} = \frac{q}{4\pi\epsilon_0 c^2}\frac{\dot{\mathbf{v}}'\times\mathbf{R}'}{R'^2 c}.$$

(17–54)

From these field vectors the Poynting vector is found to be

$$\mathbf{S} = \mathbf{E}\times\mathbf{H} = \frac{q^2}{16\pi^2\epsilon_0^2\mu_0 c^2}\frac{1}{R'^5 c^3}[\mathbf{R}'\times(\mathbf{R}'\times\dot{\mathbf{v}}')]\times[\dot{\mathbf{v}}'\times\mathbf{R}'],$$

(17–55)

which, through the use of vector identities, reduces to

$$\mathbf{S} = \frac{q^2}{16\pi^2\epsilon_0 c^3} \frac{\mathbf{R}'(\mathbf{R}' \times \dot{\mathbf{v}}')^2}{R'^5}. \tag{17-56}$$

The total radiated power is obtained by integrating this Poynting vector over a closed surface surrounding the charge. A convenient choice for such a surface is a sphere centered at the retarded position of the charge. If, furthermore, the z-axis is chosen in the direction of $\dot{\mathbf{v}}'$, then

$$P_R = -\frac{dW}{dt} = \int_S \mathbf{S} \cdot \mathbf{n}\, da$$

$$= \frac{q^2}{16\pi^2\epsilon_0 c^3} \int \frac{R'^2 \dot{v}'^2 \sin^2\theta}{R'^5} \mathbf{R}' \cdot \frac{\mathbf{R}'}{R'} R'^2 \sin\theta\, d\theta\, d\phi, \tag{17-57}$$

from which one readily obtains the well-known result

$$P_R = -\frac{dW}{dt} = \frac{q^2}{4\pi\epsilon_0} \frac{2}{3} \frac{\dot{v}'^2}{c^3} \tag{17-58}$$

for the power radiated from a slowly moving, accelerated charge.

This completes our brief survey of radiation from moving charges. The basic ideas have been presented and some elementary applications have been given in detail. For the details of other calculations reference should be made to various published works, and particularly to:

PANOFSKY and PHILLIPS, *Classical Electricity and Magnetism*, Addison-Wesley, 1955.

BECKER, *Theorie der Elektrizität*, Vol. II, Teuber (Leipzig), 1933.

LANDAU and LIFSHITZ, *The Classical Theory of Fields*, Addison-Wesley, 1951.

SOMMERFELD, *Electrodynamics*, Academic Press, 1952.

Problems

17-1. Determine the Poynting vector for the uniformly moving point charge of Section 17-2, and show that the total power radiated is zero.

17-2. When an electromagnetic wave travels through matter containing free electrons (or in which the electrons are nearly "free"), the electrons are forced to oscillate with the frequency of the electromagnetic wave. Using the expressions for small velocity in Section 17-4, show that the total power radiated by an electron in the field of an electromagnetic wave

$$E = E_0 \sin \omega(t - z/c)$$

is

$$P_R = \frac{1}{12\pi\epsilon_0} \frac{e^4 E_0^2}{m_e^2 c^3}.$$

17-3. An *unpolarized* x-ray beam of intensity I_0 is incident on matter containing free electrons. Considering one electron only and using the expressions for small velocity, show that the intensity of the scattered beam is given by

$$I_s = \frac{1}{2} I_0 \frac{e^4}{16\pi^2 \epsilon_0^2 m_e^2 c^4 r^2} (1 + \cos^2 \beta),$$

where β is the angle between OP and the original x-ray beam. Point O is the position of the electron, and P is the point where the scattered beam is to be measured.

APPENDIXES

APPENDIXES

APPENDIX I

LOGICAL DEFINITION OF MKS UNITS

The appearance of the numbers ϵ_0 and μ_0 in the formulation of Coulomb's law and the Biot law, respectively, causes an unexpected difficulty. The difficulty is simply that Coulomb's law,

$$\mathbf{F}_2 = \frac{1}{4\pi\epsilon_0} \frac{q_1 q_2 \mathbf{r}_{12}}{r_{12}^3} , \tag{I-1}$$

cannot be used to define the coulomb unless ϵ_0 is known. By the same token, it cannot be used to define ϵ_0 unless the coulomb is previously defined. A technical point is that since ϵ_0 is basically an experimentally determined number, using (I-1) to define the coulomb would result in a coulomb which would change every time ϵ_0 was redetermined. Thus it is clear that (I-1) should be used to define ϵ_0, with the coulomb otherwise defined.

A corresponding difficulty does not arise in the magnetic case because $\mu_0 = 4\pi \times 10^{-7}$ weber/amp·m, by definition. As a result, the expression

$$\frac{F}{l} = \frac{\mu_0}{2\pi} \frac{I I'}{r} \tag{I-2}$$

for the force per unit length between two parallel, current-carrying wires can be used to define the ampere, viz.:

One ampere is that steady current which, when present in each of two long parallel conductors separated by a distance of one meter, results in a force per meter of length between them numerically equal to 2×10^{-7} newton/meter.

Of course, any other geometry could be used and would result in an equally unambiguous (and, in fact, numerically identical) definition of the ampere.

Having thus defined the ampere, the coulomb is defined as the charge transported by a steady current of one ampere flowing for one second. This in turn makes it feasible to use (I-1) to define ϵ_0. There is thus no real problem, but only an artificial one arising from a desire to treat the mathematically simpler case of electrostatics before discussing the magnetic interaction of currents.

It is sometimes thought that this problem does not arise if the gaussian system of units is used. This is true only in the sense that the coefficient in Coulomb's law is chosen to be 1 dyne cm^2/esu^2, which places the burden of agreeing with experiment on the magnetic interactions. This means that the velocity of light appears either in the definition of the unit of current or else in the expression for the force between current-carrying conductors. Since in the usual treatment the conveniently defined quantity occurs first, the problem is less painfully obvious in the gaussian system than in the mks system.

APPENDIX II

OTHER SYSTEMS OF UNITS

In this book the charge-rationalized mks system of units has been used. This system has a host of virtues, not the least of which is to include the practical electrical units of potential difference (volt), current (ampere), resistance (ohm), etc. As a result of these advantages, the system rapidly gained favor with electrical engineers and is now rapidly becoming standard even with physicists for the study of electromagnetic phenomena. In other areas, notably atomic and nuclear physics, another system, known as the gaussian system, has remained popular. Most other systems have faded from use, and hence only the gaussian system will be discussed here at length.

The gaussian system is a combination of two earlier systems: the electrostatic system, esu, and the electromagnetic system, emu. The electrostatic system results from writing Coulomb's law in the form

$$\mathbf{F}_2 = \frac{q_1 q_2 \mathbf{r}_{12}}{r_{12}^3}, \tag{II-1}$$

and defining the esu of charge as that charge which when placed one centimeter from an exactly similar charge experiences a force of one dyne. It is obvious that the esu of charge is much smaller than the coulomb (in fact 1 coulomb $= 3 \times 10^9$ esu). The electromagnetic system results from writing the Biot law in the form

$$d\mathbf{F}_2 = I_1 I_2 \frac{d\mathbf{l}_2 \times (d\mathbf{l}_1 \times \mathbf{r}_{12})}{r_{12}^3} \tag{II-2}$$

and defining the abampere as the current which, when present in a long straight wire, results in a force of 1 dyne/cm when the wire is placed 1 cm from a parallel conductor carrying the same current. From $|\mu_0/4\pi| = 10^{-7}$ and 1 newton $= 10^5$ dynes, it is found that 1 abamp $= 10$ amp.

Either of the two starting points noted above can be used to initiate the development of a complete system of units. Historically, however, esu have been used primarily for electrostatic problems and emu for electromagnetic problems. This being the case, it was natural that a hybrid system using esu for electrical quantities and emu for magnetic quantities should develop. The system that has evolved in this way is known as the gaussian system. The principal point of contact of esu and emu in the gaussian system is in the current density, where

$$\mathbf{J}_{emu} = \frac{\mathbf{J}_{esu}}{c}. \tag{II-3}$$

There is no way of making a clear-cut choice between J_{emu} and J_{esu}; we will arbitrarily use J_{esu} and explicitly exhibit the velocity of light.

In gaussian units, Maxwell's equations are

$$\text{curl } \mathbf{E} + \frac{1}{c}\frac{\partial \mathbf{B}}{\partial t} = 0,$$

$$\text{div } \mathbf{D} = 4\pi\rho,$$

$$\text{curl } \mathbf{H} - \frac{1}{c}\frac{\partial \mathbf{D}}{\partial t} = \frac{4\pi \mathbf{J}}{c},$$

$$\text{div } \mathbf{B} = 0.$$

(II-4)

The fields are derived from scalar and vector potentials by means of

$$\mathbf{B} = \text{curl } \mathbf{A} \quad \text{and} \quad \mathbf{E} = -\text{grad } \varphi - \frac{1}{c}\frac{\partial \mathbf{A}}{\partial t}, \quad \text{(II-5)}$$

and the Lorentz force is

$$\mathbf{F} = q\left(\mathbf{E} + \frac{\mathbf{v}}{c}\times \mathbf{B}\right). \quad \text{(II-6)}$$

$\mathbf{D}$ and $\mathbf{B}$ are related to $\mathbf{E}$ and $\mathbf{H}$ by

$$\mathbf{D} = \mathbf{E} + 4\pi\mathbf{P} \quad \text{and} \quad \mathbf{B} = \mathbf{H} + 4\pi\mathbf{M}, \quad \text{(II-7)}$$

where $\mathbf{P}$ is the electric dipole moment ($\mathbf{p} = q\mathbf{l}$) per unit volume, and $\mathbf{M}$ is the magnetic dipole moment ($\mathbf{m} = I A \mathbf{n}/c$) per unit volume. These equations are substantially sufficient to define the gaussian system of units. For convenience, however, Table II-1 gives the numerical relationships of gaussian units to mks units.

TABLE II-1

Quantity	Gaussian units	mks units
Charge	3×10^9 esu	$= 1$ coul
Current	3×10^9 esu/sec $= 10^{-1}$ abamp	$= 1$ amp
Electric field	$\frac{1}{3} \times 10^{-4}$ dyne/esu	$= 1$ volt/m
Potential	$1/300$ erg/esu (statvolt)	$= 1$ volt
Magnetic induction	10^4 gauss	$= 1$ weber/m^2
Magnetic intensity	$4\pi \times 10^{-3}$ oersted	$= 1$ amp-turns/m
Electric displacement	$12\pi \times 10^5$ esu	$= 1$ coul/m^2
Capacitance	9×10^{11} cm	$= 1$ farad
Inductance	10^9 emu	$= 1$ henry
Magnetic flux	10^8 maxwells	$= 1$ weber

APPENDIX III

PROOF THAT DIV B = 0 AND CURL B = μ_0J

In this appendix we shall prove by rigorous mathematical manipulations that

$$\mathbf{B}(\mathbf{r}_2) = \frac{\mu_0}{4\pi} \int_V \mathbf{J}(\mathbf{r}_1) \times \frac{\mathbf{r}_2 - \mathbf{r}_1}{|\mathbf{r}_2 - \mathbf{r}_1|^3} \, dv_1 \tag{III-1}$$

implies

$$\operatorname{div} \mathbf{B} = 0, \tag{III-2}$$

and that (III-1) together with div $\mathbf{J} = 0$ implies

$$\operatorname{curl} \mathbf{B} = \mu_0 \mathbf{J}. \tag{III-3}$$

To accomplish the first of these, we take the divergence of (III-1). Using div $(\mathbf{A} \times \mathbf{B}) = -\mathbf{A} \cdot \operatorname{curl} \mathbf{B} + \mathbf{B} \cdot \operatorname{curl} \mathbf{A}$ gives

$$\operatorname{div}_2 \mathbf{B}(\mathbf{r}_2) = -\frac{\mu_0}{4\pi} \int_V \mathbf{J}(\mathbf{r}_1) \cdot \operatorname{curl}_2 \frac{\mathbf{r}_2 - \mathbf{r}_1}{|\mathbf{r}_2 - \mathbf{r}_1|^3} \, dv_1. \tag{III-4}$$

However, $(\mathbf{r}_2 - \mathbf{r}_1)/|\mathbf{r}_2 - \mathbf{r}_1|^3$ is the gradient of $-1/|\mathbf{r}_2 - \mathbf{r}_1|$ with respect to $\mathbf{r}_2$. Since the curl of any gradient is zero, it follows that

$$\operatorname{div}_2 \mathbf{B}(\mathbf{r}_2) = 0.$$

The second statement poses more difficulties. Expanding the cross product gives

$$\mathbf{J}(\mathbf{r}_1) \times (\mathbf{r}_2 - \mathbf{r}_1) = \mathbf{i}[J_y(\mathbf{r}_1)(z_2 - z_1) - J_z(\mathbf{r}_1)(y_2 - y_1)]$$

$$+ \mathbf{j}[J_z(\mathbf{r}_1)(x_2 - x_1) - J_x(\mathbf{r}_1)(z_2 - z_1)]$$

$$+ \mathbf{k}[J_x(\mathbf{r}_1)(y_2 - y_1) - J_y(\mathbf{r}_1)(x_2 - x_1)]. \tag{III-5}$$

From this, the x-component of curl B is explicitly

$$[\operatorname{curl}_2 \mathbf{B}(\mathbf{r}_2)]_x = \frac{\mu_0}{4\pi} \int_V \left(\frac{\partial}{\partial y_2} \left\{ \frac{J_x(\mathbf{r}_1)(y_2 - y_1) - J_y(\mathbf{r}_1)(x_2 - x_1)}{[(x_2 - x_1)^2 + (y_2 - y_1)^2 + (z_2 - z_1)^2]^{3/2}} \right\} \right.$$

$$\left. - \frac{\partial}{\partial z_2} \left\{ \frac{J_z(\mathbf{r}_1)(x_2 - x_1) - J_x(\mathbf{r}_1)(z_2 - z_1)}{[(x_2 - x_1)^2 + (y_2 - y_1)^2 + (z_2 - z_1)^2]^{3/2}} \right\} \right) dv_1. \tag{III-6}$$

Since

$$\frac{y_2 - y_1}{[(x_2 - x_1)^2 + (y_2 - y_1)^2 + (z_2 - z_1)^2]^{3/2}} =$$

$$= -\frac{\partial}{\partial y_2}[(x_2 - x_1)^2 + (y_2 - y_1)^2 + (z_2 - z_1)^2]^{-1/2}$$

$$= \frac{\partial}{\partial y_1}[(x_2 - x_1)^2 + (y_2 - y_1)^2 + (z_2 - z_1)^2]^{-1/2},$$

(III–6) can be written as

$$[\mathbf{curl}_2\, \mathbf{B}(\mathbf{r}_2)]_x = \frac{\mu_0}{4\pi} \int_V \left\{ -J_x(\mathbf{r}_1) \left(\frac{\partial^2}{\partial y_2^2} + \frac{\partial^2}{\partial z_2^2} \right) \right.$$

$$\times [(x_2 - x_1)^2 + (y_2 - y_1)^2 + (z_2 - z_1)^2]^{-1/2}$$

$$- \left(J_y(\mathbf{r}_1) \frac{\partial}{\partial y_2} + J_z(\mathbf{r}_1) \frac{\partial}{\partial z_2} \right)$$

$$\left. \times \frac{x_2 - x_1}{[(x_2 - x_1)^2 + (y_2 - y_1)^2 + (z_2 - z_1)^2]^{3/2}} \right\} dv_1.$$

Adding

$$-J_x(\mathbf{r}_1) \frac{\partial^2}{\partial x_2^2}[(x_2 - x_1)^2 + (y_2 - y_1)^2 + (z_2 - z_1)^2]^{-1/2}$$

$$-J_x(\mathbf{r}_1) \frac{\partial}{\partial x_2} \frac{(x_2 - x_1)}{[(x_2 - x_1)^2 + (y_2 - y_1)^2 + (z_2 - z_1)^2]^{3/2}} = 0$$

to the integrand gives

$$[\mathbf{curl}_2\, \mathbf{B}(\mathbf{r}_2)]_x =$$

$$= \frac{\mu_0}{4\pi} \int_V \left\{ -J_x(\mathbf{r}_1)\nabla_2^2 \frac{1}{[(x_2 - x_1)^2 + (y_2 - y_1)^2 + (z_2 - z_1)^2]^{1/2}} \right.$$

$$- \left[J_x(\mathbf{r}_1) \frac{\partial}{\partial x_2} + J_y(\mathbf{r}_1) \frac{\partial}{\partial y_2} + J_z(\mathbf{r}_1) \frac{\partial}{\partial z_2} \right]$$

$$\left. \times \frac{x_2 - x_1}{[(x_2 - x_1)^2 + (y_2 - y_1)^2 + (z_2 - z_1)^2]^{3/2}} \right\} dv_1. \qquad \text{(III–7)}$$

In the second term, each partial derivative with respect to an $\mathbf{r}_2$ variable can be changed to the negative of the corresponding derivative with respect to an $\mathbf{r}_1$ variable, and the resulting term integrated by parts. The integration by parts yields one term proportional to div $\mathbf{J}$ which has been assumed to vanish, and another which is a surface term. For bounded current distributions the surface can always be chosen sufficiently remote so that the surface integral vanishes. The first term of (III–7) gives

$$[\text{curl}_2\, \mathbf{B}(\mathbf{r}_2)]_x = -\frac{\mu_0}{4\pi} \int_V J_x(\mathbf{r}_1)$$

$$\times \nabla_2^2 \frac{1}{[(x_2 - x_1)^2 + (y_2 - y_1)^2 + (z_2 - z_1)^2]^{1/2}}\, dv_1.$$

The Laplacian gives zero except at $\mathbf{r}_2 = \mathbf{r}_1$; hence $J_x(\mathbf{r}_1)$ can be replaced by $J_x(\mathbf{r}_2)$ and removed from under the integral. The remaining integral is easily evaluated by using the divergence theorem:

$$\int_V \nabla_2^2 \frac{1}{[(x_2 - x_1)^2 + (y_2 - y_1)^2 + (z_2 - z_1)^2]^{1/2}}\, dv_1 = -4\pi,$$

from which

$$[\text{curl}_2\, \mathbf{B}(\mathbf{r}_2)]_x = \mu_0 J_x(\mathbf{r}_2) \tag{III–8}$$

and

$$\text{curl } \mathbf{B} = \mu_0 \mathbf{J},$$

which is the desired result.

ANSWERS TO
ODD-NUMBERED PROBLEMS

ANSWERS TO ODD-NUMBERED PROBLEMS

CHAPTER 1

1-1. $(\mathbf{A} - \mathbf{B}) \times (\mathbf{C} - \mathbf{D}) = 0$,   1:3

1-3. $\mathbf{A} \cdot \mathbf{B} = 0$, $\mathbf{A} + \mathbf{B} = \mathbf{C}$

1-7. The angle between $\mathbf{R}$ and $\mathbf{R} - \mathbf{A}$, which is 90°, may be inscribed in a semicircle with $\mathbf{A}$ as diameter. As $\mathbf{R}$ varies, the various semicircles describe the surface of a sphere.

1-11.
$$\text{div } \mathbf{F} = \frac{1}{r} \frac{\partial}{\partial r} (rF_r) + \frac{1}{r} \frac{\partial F_\theta}{\partial \theta} + \frac{\partial F_z}{\partial z}$$

CHAPTER 2

2-1. $\tan^3 \theta / (1 + \tan^2 \theta) = q^2 / 16\pi\epsilon_0 \, mg \, l^2$

2-3. $E = 2296$ volts/m (along diagonal)

2-5. (a) $E = (\sigma/2\epsilon_0)(1 - z/\sqrt{z^2 + R^2})$

  (b) $E = (\beta/2\epsilon_0) \left[\dfrac{L}{2} \left(\dfrac{L}{2} - \sqrt{\dfrac{L^2}{4} + R^2} \right) \right.$
$$\left. + R^2 \log \left(\frac{L}{2R} + \sqrt{1 + \frac{L^2}{4R^2}} \right) \right]$$

2-7. $x = \sqrt{2}a/(\sqrt{2} - 1)$, saddlepoint

2-9. $U = (\rho/4\epsilon_0) \left[(z + \tfrac{1}{2}L)\{(z + \tfrac{1}{2}L)^2 + R^2\}^{1/2} - 2zL \right.$
$$- (z - \tfrac{1}{2}L)\{(z - \tfrac{1}{2}L)^2 + R^2\}^{1/2}$$
$$\left. + R^2 \log \left\{ \frac{z + \tfrac{1}{2}L + \sqrt{(z + \tfrac{1}{2}L)^2 + R^2}}{z - \tfrac{1}{2}L + \sqrt{(z - \tfrac{1}{2}L)^2 + R^2}} \right\} \right]$$

2-11. 300,000 volts

2-13. 1.1×10^{-12} coulomb/m³, positive.

2-15. (a) $U = (A/\epsilon_0)(R - \tfrac{1}{2}r)$ for $r \le R$
  $U = AR^2/2\epsilon_0 r$ for $r \ge R$

  (b) $U = (\rho_0/2\epsilon_0)(R^2 - \tfrac{1}{3}r^2)$ for $r \le R$
  $U = R^3\rho_0/3\epsilon_0 r$ for $r \ge R$

2-17. Treat dipole as two equal but oppositely charged point charges separated by a small distance.

CHAPTER 3

3-1. Between: $U = \dfrac{r_b U_b - r_a U_a + (U_a - U_b)r_a r_b/r}{r_b - r_a}$;

  for $r > r_b$: $U = U_b r_b / r$

3-7. $U = -(1 - a^3/r^3)E_0 r \cos \theta + Q/4\pi\epsilon_0 r$

3-9. $\sigma = -\epsilon_0 A/2r^{1/2}$ on upper surface.

3-11. The mirror image of the charge distribution with ρ replaced by $-\rho$.

3-15. $M = (x_0/a) + \sqrt{(x_0/a)^2 - 1}$, image at $x_0(M^2 - 1)/(M^2 + 1)$.

3-17. $3p^2/32\pi\epsilon_0 \, d^4$, attraction.

Chapter 4

4-1. $\rho_P = -2ax$; Q_P (on ends) $= A(aL^2 + b)$, $-bA$

4-3. $E_z = \dfrac{P}{2\epsilon_0}\left[\dfrac{\frac{1}{2}L - z}{\sqrt{(\frac{1}{2}L - z)^2 + R^2}} + \dfrac{\frac{1}{2}L + z}{\sqrt{(\frac{1}{2}L + z)^2 + R^2}}\right]$

4-5. $E = (1/\epsilon_0)P\cos\gamma$

4-7. $\dfrac{\tan\theta_1}{\tan\theta_2} = \dfrac{K_1}{K_2}$

4-9. $q' = [(\epsilon_1 - \epsilon_2)/(\epsilon_1 + \epsilon_2)]q$; $\quad q'' = 2\epsilon_2 q/(\epsilon_1 + \epsilon_2)$

4-11. $D = K\epsilon_0\,\Delta U/[K\,d - (K - 1)t]$.

4-13. $E = Q/2\pi(\epsilon_1 + \epsilon_2)r^2$

4-15. Inside: $\mathbf{E} = -\mathbf{P}/3\epsilon_0$

outside: $E_r = \dfrac{2R^3 P}{3\epsilon_0 r^3}\cos\theta$

$$E_\theta = \dfrac{R^3 P}{3\epsilon_0 r^3}\sin\theta$$

Chapter 5

5-1. $\alpha = 9.7 \times 10^{-41}$ coul·m^2/volt; $R_0 = 0.96 \times 10^{-10}$ m

5-3. 2.6×10^{-16} m

5-5. 2.94×10^{-30} coul·m

Chapter 6

6-1. 18.75 cm

6-3. $4\pi R^5\rho_0^2/15\epsilon_0$

6-5. $-(R/d)q$

6-7. $\epsilon_1\epsilon_2/(\epsilon_1\,d_2 + \epsilon_2\,d_1)$

6-9. 23.8 volts

6-13. (a) $Kl(\Delta U)_0/[l + (K - 1)x]$

(b) $(K - 1)Q^2 d/2\epsilon_0 w[l + (K - 1)x]^2$

6-15. $[4\,mg/2\pi\epsilon_0(K - 1)]^{1/2}$

Chapter 7

7-1. (a) $v = 0.739 \times 10^{-7}$ m/sec

(b) $\tau = 5.0 \times 10^{-14}$ sec

7-3. $U_{\text{int}} = \dfrac{U_1 g_1(d - a) - U_2 g_2 a}{g_2 a + g_1(d - a)}$,

$$\sigma = \dfrac{(g_1\epsilon_2 - g_2\epsilon_1)(U_1 + U_2)}{g_2 a + g_1(d - a)}$$

7-5. 20 ohms

7-7. $I = 2\pi g\,\Delta U/\ln(r_2/r_1)$

7-11. $I = \pi gs\,\Delta U/\cosh^{-1}(b/2a)$

7-13. (a) $I = (\mathcal{E}_2 R_1 + \mathcal{E}_1 R_2)/(R_1 R + R_2 R + R_1 R_2)$

(b) $R_1 R_2/(R_1 + R_2)$

7-15. (a) $4R/5$ (b) $(11/20)R$

7-17. (a) $(R_4 R_5 - R_3 R_6)\mathcal{E}_1/[D + R_g(R_3 + R_4)(R_5 + R_6)]$,
   where $D = R_3 R_4 R_5 + R_4 R_5 R_6 + R_5 R_6 R_3 + R_6 R_3 R_4$

7-19. One part in 4×10^6

CHAPTER 8

8-3. (a) 0.0048 cm
   (b) 1.64×10^{-7} sec

8-5. $B = \sqrt{3}\mu_0 I / \pi a$

8-7. $\mu_0 IN/4a$

8-9. $\mu_0 NI$

8-11. (a) $\dfrac{\partial B_r}{\partial z} = \dfrac{\partial B_z}{\partial r}$

8-13. **curl curl B** $= \mu_0$ **curl J** $= 0$.

8-15. $B = \mu_0 NI/2\pi r$, $b/a = 4/3$

8-17. $A_z = (\mu_0 I/2\pi) \ln (r/b)$ between the conductors

8-19. (d) $B_r = (\mu_0 I/2a) \left[\cos \theta - \dfrac{3r^2}{4a^2} (5 \cos^3 \theta - 3 \cos \theta) + \cdots \right]$

   $B_\theta = (\mu_0 I/2a) \left[- \sin \theta + \dfrac{3r^2}{4a^2} (5 \cos^2 \theta - 1) \sin \theta + \cdots \right]$

CHAPTER 9

9-5. (a) From b to a
   (b) From b to a
   (c) From a to b

9-7. $\frac{1}{2}B^2 a^2 r^2 \omega g t$

9-9. $(\mu_0 L/2\pi) \ln (R_2/R_1)$

9-11. $\mu_0 \pi a^2 b^2 / 4r^3$

9-13. $M = (\mu_0 h/2\pi) \ln (1 + d/r)$

CHAPTER 10

10-1. $\mathbf{J}_M = $ **curl M** $= 0$.
   $j_M = \mathbf{M} \times \mathbf{n}$; $j_M = M$ on cylindrical surfaces, $j_M = 0$ on sides.

10-3. (b) $(4/3)\pi R^3 \mathbf{M}_0$

10-5. $\sigma_M = M_0 x/[x^2 + (b^4/a^4)(y^2 + z^2)]^{1/2}$
   $\rho_M = 0$.

10-7. (b) $B_z = \frac{1}{2}\mu_0 M \left[\dfrac{\frac{1}{2}L - z}{\sqrt{(\frac{1}{2}L - z)^2 + R^2}} + \dfrac{\frac{1}{2}L + z}{\sqrt{(\frac{1}{2}L + z)^2 + R^2}} \right]$

10-9. (a) 0.25 w/m^2
   (b) 0.95 w/m^2
   (c) 1.52 w/m^2

10-11. 0.002 henry

10–13. (a) Sintered oxide 0.4 w/m^2
           35% Co steel   0.22 w/m^2
      (b) Sintered oxide 0.53 w/m^2
           35% Co steel   0.96 w/m^2

10–15. 0.64 w/m^2

10–17. $\mathbf{B}_i = 2(\mu/\mu_0)\mathbf{B}_0/(1 + \mu/\mu_0)$

Chapter 11

11–3. 3.69×10^{-4}

11–5. $\gamma = 976$

Chapter 12

12–3. $W = \dfrac{1}{s + 2}\,[L_1^{(f)}I_1^{(f)^2} + 2M_{12}^{(f)}I_1^{(f)}I_2^{(f)} + L_2^{(f)}I_2^{(f)^2}]$

12–5. $\dfrac{N^2 I^2 A\mu^2}{\mu_0(l + d)^2}$

12–7. (a) $F = B_0^2 \chi_m A/2\mu_0(1 + \chi_m)$
      (b) 1.76×10^{-4} newton

12–11. Commercial iron: 0.018 watt/cm^3
        Tungsten steel: 0.395 watt/cm^3

12–13. $-d(\mathbf{m} \cdot \mathbf{B})$

Chapter 13

13–1. (a) $I = 0.605$ amp,
         $dI/dt = 1.59$ amp/sec
      (b) $I = 1.295$ amp,
         $dI/dt = 0.558$ amp/sec
      (c) $I = 1.663$ amp,
         $dI/dt = 0.0062$ amp/sec

13–3. $Q = C\mathcal{E}_0[1 - e^{-t/RC}]$

13–5. $Z = \dfrac{R\alpha - \omega C'R(\omega L - 1/\omega C) + j[\omega C'R^2 + (\omega L - 1/\omega C)\alpha]}{\alpha^2 + \omega^2 C'^2 R^2}$,
      where $\alpha = 1 + \omega^2 C'L - C'/C$

13–7. (a) 3.2×10^{-2} deg
      (b) zero to 1.8 megacycles/sec

13–9. (a) $f = 1.78 \times 10^3$ cycles/sec
      (b) $f = 1.78 \times 10^3$ cycles/sec
      (c) $f = 0.796 \times 10^3$ cycles/sec

13–11. (a) $L/C = 2R^2$
       (b) $L = \sqrt{2}\,R/\omega_c$; $C = 1/\sqrt{2}\,R\omega_c$

13–13. $0.0713 - 0.0034j$ milliamp

13–15. $1/\sqrt{3LC}$

13–17. $V_1 = -100 - 700j$ volts
        $V_2 = 150 - 750j$ volts

CHAPTER 15

15-1. (a) $Q = C(\Delta U)e^{-gt/\epsilon}$

(b) $-(g/\epsilon)C(\Delta U)e^{-gt/\epsilon}$

(c) Zero

15-5. $\mathbf{B} = -\mathbf{i}E_0\sqrt{\epsilon\mu}\sin\omega(\sqrt{\epsilon\mu}z - t) + \mathbf{j}E_0\sqrt{\epsilon\mu}\cos\omega(\sqrt{\epsilon\mu}z - t)$

$\mathbf{S} = \mathbf{k}\sqrt{\dfrac{\epsilon}{\mu}}\,E_0^2$

15-7. $E = 686$ v/m; $B = 2.29 \times 10^{-6}$ w/m^2, rms.

15-9. $\mathbf{A} = -\mathbf{i}(\lambda E_0/2\pi c)\cos[2\pi(z - ct)/\lambda]$

CHAPTER 16

16-1. $R = \dfrac{2r[1 + \cos(2\omega nd/c)]}{1 + r^2 + 2r\cos(2\omega nd/c)}$, where $r = \left[\dfrac{n-1}{n+1}\right]^2$

16-3. (1) $E_{1,0} + E_{2,0} = E_{3,0}$

(2) $\sqrt{\epsilon_1/\mu_1}\cos\theta_1(E_{1,0} - E_{2,0}) = \sqrt{\epsilon_2/\mu_2}\,E_{3,0}\cos\theta_3$

16-5. (a) $\dfrac{E_{2,0}}{E_{1,0}} = \dfrac{\sqrt{(n_2/n_1)^2 - \sin^2\theta_1} - (n_2/n_1)^2\cos\theta_1}{\sqrt{(n_2/n_1)^2 - \sin^2\theta_1} + (n_2/n_1)^2\cos\theta_1}$,

$\dfrac{E_{3,0}}{E_{1,0}} = \dfrac{2(n_2/n_1)\cos\theta_1}{\sqrt{(n_2/n_1)^2 - \sin^2\theta_1} + (n_2/n_1)^2\cos\theta_1}$

(b) Total internal reflection

16-7. $B_x = B_1\cos(\kappa y\cos\theta)e^{j(\kappa z\sin\theta - \omega t)}$

$E_y = -cB_1\sin\theta\cos(\kappa y\cos\theta)e^{j(\kappa z\sin\theta - \omega t)}$

$E_z = jcB_1\cos\theta\sin(\kappa y\cos\theta)e^{j(\kappa z\sin\theta - \omega t)}$

16-9. $\dfrac{\lambda}{2} < a < \dfrac{\lambda}{\sqrt{2}}$

16-11. $B_\theta = \dfrac{\mu_0 I_0}{4\pi}\,A\,\dfrac{\omega^2}{c^2 r}\sin\theta\cos\omega\left(t - \dfrac{r}{c}\right)$

$E_\phi = -\dfrac{I_0 A}{4\pi\epsilon_0}\,\dfrac{\omega^2}{c^3 r}\sin\theta\cos\omega\left(t - \dfrac{r}{c}\right)$, where A is the area of the circular loop.

$P = \dfrac{\mu_0}{6\pi}\,I_0^2 A^2\,\dfrac{\omega^4}{c^3}\cos^2\omega\left(t - \dfrac{r}{c}\right)$

CHAPTER 17

17-1. $\mathbf{S} = \dfrac{q^2}{16\pi^2\epsilon_0 R^{*6}}\left(1 - \dfrac{v^2}{c^2}\right)^2[R^2\mathbf{v} - (\mathbf{v}\cdot\mathbf{R})\mathbf{R}]$

INDEX

INDEX